Justine Latremouille.

Justine Latremouille

NELSON

Science & Technology 8

Authors

Unit 1
Bob Ritter

Unit 2
Nora L. Alexander

Unit 3
Carol Glegg
Peter Williams

Unit 4
Chuck Hammill

Unit 5
Alan J. Hirsch

Program Consultant
Marietta (Mars) Bloch

Contributing Authors

Skills Handbook
Nancy Dalgarno Alldred
Stephen Haberer

Nelson
Thomson Learning™

Australia • Canada • Denmark • Japan • Mexico • New Zealand • Philippines
Puerto Rico • Singapore • South Africa • Spain • United Kingdom • United States

1120 Birchmount Road
Scarborough, Ontario M1K 5G4
www.nelson.com
www.thomson.com

Printed and bound in Canada
5 6 7 8 9 0 /ITIB/ 8 7 6 5 4 3 2

Canadian Cataloguing in Publication Data

Main entry under title:
Nelson science & technology 8
Includes index.
ISBN 0-17-607497-4

1. Science – Juvenile literature. I. Ritter, Bob, 1950-   . II. Title: Science 8.

Q161.2.N44 1999   500   C99-930748-7

Nelson Science & Technology 8 Project Team

Artplus Design & Communication

Marnie Benedict

Colin Bisset

Beverley Buxton

Angela Cluer

Bob Cooper

Ruta Demery

Peggy Ferguson

Kyle Gell

Susan Green

Julie Greener

Geraldine Kikuta

Margo Davies Leclair

Julia Lee

Kevin Linder

Kevin Martindale

Dave Mazierski

Allan Moon

Renate McCloy

Ruth Peckover

Suzanne Peden

Ken Phipps

Peggy Rhodes

Todd Ryoji

Silver Birch Graphics

David Steele

Rosalyn Steiner

Rosemary Tanner

Karen Taylor

Theresa Thomas

Bart Vallecoccia

Ilana Weitzman

Acknowledgments

Nelson Science & Technology 8 is the result of the efforts of a great many people. The publisher would like to thank those who assisted in the development of this learning resource.

Program Assessment Consultants
Damian Cooper
Halton District School Board

Nanci Wakeman-Jones
Halton District School Board

Safety Review
Patrick Hogan
Catholic District Board of Eastern Ontario

Margaret Redway
Fraser Scientific and Business Services

Expert Review
Steve Alsop
York University, Faculty of Pure and Applied Science

David Logan
York University, Faculty of Pure and Applied Science

Steve Rogers
Technology Teaching Systems

Peter I. Russell
Earth Sciences Curator, University of Waterloo

Sean D. Spencer, P. Eng.
Product Engineer, Dimtex North America Ltd.

Materials Review
Paul Hannan

Web Consultant
Peter Sovran

Reviewers

Roni Abrahamsohn
The Leo Baeck Day School

Diane Aitken
Hamilton Wentworth District School Board

Karen Barnes
Toronto District School Board

Barbara Behan
Dufferin-Peel Catholic District School Board

David Bell
York Centre for Applied Sustainability

Al Bernacki

Steve Bibla
Toronto District School Board

Ray Bowers
North York Board of Education

Bob Cooper
The Leo Baeck Day School

Jim Dawson
Faculty of Education, University of Windsor

Chris Eaton
Waterloo District Catholic School Board

Gord Felix
Dufferin-Peel Catholic District School Board

Maureen Innes
Waterloo Catholic District School Board

Claudia Jones
Dufferin-Peel Catholic District School Board

Paul Podesta
Dufferin-Peel Catholic District School Board

Franca Porcelli
York Catholic District School Board

Margaret E. Ramsay
Dufferin-Peel Catholic District School Board

Steve Rogers
Technology Teaching Systems

Elaine Rubinoff
Learning for a Sustainable Future

Melissa Stout
Toronto District School Board

Pamela Schwartzberg
Learning for a Sustainable Future

Linda Strey
Lakehead District School Board

Mary Jane Vowles
Dufferin-Peel Catholic District School Board

Allison Weagle
York Region District School Board

Janice Weir
York Region District School Board

Otto Wevers
Toronto District School Board

Table of Contents

UNIT 1: CELLS, TISSUES, ORGANS, AND SYSTEMS   10

OVERVIEW   12

GETTING STARTED: The Building Blocks of Living Things   14

1.1 Characteristics of Living Things   16

1.2 INQUIRY INVESTIGATION: Using the Microscope   18

1.3 Plant and Animal Cells   20

1.4 INQUIRY INVESTIGATION: Comparing Plant and Animal Cells   22

1.5 Technological Advances of the Microscope   24

1.6 Parts of a Cell Seen with an Electron Microscope   26

1.7 Cells in Their Environment   28

1.8 Osmosis   30

1.9 INQUIRY INVESTIGATION: Observing Diffusion and Osmosis   34

1.10 INQUIRY INVESTIGATION: How Does the Concentration of a Solution Affect Osmosis?   36

1.11 CAREER PROFILE: Modellers   38

1.12 Cells and Cell Systems   40

1.13 Unicellular Organisms   42

1.14 The Need for Cell Division   46

1.15 Cell Specialization   48

1.16 CASE STUDY: Cell Wars   50

1.17 INQUIRY INVESTIGATION: Water Movement in Plants   52

1.18 From the Ground Up   54

1.19 Examining the Leaf   58

1.20 CASE STUDY: Observations of a Naturalist   60

1.21 CASE STUDY: Animal Organ Systems Working Together   62

1.22 Fluid Movement in Animals   64

1.23 Animal Digestive Systems   68

1.24 INQUIRY INVESTIGATION: Factors That Affect Reaction Time   70

1.25 EXPLORE AN ISSUE: Tinkering with Cells   72

DESIGN CHALLENGE: Design and Build a Model or Simulation of Cells   74

SUMMARY   76

REVIEW   78

UNIT 2: FLUIDS 82

OVERVIEW 84

GETTING STARTED:
Fluids in Our Lives 86

2.1 A Close-Up Look at
Fluid Flow 88

2.2 Fluid Flow Around Objects 90

2.3 Viscosity: A Property
of Fluids 92

2.4 INQUIRY INVESTIGATION:
Liquids Can Be Thick or Thin 94

2.5 CAREER PROFILE: Viscosity
and the Chocolate Factory 96

2.6 Measuring Matter: Mass,
Weight, and Volume 98

2.7 INQUIRY INVESTIGATION:
Relating Mass and Volume 100

2.8 Density: Another Property
of Fluids 102

2.9 INQUIRY INVESTIGATION: Some
Liquids Just Don't Mix 104

2.10 Comparing Densities 106

2.11 The Ups and Downs of
Buoyancy 108

2.12 How and Why Do Things
Float? 110

2.13 DESIGN INVESTIGATION:
Another Way to Measure
the Density of a Liquid 112

2.14 CASE STUDY: From Bladders
to Ballast: Altering Buoyancy 114

2.15 EXPLORE AN ISSUE:
Human Impact on Natural
Fluid Systems 116

2.16 How Does Temperature
Affect Viscosity and Density? 118

2.17 CASE STUDY: Fluids and the
Confederation Bridge 120

2.18 INQUIRY INVESTIGATION:
How Fluids Handle Pressure 122

2.19 Confined Fluids Under
Pressure 124

2.20 Pressurized Fluid Systems:
Hydraulics 126

2.21 Pressurized Fluid Systems:
Pneumatics 128

2.22 DESIGN INVESTIGATION:
A Closer Look at Fluid
Power 130

2.23 Fluid Power at Work for Us 132

DESIGN CHALLENGE: Design and
Build a Device That Uses
the Properties of Fluids 134

SUMMARY 136

REVIEW 138

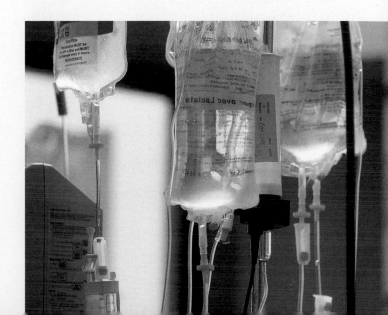

UNIT 3: MECHANICAL ADVANTAGE AND EFFICIENCY 142

OVERVIEW 144

GETTING STARTED: Using Machines to Get Things Done 146

3.1 Designing Machines 148

3.2 Levers: How They Work 150

3.3 DESIGN INVESTIGATION: Raise It Up 154

3.4 Simulating Human Movement 156

3.5 Pulleys, Wheel and Axle, and Gears 158

3.6 CASE STUDY: Mechanisms in Giant Machines 162

3.7 Moving Efficiently 164

3.8 Friction and Mechanical Advantage 166

3.9 DESIGN INVESTIGATION: Moving the Couch 168

3.10 CAREER PROFILE: Testing Force and Endurance 170

3.11 INQUIRY INVESTIGATION: Testing Shoes 172

3.12 Force, Area and Pressure 174

3.13 Pressure on Liquids and Gases 176

3.14 INQUIRY INVESTIGATION: Squeezing Liquids and Gases 178

3.15 Pressure in Fluid Systems 180

3.16 DESIGN INVESTIGATION: A Hydraulic Solution for a Pain in the Neck 182

3.17 CASE STUDY: A Student-Friendly Classroom 184

3.18 Designing for People with Special Needs 186

3.19 CASE STUDY: Mountain Bike or Road Bike? 188

3.20 The Life of a Product 190

3.21 EXPLORE AN ISSUE: A World Without Cars? 192

DESIGN CHALLENGE: Design and Build a Mechanical Model or Device 194

SUMMARY 196

REVIEW 198

UNIT 4: WATER SYSTEMS   202

OVERVIEW   204

GETTING STARTED: How Does
   Water Shape Our World?   206

4.1   Water in Our World   208

4.2   INQUIRY INVESTIGATION:
   Comparing Salt Water and
   Fresh Water   210

4.3   The Water Cycle   212

4.4   CASE STUDY: The Power
   of Water   214

4.5   The Water Table   216

4.6   The Human Side of Water
   Systems   218

4.7   Water Treatment and
   Disposal   220

4.8   CAREER PROFILE:
   Floods: Water Untamed   222

4.9   Geological Features at Sea
   and on Land   224

4.10   Glaciers: Rivers of Ice   228

4.11   INQUIRY INVESTIGATION:
   Rising and Falling   230

4.12   Currents   232

4.13   CASE STUDY: Water, Weather,
   and Climate   234

4.14   Waves   236

4.15   INQUIRY INVESTIGATION:
   Investigating Tides   238

4.16   Exploring the Deep   240

4.17   Oil: Wealth from the
   Ocean Floor   242

4.18   Diversity   244

4.19   INQUIRY INVESTIGATION:
   Productivity of Organisms   248

4.20   INQUIRY INVESTIGATION:
   The Brine Shrimp
   Experiment   250

4.21   EXPLORE AN ISSUE:
   People, Resources, and
   Water Systems   252

DESIGN CHALLENGE: Design and
   Build a Device to Live Safely
   with Water   254

SUMMARY   256

REVIEW   258

UNIT 5: OPTICS

UNIT 5: OPTICS   **262**

OVERVIEW   264

GETTING STARTED: Viewing Light Energy   266

5.1   Light Energy and Its Sources   268

5.2   INQUIRY INVESTIGATION: Watching Light Travel   272

5.3   Getting in Light's Way   274

5.4   Describing Images   276

5.5   INQUIRY INVESTIGATION: Reflecting Light Off a Plane Mirror   278

5.6   Reflecting Light Off Surfaces   280

5.7   INQUIRY INVESTIGATION: Viewing Images in a Plane Mirror   282

5.8   INQUIRY INVESTIGATION: Curved Mirrors   284

5.9   Using Curved Mirrors   286

5.10   INQUIRY INVESTIGATION: The Refraction of Light   288

5.11   Refracting Light in Lenses   290

5.12   INQUIRY INVESTIGATION: Investigating Lenses   292

5.13   The Human Eye and the Camera   294

5.14   The Visible Spectrum   296

5.15   The Electromagnetic Spectrum   298

5.16   CASE STUDY: A Telescope for Every Wave   300

5.17   INQUIRY INVESTIGATION: Mixing the Colours of Light   302

5.18   Additive Colour Mixing   304

5.19   CAREER PROFILE: Light Entertainment   306

5.20   DESIGN INVESTIGATION: Pigments and Filters for the Stage   308

5.21   Subtractive Colour Mixing   310

5.22   EXPLORE AN ISSUE: Solar Panels   312

DESIGN CHALLENGE: Design and Build a Device or System That Controls Light   314

SUMMARY   316

REVIEW   318

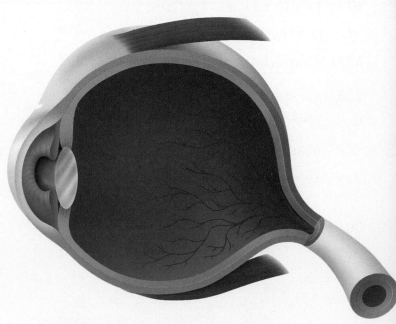

UNIT 6: SKILLS HANDBOOK 322

Safety in Science & Technology 324

Process of Scientific Inquiry 329

2A Process of Scientific Inquiry 329

2B Asking a Question 332

2C Predicting and Hypothesizing 334

2D Identifying Variables and Controls 335

2E Designing an Inquiry Investigation 337

Process of Design 339

3A The Problem-Solving Cycle 339

3B Identifying a Problem 342

3C Selecting the Best Alternative 343

3D Planning a Prototype 345

3E Building a Prototype 346

3F Testing and Evaluating a Prototype 347

3G Patents, Trademarks, & Copyrights 349

Researching 350

4A Research Skills 350

4B Interviewing and Survey Skills 352

4C Critical Thinking 354

Using Equipment in Science & Technology 356

5A Using the Microscope 356

5B Working with Scales and Balances 360

5C Using Other Scientific Equipment 362

5D Using Technology Equipment 363

5E Fabrication Techniques 366

Observing and Recording Data 372

6A Obtaining Qualitative Data 372

6B Obtaining Quantitative Data 375

6C Scientific & Technical Drawing 379

6D Creating Data Tables 383

Analyzing Results 384

7A The Need to Graph 384

7B Reading a Graph 386

7C Constructing Graphs 387

7D Using Math in Science & Technology 392

7E Reaching a Conclusion 394

7F Reflecting on Your Work 395

Communicating 396

8A Writing a Report 396

8B Creating a Design Folder 399

8C Multimedia Presentations 401

8D Exploring an Issue 403

Study Skills 404

9A Setting Goals and Monitoring Progress 404

9B Good Study Habits 406

9C Using Your Computer Effectively 408

9D Working Together 411

9E Graphic Organizers 413

PHOTO CREDITS 417

GLOSSARY 420

INDEX 425

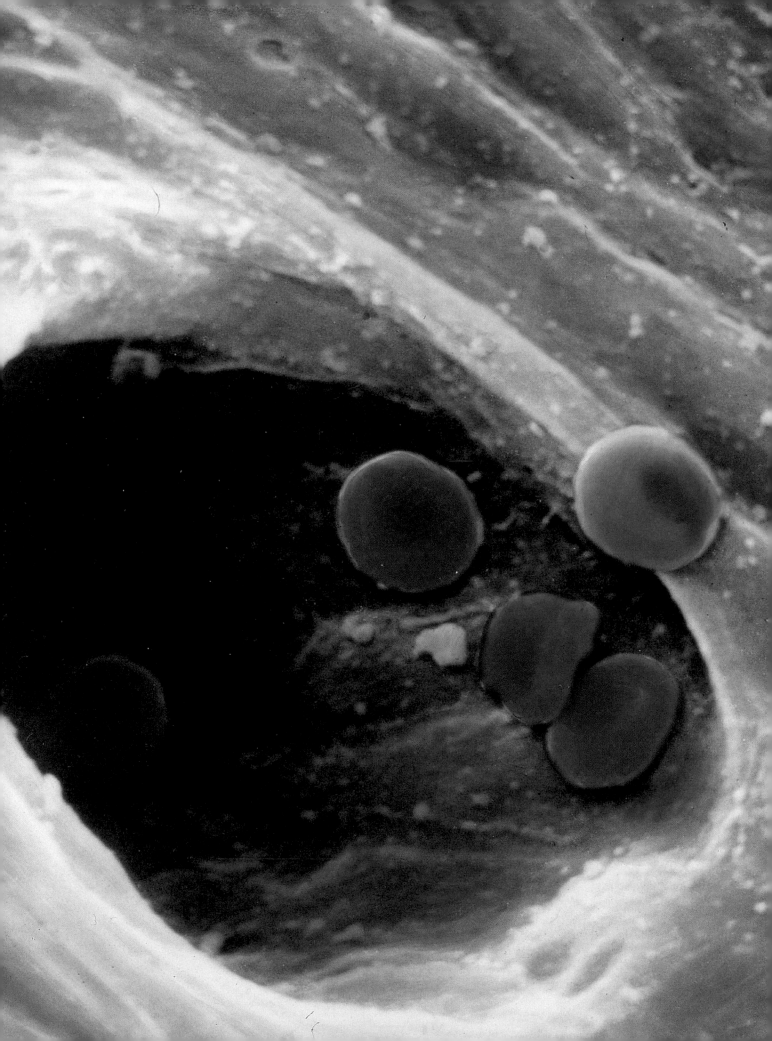

Unit 1

Cells, Tissues, Organs, and Systems

Unit 1 Overview

Getting Started: The Building Blocks of Living Things

1.1   Characteristics of Living Things

1.2   Inquiry Investigation: Using the Microscope

1.3   Plant and Animal Cells

1.4   Inquiry Investigation: Comparing Plant and Animal Cells

1.5   Technological Advances of the Microscope

1.6   Parts of a Cell Seen with an Electron Microscope

1.7   Cells in Their Environment

1.8   Osmosis

1.9   Inquiry Investigation: Observing Diffusion and Osmosis

1.10   Inquiry Investigation: How Does the Concentration of a Solution Affect Osmosis?

1.11   Career Profile: Modellers

1.12   Cells and Cell Systems

1.13   Unicellular Organisms

1.14   The Need for Cell Division

1.15   Cell Specialization

1.16   Case Study: Cell Wars

1.17   Inquiry Investigation: Water Movement in Plants

1.18   From the Ground Up

1.19   Examining the Leaf

1.20   Case Study: Observations of a Naturalist

1.21   Case Study: Animal Organ Systems Working Together

1.22   Fluid Movement in Animals

1.23   Animal Digestive Systems

1.24   Inquiry Investigation: Factors That Affect Reaction Time

1.25   Explore an Issue: Tinkering with Cells

Design Challenge: Design and Build a Model or Simulation of Cells

Unit 1 Summary

Unit 1 Review

Unit 1 Overview

Y ou are made of millions and millions of cells. Everything you do, everything you think, everything you feel requires millions of those cells to work together. Your cells have many tasks, and often those tasks must be carried out at the same time. How can so many cells be organized? Can they possibly all be the same? How do cells work, anyway?

Cells

All plants and animals, dead or alive, are made of cells.

You will be able to:

- determine if all cells are alike
- describe how living things made of a single cell are able to survive
- recognize how cells are organized into systems
- use a microscope to observe and draw plant and animal cells

Animal Systems

Animals are composed of one cell or systems of cells.

You will be able to:

- recognize that animals are made of one cell or groups of specialized cells
- use a microscope to observe and record how a single-cell animal moves and feeds
- question and find answers on how the cells in your body are organized into tissues, organs, and organ systems
- describe how food enters your blood
- recognize that your health depends on how well your cell systems work together
- collect data and analyze what can affect your reaction time

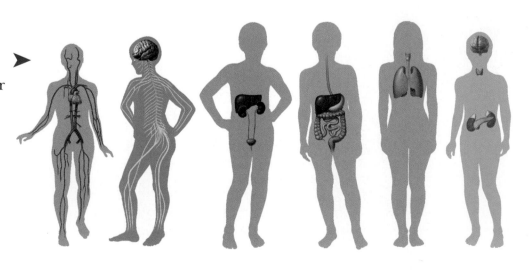

Plant Systems

Plants must be able to gather water and transport it to their leaves to survive.

You will be able to:

- recognize that plants are made of one cell or groups of specialized cells
- identify the structure and function of cells in plant tissues
- experiment and observe how water moves in a plant
- record your observations on diffusion
- design an investigation to show the effects of osmosis
- predict how plants can survive in different environments

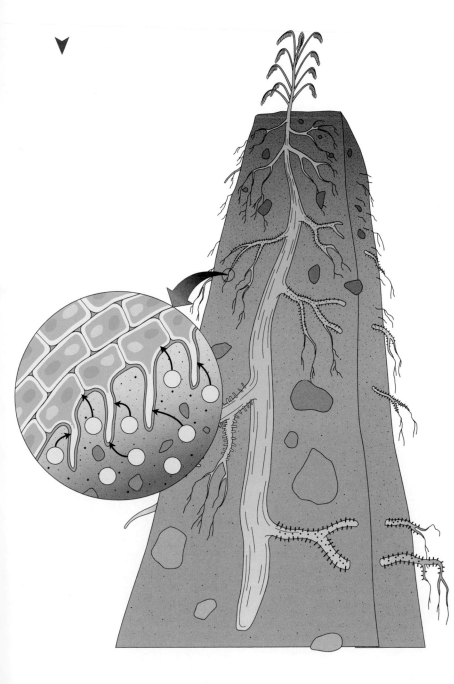

Design Challenge

You will be able to...

demonstrate your learning by completing a Design Challenge.

Model or Simulation of Cells

Scientists and technologists are trying to create artificial cells. They use the artificial cells as models of real cells, so they can understand how human cells work together.

In this unit you will be able to design and build:

1 **A Cell That Carries Oxygen**
Design and build a simulation of a red blood cell that carries oxygen to other cells.

2 **A Cell That Removes Dirt**
Design and build a model of a cell that could remove dirt from the lung.

3 **Artificial Skin**
Design and build a model of skin that will protect other cells.

To start your Design Challenge, see page 74.

Record your thoughts and design ideas for the Challenge when you see

Design Challenge

Getting Started

The Building Blocks of Living Things

1 You have no difficulty identifying your friend and yourself. But imagine how different the world would look if you could magnify with your eyes the way microscopes do. Imagine you could zoom right down to your friend's cells. Could you tell the difference between a cell from your arm and a cell from your friend's arm? What if you could see a cell from a fish's fin and a cell from your arm—could you tell which was which? And if you could see a cell in a lettuce leaf, could you tell it apart from a cell from your arm?

2 Just as a network of roads carries people and goods throughout a city, so a network of blood vessels, thousands of kilometres long, carries a living fluid throughout your body. The driving force is your heart, beating continuously over 40 million times a year, whether you are asleep or awake. Why do you need this system? What does it mean to say that blood is a living fluid?

3 Plants are an essential part of the circle of food and energy that connects all life on Earth. Plants make food, and you need that food either directly or indirectly to stay alive. To make that food, plants need water. But water flows downhill. How does water get from the ground up to the tip of the tallest tree? Is there any similarity between this movement, and the movement of blood from your heart to your head?

Reflecting

Think about questions **1**, **2**, **3**. What other questions do you have about cells, tissues, and organs? As you progress through this unit, reflect on your answers and revise them based on what you have learned.

 **The Apple Juice Test**

You would probably agree that you and your friend, the blood in your veins, the tallest tree, and the smallest speck of algae in a pond are all alive. But how can you tell what is living and what is not?

• Examine a small amount of sand and an equal amount of dry yeast.

1. Is there anything that you can see that makes sand different from yeast? You may want to look at differences in size, texture, colour, or shape.

• Pour equal amounts of apple juice into two containers, either 250-mL beakers or glasses.

2. (a) What do you think will happen when you put yeast in one of the containers? Record your prediction.

(b) Predict what will happen when you put sand in the other container. Record your prediction.

• Put 25 mL of sand in one container. Put 25 mL of yeast in the second container.

3. What happened in each of the containers?

4. Were you surprised by what you observed? How was what you predicted different from what you saw?

5. Why was it important to use an equal amount of sand and yeast, and an equal amount of apple juice in each container?

6. (a) Speculate about what happened in each container.

(b) From your observations and speculations, what new questions do you have that might be worth investigating?

Characteristics of Living Things

How do you know if something is alive? What do you look for in living things that tells you that they are alive? For example, is the volcano in **Figure 1** alive? You would probably say "no," but why?

The lava flowing down the sides of a volcano moves, just as some living things do. Is movement alone enough to identify living things?

In time, the volcano may get larger. Is this growth? Is change in size enough to identify a living thing?

Human beings breathe out gases. Gases also burst from the top of the volcano. Does this "breathing out" of gases mean that the volcano is alive?

To answer the question about the volcano, you must examine the characteristics of living things, shown in **Figure 2**. As you have seen, many non-living things show one characteristic of living things, and some, like the volcano, show several. Living things are often referred to as **organisms**. Before a thing can be classified as an organism, it must show *all* of the characteristics of living things.

Figure 1
Volcanoes "grow" and "breathe." Are they alive?

Figure 2
Characteristics of living things

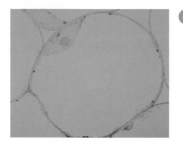

a Living things are composed of cells.

All cells are similar. This plant cell has similar features to other plant cells.

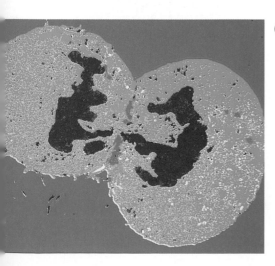

b Living things reproduce, grow, and repair themselves.

Cells reproduce by dividing in two. New cells are needed for growth and repair.

c Living things require energy.

Plants get their energy from the Sun. Animals get the energy they need by eating plants, or by eating other animals that got their energy from plants.

d Living things respond to the environment.

The response might be to another organism or to many other factors.

Cell Theory

By looking closely at living things over the centuries, scientists have gathered a great deal of evidence to support what they call the cell theory:

• All living things are composed of cells.

• All cells come from pre-existing cells.

The cell theory has proven very powerful in helping scientists to understand the workings of the human body and the bodies of other animals and plants.

(e) Living things have a life span.

Living things exist for only a limited period of time.

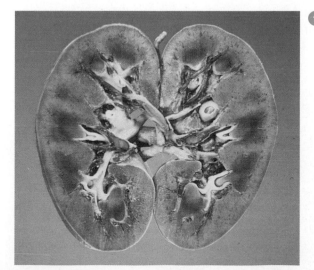

(f) Living things produce wastes.

Your kidneys filter wastes from your blood.

Understanding Concepts

1. What are the important differences between living and non-living things?

2. Are volcanoes living things? Explain.

3. Name at least one characteristic of living things that is shown in each of the following examples.

   (a) A plant bends toward the light.

   (b) A tadpole develops into a frog.

   (c) Human lungs breathe out carbon dioxide.

   (d) A blue jay feeds on sunflower seeds.

   (e) A cat gives birth to kittens.

4. Make a table listing the six characteristics of living things in one column. In the second column, next to each characteristic, suggest a non-living thing that shows the characteristic.

Reflecting

5. How do scientists determine whether to consider something as an organism?

Design Challenge

In your Challenge you will create a model to represent a living cell or a group of cells that work together. What kinds of difficulties do you expect when using non-living materials to represent a living thing?

Using the Microscope

Because cells are very small, you must make them appear larger in order to study them. Since a hand lens isn't powerful enough, you will need to use a compound light microscope to view cells closely. **Figure 1** shows a compound light microscope.

Question

Can a microscope be used to estimate the size of small objects?

Hypothesis

If you can estimate the number of objects that you can fit across a microscope's field of view, then you can estimate the size of each object.

Experimental Design

In this investigation you will find the diameter of the field of view of your microscope under low and medium power using a ruler. (The **field of view** is the circle of light you see through the microscope.)

Most high-power lenses have a field of view that is less than 1 mm wide, so you won't be able to use a ruler for the high-power lens. You will use a ratio. You will then estimate how many objects could fit into each field to determine the size of an object.

5A

Materials

- compound microscope
- transparent ruler
- newspaper
- scissors
- microscope slides
- cover slips
- lens paper

🛑 Never use the coarse-adjustment knob with medium or high power.

Use care when handling slides and cover slips. They are made of glass and may shatter if dropped.

Procedure

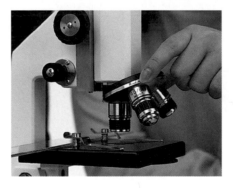

1 With the low-power lens in place, put a transparent ruler on the stage.
- Position the millimetre marks of the ruler below the objective lens.
- Using the coarse-adjustment knob, focus on the marks of the ruler.
- Measure the field of view.

✏️ (a) Record the diameter of the field of view under low power.

2 Rotate the nosepiece to the medium-power lens.
- Use the fine-adjustment knob to bring the lines on the ruler into focus.

(a) Why should the coarse-adjustment knob not be used with the medium- and high-power lenses?
- Measure the field of view.

✏️ (b) Record the diameter of the field of view under medium power.

3 To determine the field of view under high power, follow these steps:
- Calculate the ratio of the magnification of the high-power lens to the low-power lens.

$$\text{Ratio} = \frac{\text{magnification of high-power lens}}{\text{magnification of low-power lens}}$$

- Use the ratio to determine the diameter of the field of view under high-power magnification.

$$\text{Diameter of field (high power)} = \frac{\text{diameter of field (low power)}}{\text{ratio}}$$

✏️ (a) Show your calculations.

Figure 1
A compound light microscope.

coarse-adjustment knob

fine-adjustment knob

low-power objective lens
medium-power objective lens
high-power objective lens

Exploring

1. (a) Use convex lenses and a cardboard tube to construct a microscope.

(b) How does your microscope compare with the compound light microscope shown? Calculate the magnification of your microscope using the techniques discussed.

Analysis

6 Analyze your results by answering the following.

(a) What happens to the diameter of the field of view as you move from low to high magnification?

(b) Explain why the size of objects viewed under high power is usually recorded in micrometres (μm), rather than millimetres (mm) (1000 μm = 1 mm).

(c) Devise a way to estimate the size of the letter *f*.
  • Describe your method.
  • Construct an equation that could be used in calculating size.
  • Calculate the size of the letter you viewed under the microscope.

(d) Which magnification would be best for scanning several objects?

(e) The cell shown in **Figure 2** is viewed under low power. When you rotate the microscope to high power, you cannot see an image, no matter how much you try to focus.
  • Why can't the image be seen?
  • Suggest a solution.

Figure 2
A cell under low power

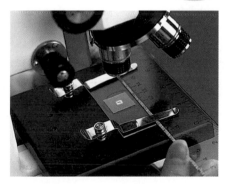

4 Find and cut out an *f* from a newspaper.
  • Place the *f* in the centre of a microscope slide.
  • Hold a cover slip between your thumb and forefinger. Place the edge of the cover slip down on one side of the letter.
  • Gently lower the cover slip onto the slide so that it covers the letter.

5 Place the slide on the centre of the microscope stage with the letter right-side up.
  • Use the stage clips to hold the slide in position.
  • Estimate the number of copies of the letter *f* that could fit across the field of view.

  (a) Record your estimate.

Plant and Animal Cells

"Because there are so many different kinds of organisms, there must be at least as many different kinds of cells." Do you agree with this hypothesis? Surprisingly, there are more similarities than differences among cells. The cells of all plants and the cells of all animals have many structures in common.

Using a microscope, it is quite easy to tell plant cells from animal cells, as you will discover. However, it is difficult to tell which plant cell came from which plant, and which animal cell came from which animal. It is much easier to tell what the cell does, and in what part of the animal or plant it was found. The features of cells that you can see through a light microscope are shown in **Figure 1**.

Animal Cell Structures

Most animal cells have these structures.

1. Control: The Nucleus

The **nucleus** is the control centre. It directs all of the cell's activities.

2. Control: Chromosomes

Chromosomes are found inside the nucleus. **Chromosomes** contain genetic information, which holds "construction plans" for all of the pieces of the cell.

3. Materials: The Cell Membrane

The **cell membrane** acts like a gatekeeper, controlling the movement of materials like nutrients and waste into and out of the cell.

4. Materials: The Cytoplasm

Most of the cell is cytoplasm, a watery fluid. The **cytoplasm** allows materials to be transported quickly between structures in the cell. The cytoplasm also stores wastes until they can be disposed of.

5. Materials Storage: The Vacuole

Each vacuole is filled with fluid. A **vacuole** is used to store water and nutrients, such as sugar and minerals.

Figure 1

Features of cells that can be seen using a light microscope

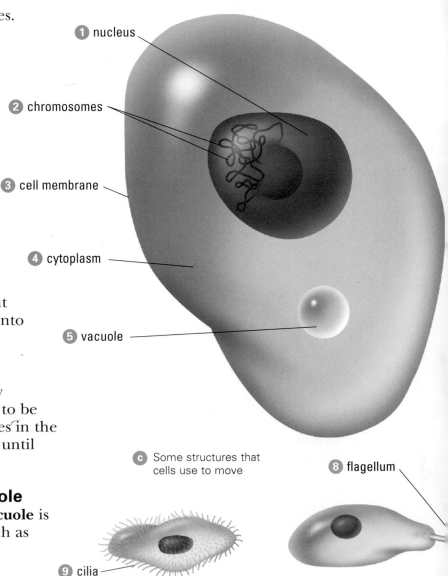

a Structures that can be seen in most animal cells

1 nucleus
2 chromosomes
3 cell membrane
4 cytoplasm
5 vacuole

c Some structures that cells use to move

8 flagellum

9 cilia

Plant Cell Structures

Plant cells contain the same features as animal cells, but they also have some special structures not found in animal cells. (As you look at a plant cell, it may appear that the cell doesn't have a cell membrane. The cell membrane is just hard to see.)

5. Materials Storage: The Vacuole

Just as in animal cells, the **vacuole** is filled with nutrients. However, the vacuole takes up a much larger part of the cytoplasm of a plant cell.

6. Protection: The Cell Wall

The **cell wall** protects and supports the plant cell. Gases, water, and some minerals can pass through small pores (openings) in the cell wall.

7. Food Production: Chloroplasts

Chloroplasts contain many molecules of a green chemical called chlorophyll. Chlorophyll allows plant cells to make their own food, using light from the sun. Animal cells cannot do this.

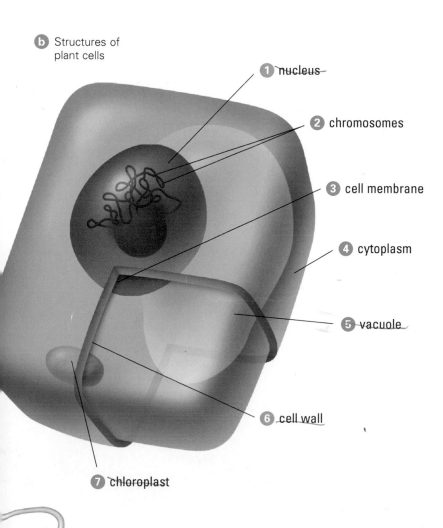

b Structures of plant cells

1 nucleus
2 chromosomes
3 cell membrane
4 cytoplasm
5 vacuole
6 cell wall
7 chloroplast

Understanding Concepts

1. Construct a table summarizing the similarities and differences of animal and plant cell structures.

Structure	Plant Cell	Animal Cell	Function
nucleus	yes	yes	• control centre • directs cell activities
?	?	?	

2. Where in a cell is genetic information found?

Making Connections

3. A biologist finds a cell with what appears to be two nuclei (plural of nucleus). What conclusion might you make about why this cell appears to have two nuclei?
4. Predict what might happen to a cell if the cell membrane were replaced by a plastic coat that prevented molecules from entering or leaving the cell.

Structures for Movement

Some cells must move. They may have special structures to help them move.

8. Movement: The Flagellum

The flagellum is a whiplike tail that helps some cells to move. They are not found on all cells.

9. Movement: Cilia

Cilia are tiny hairs that work together to move a cell or to move the environment surrounding the cell. They are not found on all cells.

Design Challenge

When you are building your model cell, what structures will you have to include? How can you represent them in the model?

1.4 Inquiry Investigation

SKILLS MENU
○ Questioning   ● Conducting   ● Analyzing
○ Hypothesizing   ● Recording   ● Communicating
○ Planning

Comparing Plant and Animal Cells

You have learned about some of the structures inside plant and animal cells. In this investigation you will examine plant and animal cells under a microscope. Being able to identify cell structures is important in understanding their functions.

Question
How do plant cells differ from animal cells?

Hypothesis
If a microscope is used, then plant cells can be differentiated from animal cells by their structures.

Experimental Design
In this investigation you will prepare a wet mount of onion cells. You will use the slide to identify structures within plant cells. You will use a prepared slide to examine the parts of an animal cell.

Materials
- onion
- tweezers
- microscope slide
- medicine dropper
- water
- cover slip
- light microscope
- safety goggles
- rubber gloves
- iodine stain (Lugol's)
- paper towel
- lens paper
- prepared slide of human epithelium (skin cells)

Procedure

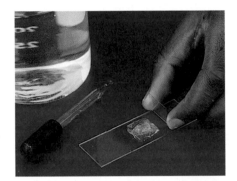

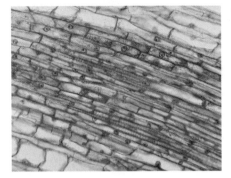

1 Using a knife, your teacher will remove a small section (about 2 cm^2) from an onion.
- Use tweezers to remove a single layer from the inner side of the onion section. If the layer you removed is not translucent to light, then try again.

 Iodine will irritate eyes, mouth, and skin. It may stain skin and clothing. Do not touch the stain with bare hands, and do not touch your face after using the stain.

2 Place the onion skin in the centre of a slide. Make sure the skin does not fold over.
- Place two drops of water on the onion skin.
- From a 45° angle to the slide, gently lower a cover slip over the onion skin, allowing the air to escape. This is called a **wet mount**.
- Gently tap the slide with the eraser end of a pencil to remove any air bubbles.

3 Place the slide on the stage and focus with the **5A** low-power objective lens in place.
- Move the slide so the cells you wish to study are in the centre of the field of view.
- Rotate the nosepiece of the microscope to the medium-power objective lens and use the fine-adjustment knob to bring the cells into view.

(a) Draw and describe **6C** what you see.

SKILLS HANDBOOK: **5A** Using the Microscope   **6C** Scientific & Technical Drawing

Figure 1

By looking at cells under a microscope, you can tell if they came from a plant or an animal.

Exploring

1. Do the cells of bananas and green peppers have the same shape as the onion cells? A toothpick can be used to scrape cells from a banana or a green pepper.

   (a) Devise a technique that allows you to view these cells.

   (b) Describe the technique.

   (c) Are all plant cells the same?

4 Switch to low power and remove the slide. Put on rubber gloves and goggles.
- Place a drop of iodine stain at one edge of the cover slip. Touch the opposite edge of the cover slip with paper towel to draw the stain under the slip.
- View the cells under medium and high power.

   (a) What effect did the iodine have on the cells?

   (b) Draw a group of four cells. Label structures you see.

   (c) Estimate the size of one cell.

5 Switch to low power.
- Remove the slide containing plant cells.
- Dispose of the onion skin, as directed by your teacher.
- Clean the slide and cover slip with lens paper.

6 Place the prepared slide of human epithelial cells on the stage.
- Using the coarse-adjustment knob, locate and focus on a group of the cells.
- Switch to medium power and focus using the fine-adjustment knob.

   (a) Is the arrangement of plant and animal cells different? Explain.

   (b) Draw a group of four cells and label the cell structures you can see.

   (c) Estimate the size of each cell.

Analysis

7 Analyze your results by answering the following.

   (a) In what ways do the onion skin cells differ from the human skin cells?

   (b) Why is it a good idea to stain cells?

   (c) Predict the function of the onion cells that you observed under the microscope. What prominent cell structures would justify your prediction?

   (d) Explain why the cells of an onion bulb do not appear to have any chloroplasts. (Don't all plant cells have chloroplasts?)

   (e) A student viewing onion cells sees just large, dark circles. What might have caused the dark circles? Did anyone in your class experience this difficulty?

1.5

Technological Advances of the Microscope

Advances in cell biology are directly linked with advances in optics. As biologists see and learn more about cells, they want instruments that provide them with greater detail. Optical scientists and technologists respond by investigating light and solve the problems of the biologists by creating better and better microscopes. Better microscopes allow biologists to develop a deeper understanding of how the cells that make up organisms function.

The Single-Lens Microscope

Some of the best of the earliest microscopes were made by Anton van Leeuwenhoek in the 1660s. He was curious about the microscopic world and constantly worked at improving his design. His microscopes, **Figure 1**, had only a single lens that magnified things 10 or more times. Nevertheless, he was astonished when he looked at a water drop and saw numerous tiny organisms.

The Compound Light Microscope

Biologists found a single lens limiting—they couldn't see the details needed to understand how cells work. An important advance came when a second lens was added to the microscope. An image magnified 10× by the first lens and 10× by the second lens is viewed as 100× larger.

There is a limit to what can be done with glass lenses and light. To make images larger, lenses must become thicker. But as lenses become thicker, the images they produce begin to blur. Eventually the image is so blurred that no detail can be seen.

The light microscope (**Figure 2**) is limited to about 2000× magnification. To see the detail within a human cell, greater magnification is needed. The development of the electron microscope provided this window.

Figure 1

Leeuwenhoek's microscopes used a single lens mounted between two brass plates to magnify objects.

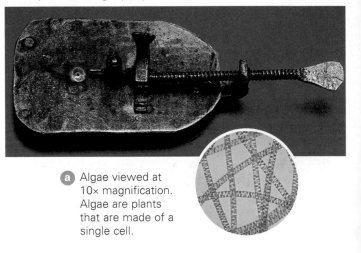

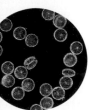

a Algae viewed at 10× magnification. Algae are plants that are made of a single cell.

Figure 2

Light microscope

a Algae cells seen through a light microscope

The Transmission Electron Microscope

These microscopes are capable of 2 000 000×
magnification! Instead of light, transmission electron
microscopes use a beam of electrons that pass through
the specimen of cells or tissues. (Electrons are tiny
particles that travel around the nucleus of an atom.)

Transmission electron microscopes (**Figure 3**) have
two major limitations. First, specimens that contain many
layers of cells, such as a blood vessel, cannot be examined.
The electrons are easily deflected or absorbed by a thick
specimen. Very thin slices of cells (sections) must be used.
These thin sections are obtained by encasing a specimen
in plastic, and then shaving very thin layers off the plastic.
The second limitation is that mounting cells in plastic kills
them. That means only dead cells can be observed.
Although the transmission electron microscope is ideal for
examining structures within a cell, it does not allow you to
examine the details of a many-celled insect eye, or a living
cell as it divides.

The Scanning Electron Microscope

The scanning electron microscope (**Figure 4**) was a
response to the limitations of the transmission
microscope. It uses electrons that are reflected off a
specimen. This allows a digital three-dimensional
image to be created. Because this instrument uses
only reflected electrons, it doesn't matter how thick
the specimen is, but only the outside of the specimen
can be seen. Also, the scanning electron microscope
cannot magnify as much as the transmission microscope.

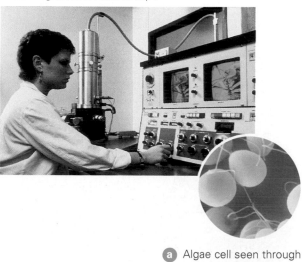

Figure 4
Scanning electron microscope

(a) Algae cell seen through
the scanning electron
microscope

Figure 3

The transmission electron microscope uses
magnets to concentrate a beam of electrons
directed at a specimen.

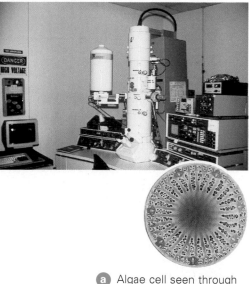

(a) Algae cell seen through
a transmission electron
microscope

Understanding Concepts

1. Give one advantage of a
compound light microscope over
a single-lens microscope.

2. Give one advantage of a scanning
electron microscope over a
transmission electron microscope.

3. Describe differences in the
appearance of algae cells when
viewed with each of the
microscopes.

4. Which microscope would you
recommend for viewing each of
the following? Give reasons for
your choice.

   (a) the detailed structure of a
   cell's nucleus

   (b) a single cell

Reflecting

5. Imagine that you could direct a
team of technologists to invent a
new microscope. What would you
want that new microscope to do?
How would this benefit society?

Parts of a Cell Seen with an Electron Microscope

The cytoplasm, the working area of every cell, contains special structures called **organelles**. Many of these tiny structures can be seen only with a transmission electron microscope. The organelles described below are found in both plant and animal cells, although **Figure 1** shows an animal cell.

1. Energy: Mitochondria

Mitochondria (singular is mitochondrion) provide the cells with energy. In a process called **respiration**, mitochondria release energy by combining sugar molecules with oxygen to form carbon dioxide and water. This energy is used in almost every other function of the cell.

2. Protein Manufacturing: Ribosomes

Proteins are put together on **ribosomes** using information from the nucleus and molecules from the cytoplasm. Proteins are large molecules that are needed for cell growth, for repair, and for reproduction.

3. Material Transport: Endoplasmic Reticulum

A series of folded membranes, called **endoplasmic reticulum**, carry materials through the cytoplasm. "Rough" endoplasmic reticulum has many ribosomes attached to it.

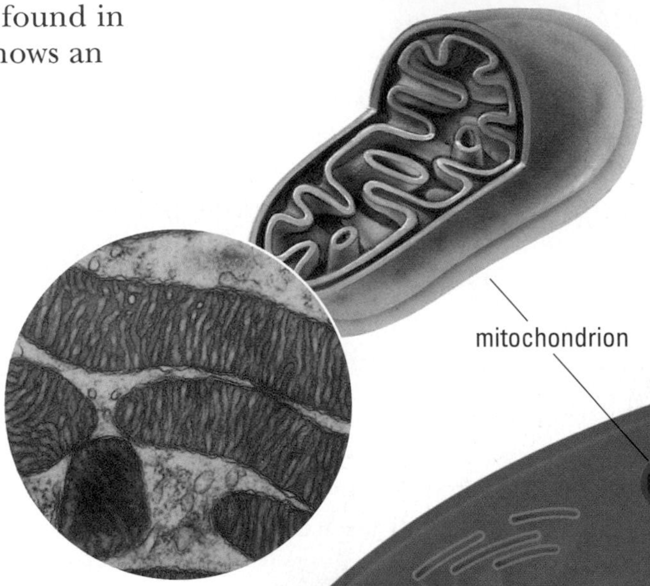

1. Mitochondria, often referred to as the "powerhouse" of the cell, are the largest of the cytoplasmic organelles.

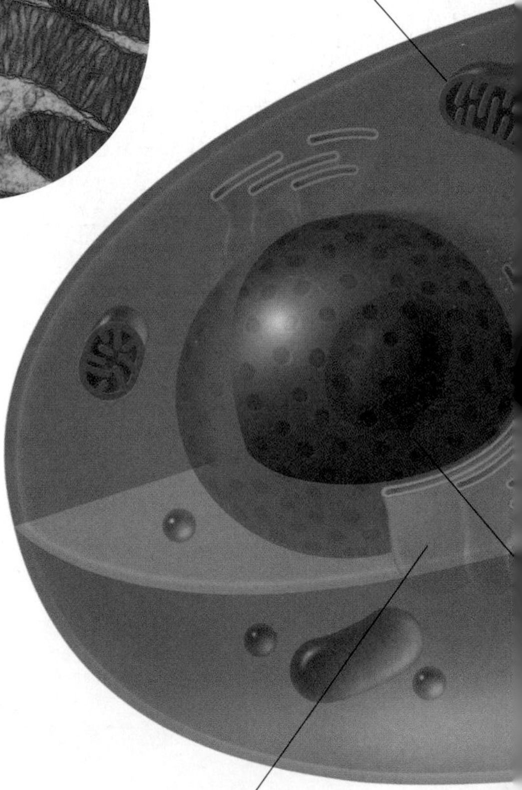

mitochondrion

Figure 1

These organelles are found in animal and plant cells.

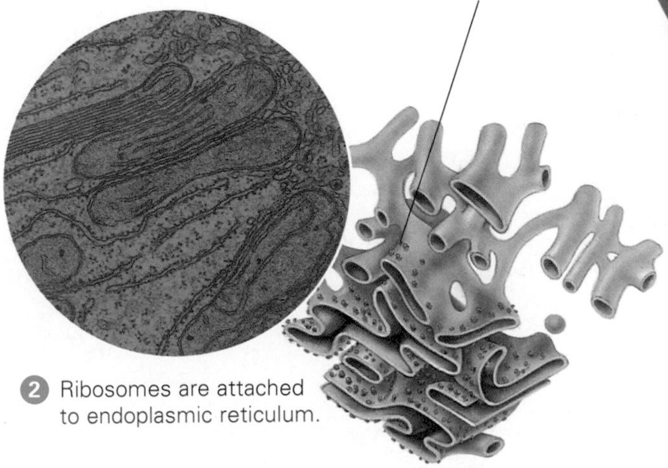

ribosome

endoplasmic reticulum

3. Endoplasmic reticulum may appear rough or smooth. It looks rough when it is supporting ribosomes.

2. Ribosomes are attached to endoplasmic reticulum.

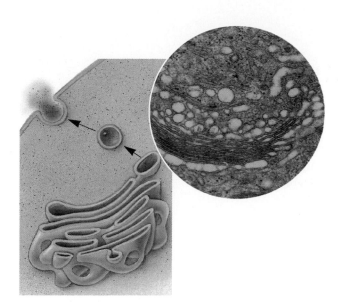

4. Protein Storage: The Golgi Apparatus

Proteins are stored inside the **Golgi apparatus**. This organelle also puts proteins into packages, called vesicles. Vesicles carry the protein molecules to the surface of the cell, where they are released to the outside. The proteins in the vesicles vary, depending on their function.

5. Recycling: Lysosomes

Lysosomes patrol the cytoplasm, cleaning up. They contain special proteins that are used to break down large molecules into many smaller molecules. The smaller molecules can be reused as building blocks for other large molecules. In humans and other animals, lysosomes are also used to kill and digest invading organisms.

Golgi apparatus

4 The Golgi apparatus, named after its discoverer, Camillo Golgi, may release packages of molecules to the outside of the cell.

cell membrane

lysosome

nucleus

5 Damaged and worn-out cells are destroyed by their own lysosomes. Therefore, lysosomes are sometimes referred to as "suicide sacs."

Understanding Concepts

1. What are organelles?

2. Make a concept map showing cell structures and their functions. Include the structures that are visible with a light microscope and an electron microscope.

3. Predict what would happen to a cell if its mitochondria stopped working.

Making Connections

4. Cells lining the stomach release enzymes that aid digestion. Digestive enzymes are protein molecules. Explain why many Golgi apparatuses are found in stomach cells.

Design Challenge

You have learned about the organelles inside a cell. When you build a specialized cell, should your design include some of these organelles? Explain.

Cells in Their Environment

Imagine if you had to live inside a sealed plastic bag. How long would you survive? Well, not long without holes so oxygen could enter. Soon, you would need a way to get water and food through the plastic. Even this would not be enough. You would also need a way of removing wastes, such as carbon dioxide and urine.

In some ways, the cell membrane is like that plastic bag. However, the cell membrane is also much more complex, as you can see in **Figure 1**.

Cell Membranes

Cells allow some materials to enter or leave, but not others. They are said to be permeable to some materials and impermeable to others. Permeable means permitting passage, and impermeable means not permitting passage.

In general, small molecules pass easily through the cell membrane, medium-sized molecules move through less easily, and large ones cannot pass through without help from the cell. Because it allows certain substances to enter or leave, but not others, the cell membrane is said to be **selectively permeable**.

Figure 1

The cell membrane has two layers of fat (lipid). Embedded in the fat layers are protein molecules (coloured blobs) and pores made of protein. There are pores of several different sizes.

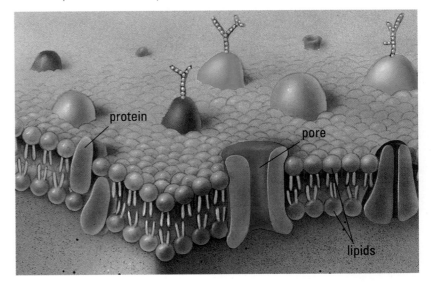

Diffusion

In **Figure 2** a blob of ink gradually spreads out and colours the whole beaker of water. Why doesn't the ink remain as a small blob? What causes it to move outward?

The molecules of the ink blob are constantly moving and colliding with other ink molecules and with the molecules of the water. When they collide, they bounce off each other. This causes molecules that are concentrated in one area to gradually spread outward. **Diffusion** is the movement of molecules from an area of high concentration to an area of lower concentration.

Figure 2

Ink diffusing in water.

Diffusion and Cells

Diffusion is one of the ways substances move into and out of cells. A substance that a cell uses up, such as oxygen, will be in low concentration inside the cell. Outside the cell, the concentration of the substance will be higher. The molecules of the substance will diffuse across the cell membrane into the cell. Diffusion will continue until the concentration of the substance is the same inside and outside the cell.

Waste products, such as carbon dioxide, tend to become more concentrated inside the cell than outside, so they will diffuse out of the cell.

Try This Models of Membranes

Look at **Figure 3**. Compare the permeability of the three materials—glass, mesh, and cloth—covering the jars.

1. Which covering is impermeable to all three substances?

2. Which covering is permeable to all three substances?

3. Which covering is impermeable to some substances, but permeable to others?

4. Name two other materials that are permeable to some of the substances shown, but impermeable to the others. Test the permeability of the substances for yourself.

Figure 3
Three "membranes"—glass, wire or plastic mesh, and cloth.

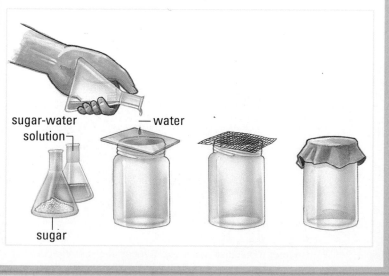

sugar-water solution
water
sugar

Understanding Concepts

1. Explain in your own words the process of *diffusion*.

2. Explain what is meant by impermeable, permeable, and selectively permeable materials.

3. What type of membrane do cells have? Explain why.

4. Hypothesize why the pores in the cell membrane are of different sizes.

Making Connections

5. The pores of cells aren't always open. Sometimes they are locked. In humans and many other animals, insulin acts like a key to a lock. Insulin is a protein released by the pancreas into the blood. Once in the blood, insulin molecules can reach all the cells of the body. An insulin molecule is able to attach itself to the cell membrane of cells. When it does, one kind of pore opens. Sugar from the blood can then enter the cell through the open pore.

   (a) Imagine a mechanism that would allow insulin to open a pore. Draw a diagram showing how insulin would open the pore.

   (b) People who are unable to produce insulin have diabetes. What problem would be caused by not producing insulin?

   (c) What organelles within the cell would be most affected by a lack of insulin? Explain your choice.

Osmosis

Have you ever gone to the refrigerator to snack on some crisp vegetables, only to find that the celery stalks are limp? As it loses water, celery droops, as you can see in **Figure 1**. It will become crisp again if water moves back into the cells of the vegetable. Osmosis is the reason wilted celery becomes crisp after being put in water.

Water molecules are small, and they move across cell membranes easily by diffusion. The diffusion of water through a selectively permeable membrane is called **osmosis**. In a normal situation, water molecules are constantly passing through the cell membrane, both into and out of the cell. If there is an imbalance, more water will move in one direction than in the other. The direction of the water movement depends on the concentration of water inside the cell compared with the concentration outside the cell.

Figure 1

This stalk of celery will become crisp again if put in water.

A Model of Osmosis

Water can pass freely through the membrane in **Figure 2**, but the protein molecules are too large to move through the pores. The membrane is permeable to water, but impermeable to the larger protein molecules. Osmosis refers only to the diffusion of water from an area of greater concentration of water to an area of lesser concentration of water.

Figure 2

This model of a semi-permeable membrane shows osmosis at work.

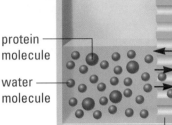

protein molecule
water molecule

selectively permeable membrane

a The concentration of pure water is 100%. When materials are dissolved in pure water, the concentration of water is lowered.

Which side has the greater concentration of water? (Water molecules are shown in blue.) There are fewer protein molecules on side X, but many more water molecules. Side X has a greater concentration of water. Water will diffuse from side X, the area of higher water concentration, to side Y, the area of lower water concentration.

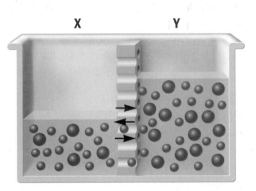

b The membrane allows water to move back and forth through it. However, more water is passing from X to Y then from Y to X.

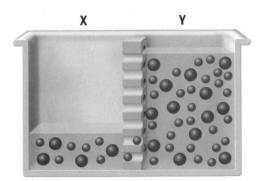

c When the concentration of water on sides X and Y is equal, water molecules still move through the membrane. However, they move in and out at the same rate.

Cells in Solutions of Different Concentrations

The movement of water into and out of cells is vital to living things, and it is driven by imbalances in concentration. Ideally, the solute concentration outside the cell is equal to that inside the cell. A solute is a substance that is dissolved in another substance, the solvent. In cells, salts and sugars are common solutes, and water is the solvent.

Figure 3 shows the three different environments that a cell may find itself in.

a

b
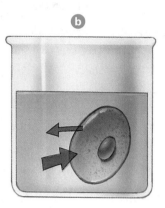

c
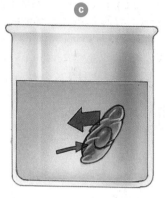

In **A**, the concentration of solute molecules outside the cell *is equal to* the concentration of solute molecules inside the cell. This means that the concentration of water molecules inside the cell is the same as the concentration outside the cell. There is no net movement of water into or out of the cell. The size and shape of the cell remain the same.

In **B**, the concentration of solutes outside the cell *is less than* that found inside the cell. This means that the concentration of water molecules is greater outside the cell than inside the cell. More water molecules move into the cell than out of the cell. The cell increases in size. Cell walls protect plant cells, but animal cells may burst if too much water enters.

In **C**, the concentration of solutes outside the cell *is greater than* that found inside the cell. This means that the concentration of water is greater inside the cell than outside the cell. More water molecules move out of the cell than into the cell. The cell decreases in size. If enough water leaves, the cell may die.

Figure 4

Markets spray their produce with water. Can you explain why?

Turgor Pressure

Have you ever noticed that when salt is used on sidewalks and roads during the winter, the surrounding grass may wilt or die in the spring?

If the concentration of water outside a plant cell is higher than inside it, water molecules enter the cell by osmosis. The water fills the vacuoles and cytoplasm, causing them to swell up and push against the cell wall. This outward pressure is called **turgor pressure**. When the cell is full of water, the cell wall resists the turgor pressure, preventing more water from entering the cell. As you can see in **Figure 5**, turgor pressure supports plants, causing their leaves and stems to stay rigid.

In the spring, the salt used on the road during the winter combines with water from the snow to create a solution. The concentration of salt in this solution is much higher than the concentration of salt in the cells of the grass. There is a higher concentration of water inside the cell, so water moves out of the grass cells by osmosis. As water leaves the cells, the cells shrink—their cytoplasm pulls away from the cell wall. Without this support, the grass wilts. If water is not restored to the cells, the grass will die.

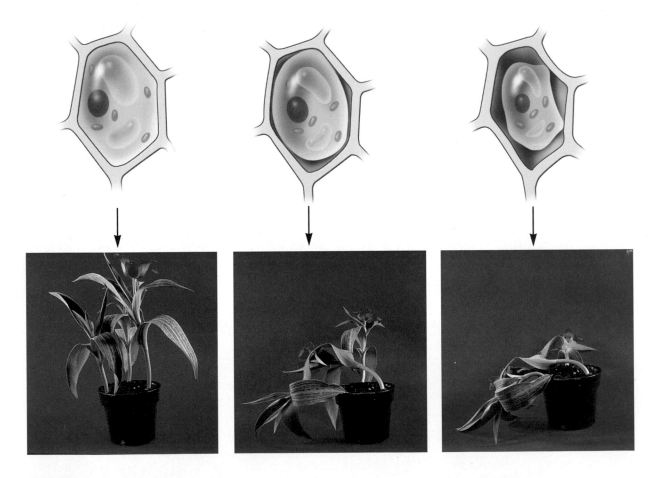

Figure 5

As a plant loses turgor pressure, it begins to wilt.

Try This An Egg as an Osmosis Meter

You can use an egg to study osmosis.

- Place an uncooked egg, with its round end down, in a small jar that can hold it as shown in **Figure 6**. Note how far down the egg sits.
- Remove the egg and fill the jar with vinegar, until the vinegar reaches the level where the egg was.
- Put the egg back in the jar and allow it to stand with its bottom touching the vinegar for 24 h. (The vinegar will dissolve the bottom of the egg's shell.)
- Remove the egg and rinse it with cold water.
- Dispose of the vinegar. Rinse the jar and refill it with distilled water.
- Using a spoon, gently crack the pointed end of the egg and remove a small piece of shell, without breaking the membrane underneath.
- Insert a glass tube through the small opening and the membrane. Seal the area around the tube with candle wax, as shown in **Figure 6**.
- Place the egg in the jar of water.

1. Predict what will happen to the level of water in the glass tube.
2. Observe your egg osmosis meter after 24 h.
3. Explain your observations.

Figure 6

An egg osmosis meter

Understanding Concepts

1. How are osmosis and diffusion different? How are they the same?
2. What determines the direction of water movement into or out of cells?
3. What prevents a plant cell from bursting when it is full of water?
4. Explain why animal cells are more likely than plant cells to burst when placed in distilled water.
5. Describe turgor pressure in your own words.

Making Connections

6. Based on what you have learned about osmosis, explain why grocery stores spray their vegetables with water.
7. You lose a solution of salt and water when you perspire. After extreme exertion on a very hot day, a person who drinks only water to replace lost fluid may become ill. An examination of the person's blood after drinking the water would reveal that many red blood cells have become swollen and that some have ruptured. Why would the red blood cells burst?

Design Challenge

All cells are subject to osmosis if they are immersed in a pure water solution. How does an understanding of osmosis help you to modify your design? Make a list of problems that must be solved to prevent the cell from shrinking or bursting.

Observing Diffusion and Osmosis

Smaller molecules move easily through cell membranes, while larger molecules, such as proteins, cannot. By studying the movement of molecules across a membrane, you will develop a better understanding of how cells respond to different environments.

In this investigation you will use dialysis tubing to represent a cell membrane. Dialysis tubing is a non-living, selectively permeable cellophane material. It is used in dialysis treatment of a person with damaged kidneys (**Figure 1**).

Question

Which molecules move through a dialysis membrane?

Hypothesis

1 Read the Experimental Design and Procedure and write a hypothesis for this investigation.

Experimental Design

This is a controlled investigation of the movement of a substance through a selectively permeable membrane.

Materials

- apron
- safety goggles
- rubber gloves
- 2 medicine droppers
- distilled water in wash bottle
- 4% starch solution
- microscope slide
- iodine solution
- 100-mL graduated cylinder
- funnel
- 2 beakers, 250 mL
- dialysis tubing
- scissors

Iodine solution is toxic and an irritant. It may stain skin and clothing. Use rubber gloves when cleaning up spills and rinse the area of the spills with water.

Procedure

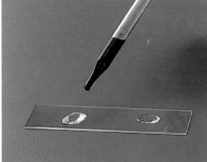

2 Put a drop of water on one end of a microscope slide and a drop of starch solution on the other end.

- Add a small drop of iodine solution to each of the drops on the slide.

(a) Record your observations.

(b) Iodine is used as an indicator. Which substance can be identified using iodine?

3 Cut two strips of dialysis tubing (about 25 cm long) and soak them in a beaker of tap water for 2 min.

- Tie a knot near one of the ends of each strip of dialysis tubing.
- Rub the other end of the dialysis tubing between your fingers to find an opening (as you would to open a flat plastic bag).

4 Using a graduated cylinder, measure 15 mL of the 4% starch solution.

- Use a funnel to help pour the solution into the open end of a dialysis tube.
- Twist the open end of the dialysis tube and tie it in a knot.
- Rinse the funnel and graduated cylinder and use them to put 15 mL of distilled water in the second dialysis tube.

SKILLS HANDBOOK: **2C** Predicting and Hypothesizing   **6C** Scientific & Technical Drawing

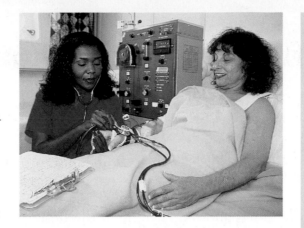

Figure 1

Kidneys normally filter waste from the blood by taking advantage of osmosis and diffusion. Patients whose kidneys are damaged cannot remove this waste without the help of a dialysis machine.

Figure 2

Dialysis tubings with different solutions

distilled water   distilled water   4% starch solution

4% starch solution   distilled water   distilled water

5 Rinse the outside of the dialysis tubes with distilled water to remove any fluids that may have leaked out.

- Place each dialysis tube in a 250-mL beaker containing 100 mL of distilled water.

Design Challenge

What materials would best represent a cell membrane for your Challenge?

6 Add 20 drops of iodine to the beakers.

  (a) Observe the dialysis tubes for any colour change and record your observations.

- After 10 min, remove the dialysis tubes from the beakers.

  (b) Do the tubes seem different in mass? Record your observations.

Making Connections

1. Explain why dialysis tubing provides a good model for a cell membrane.

2. What are some of the limitations of dialysis tubing as a model of a cell membrane?

Exploring

3. How do cells respond to environments with different solute concentrations? Investigate how a concentrated salt solution and distilled water affect onion cells and liver cells. The technique developed in 1.4 can be used for this investigation.

Analysis

7 Analyze your results by answering the following.

(a) List some molecules that move by diffusion and osmosis. Include any laboratory evidence you have.

(b) Which dialysis tube acted as a control?

(c) Do your observations support your hypothesis?

6C Draw a diagram showing what you believe happened in each of the beakers and showing movement of molecules.

(d) What would you have observed if dialysis tubing were permeable to starch?

(e) **Figure 2** shows three different situations. Predict and explain any changes that would occur for each dialysis tube.

Cells, Tissues, Organs, and Systems   **35**

1.10 Inquiry Investigation

SKILLS MENU
○ Questioning   ● Conducting   ● Analyzing
● Hypothesizing   ● Recording   ● Communicating
● Planning

How Does the Concentration of a Solution Affect Osmosis?

One method of increasing food production is to increase the amount of land used to grow plants. (Humans around the world use about 10% of the available land for growing crops, **Figure 1**.) Deserts seem a good place to start. Adding water, as in **Figure 2**, has allowed farming in the desert. Unfortunately, the irrigation of arid land is not a complete technological solution to feeding the world. Like most technologies, irrigation brings benefits and risks.

Most of the water used for irrigation contains small amounts of salts. During the heat of the day, some of the water evaporates from the soil, leaving the salts behind. After years of watering, a salty crust of minerals forms on top of the soil. Salts draw water from plant cells by osmosis, causing wilting.

Question

How does the concentration of salts in the soil affect potatoes?

Hypothesis

(2C) **1** Write a hypothesis for this experiment.

Experimental Design

2 Plan an experiment to test your hypothesis.

(2E) Things to consider:
- Potato cubes, placed in salt solutions of various concentrations, will change in volume and mass as water moves into or out of the potato cells.
- How will you measure the movement of water into and out of the pieces of potato?
- What are your independent and dependent variables?
- What variables will you attempt to control during the experiment?

3 Explain in detail how you will investigate the relationship between water loss from potatoes and the salt concentration of the soil.

4 Create a table for recording your data.

5 Submit your procedure and your table to your teacher for approval.

Materials

- potato cubes
- salt (to make solutions of various concentrations)
- distilled water
- 10-mL graduated cylinder
- ruler
- triple-beam balance
- test tubes
- beakers
- medicine droppers
- goggles

Procedure

6 Conduct your experiment.

Analysis

7 Analyze your results by answering the following.

(a) Plot a graph showing any changes you measured, with mass or volume along the y-axis and time along the x-axis.

(b) Interpret your data and draw a conclusion. How good was your hypothesis?

SKILLS HANDBOOK: (2C) Predicting and Hypothesizing   (2E) Designing an Inquiry Investigation

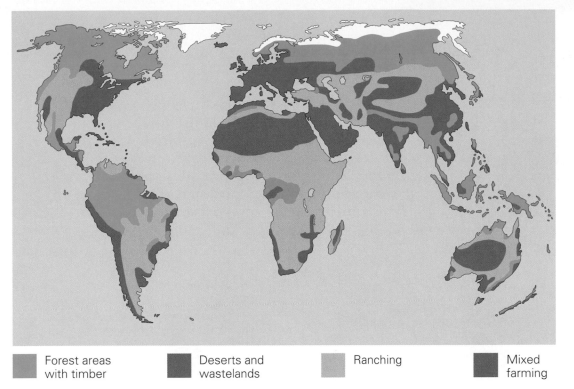

■ Forest areas with timber	■ Deserts and wastelands	■ Ranching	■ Mixed farming

Figure 2
An irrigation system enables crops to grow on arid land.

(c) Explain how it might be possible for two groups of students to perform the same experiment, yet collect different data (measurements of mass or volume).

(d) Write your investigation as a report.

Making Connections

1. Why would the irrigation of plants with sea water be harmful?

2. Predict why potatoes grown in mineral-rich soils, such as those found in Prince Edward Island, are better tasting than those grown hydroponically (in water).

Reflecting

3. What would you change to improve your procedure? How would these changes give more accurate results?

Design Challenge

How can the principles of experimental design be used to test your model cell?

Cells, Tissues, Organs, and Systems **37**

Modellers

Engineers have often looked to nature for their designs. Soaring birds have inspired designers of gliders and airplanes. Feathers and fur were models for synthetic fabrics designed to trap body heat and repel water and wind. The structure of the human ear has served as a model for the telephone, stereo speakers, and radio receivers.

Figure 1

Inspired by gliding birds, engineers perfected the basic form of human flight machines — large wingspan, lightweight body construction, and tailfins for balance.

Models of the Body

Medical researchers have also studied our bodies, seeking ways to replace parts that are damaged or worn out with model parts similar to the original. Artificial limbs were likely the first of these structures. For many years now machines that imitate kidneys (dialysis machines) have filtered the blood of people who have severely damaged kidneys. Artificial pacemakers set the heart rate for patients with a failed heart rhythm. Artificial Teflon and ceramic hips have allowed people a second chance to walk.

Figure 2

A dialysis machine is designed to work like a large exterior kidney.

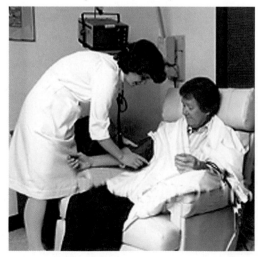

Models of Cells

Scientists have begun to make their models smaller and smaller as they attempt to learn more about what happens inside cells. Dr. Thomas Chang, a scientist from McGill University, has devoted more than three decades to building and investigating artificial cells. His artificial cells function much like natural cells. He uses them as models in order to find out how real cells are damaged by poisons in the environment. For example, artificial cells were important in developing treatments for blood poisoning resulting from metals such as aluminum and iron.

Artificial cells have also been tested in the treatment of diabetes and liver failure. Still other types of artificial cells are being tested for the treatment of hereditary diseases. The cell membranes of artificial cells are being studied to gather information about drug delivery systems. The possibilities seem almost limitless.

Buildings have "bones" too.

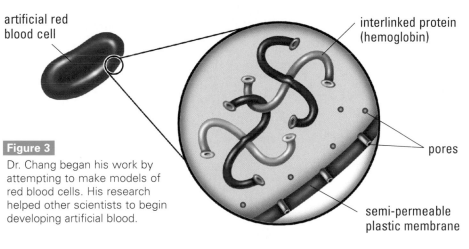

Figure 3

Dr. Chang began his work by attempting to make models of red blood cells. His research helped other scientists to begin developing artificial blood.

Labels: artificial red blood cell; interlinked protein (hemoglobin); pores; semi-permeable plastic membrane

---

Try This — Make a Model of Primitive Cells

Scientists believe that life began somewhere between 3.9 and 3.5 billion years ago. One of the important steps in the process was the formation of a cell membrane. One hypothesis for how the first cell membranes formed involves tiny structures called microspheres, made of protein and fats.

• Put approximately 6 mL of water in a large test tube.

• Using an eyedropper, add 10 drops of vegetable fat and then carefully add a single drop of sudan IV indicator.

• Place a stopper in the test tube and shake it well.

1. Describe the microspheres.

2. What happens when two microspheres touch?

3. How is the barrier created by the microsphere similar to a cell membrane?

Cells and Cell Systems

Have you ever been part of a team? Successful teams are not always the ones with the most gifted players; success depends upon how well the players cooperate.

A multicellular organism, such as yourself, can be compared to a team: all of your cells must work together. A cell that works on its own faster or more efficiently than other cells is not necessarily a better cell. It can even be life-threatening. For example, a cell that uses nutrients more quickly or reproduces faster than other cells could be a cancer cell.

Cell Organization

A group of cells that are similar in shape and function is called a **tissue**. For example, skin that covers the outside surfaces of your body is made of epithelial tissue. Epithelial tissue also covers the inside surfaces of your body and provides support and protection for your body structures.

Tissues are often organized into larger structures called **organs**. Many organs are composed of several different types of tissues. Each organ has at least one function. For example, the heart is an organ. It pumps blood through your body. It is made of several tissues, as you can see in **Figure 1**.

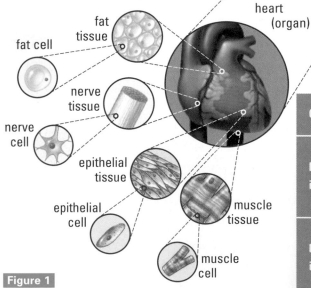

Figure 1

Your heart, an organ, is made of several different kinds of tissue. Each tissue is made of cells that are similar. For example, epithelial cells tend to be long and flat. Cells from different tissues look different. Cells in nerve tissue do not look like cells in muscle tissue.

Organ system	Circulatory system	Nervous system	
Major organs in the system	heart, arteries, capillaries, veins	brain, spinal cord, eyes, ears, nerves to and from body parts	
Major tissues in the system	epithelial, nerve, connective, muscle, blood	nerve, connective, epithelial	
Major functions	transportation of nutrients, dissolved gases, and wastes to and from body cells	response to environment and control of body activities	

LEVELS OF CELL ORGANIZATION

Organ systems are groups of organs that have related functions. The circulatory system includes the heart; arteries that carry blood from the heart to the tissues; capillaries where nutrients and wastes are exchanged; and veins that carry blood and wastes from the tissues back to the heart. Nerve tissue, blood, epithelial tissue, connective tissue, and muscle tissue are all found in the circulatory system. Many of the other organ systems in the body appear in **Figure 2**, the Levels of Cell Organization chart.

Figure 2

The organs of the human body and the bodies of all large organisms are organized into organ systems.

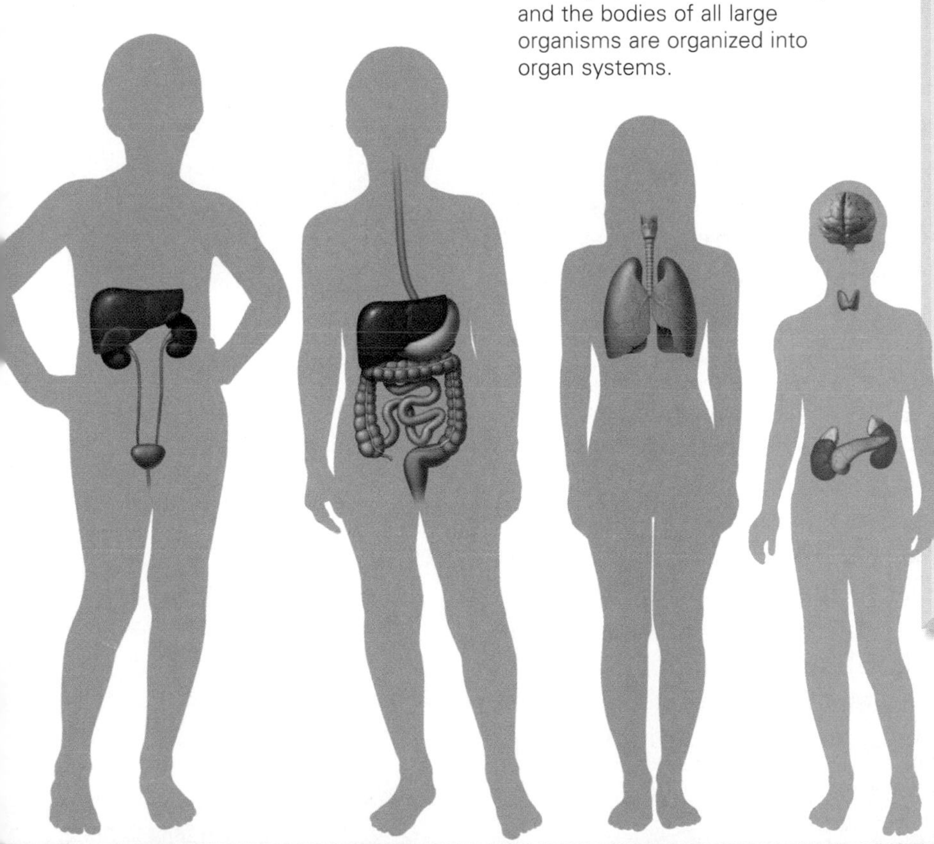

Understanding Concepts

1. Define *tissue*, *organ*, and *organ system*. Describe three levels of organization in complex, multicellular organisms. Give an example of each.

2. Organize the following structures from smallest to largest and give an example of each: *organ system*, *tissue*, *cell*, *organ*, and *molecule*.

3. Choose one of the human organ systems and construct a concept map. Arrange the structures in your concept map from smallest to largest.

Making Connections

4. Make a chart comparing the levels of cell organization to the levels in an organization that you are familiar with, such as a sports organization.

Reflecting

5. If cells are the basic unit of life, why are tissues, organs, and organ systems required in large multicellular organisms?

	Excretory system	Digestive system	Respiratory system	Endocrine system
	kidneys, bladder, ureters, urethra, liver	esophagus, stomach, intestines, liver	lungs, windpipe, blood vessels	pancreas, adrenal glands, pituitary gland
	epithelial, nerve, connective, muscle	epithelial, nerve, connective, muscle	epithelial, nerve, connective, muscle	epithelial, nerve, connective
	removal of wastes	chemical and physical breakdown of food into molecules small enough to pass into cells	gas exchange	coordination and regulation of body activities

Unicellular Organisms

You are a multicellular organism. You have many specialized cells that work together to carry out all of life's functions. However, many living things are composed of just one cell. These unicellular organisms, referred to as **microorganisms** or microbes because they are only visible under a microscope, must also carry out all of life's functions. The single cell is responsible for feeding, digestion, excretion, and reproduction.

The Importance of Microorganisms

Most people become aware of microorganisms when they get sick. However, it is unfair to think of microorganisms just in terms of disease. It's true that they cause many diseases, but most are harmless and many are even helpful, as you can see in **Figure 1**. Dairy products such as buttermilk, cottage cheese, and yogurt are produced by the action of microorganisms.

Bacteria

Bacteria (singular form is *bacterium*) are among the most primitive and also the most plentiful organisms on the planet. They are said to be very successful because they have survived and changed little over several billion years (**Figure 2**). Some, like plants, can make their own food. Others are parasites. (Parasites can live by invading the body of an animal or a plant.) Some bacteria can even live with little or no oxygen. There are bacteria in every Earth environment, even in hot springs. Bacteria are different from animal and plant cells in that they have no nucleus, no mitochondria, and no ribosomes.

a Each droplet sprayed into the air during a sneeze could contain thousands of microorganisms.

b Microorganisms decompose dead plants and animals into chemical building blocks that can be recycled by plants into food for humans and other animals.

Figure 1

Some microorganisms make us sick, but without the others we could not survive.

pili: These hairlike structures help bacteria to attach to each other and to surfaces. They also help bacteria to move.

flagellum: Some bacteria have whiplike tails to help them move.

chromosome: The genetic material of bacteria is organized in one chromosome. There is no nucleus.

cell membrane: Regulates movement of materials into and out of the cell

Figure 2

A typical bacterium

cell wall: Provides rigid support

capsule: A sticky coating surrounds disease-causing bacteria. The capsule makes it difficult for animals' white blood cells to destroy these bacteria.

Protists

If you look into a drop of pond water, you will find an incredible collection of **protists**. Almost anywhere there is water, even in moist soil or in rotting leaves, you will find protists. Unlike bacteria, protists have a nucleus and contain organelles such as mitochondria, ribosomes, and lysosomes.

Plantlike Protists

Diatoms

Diatoms are found in both fresh and salt water. They contain chlorophyll and can make their own food. Diatoms are encased in two thin shells joined together. **Figure 3** shows some diatoms.

Euglena

Euglena (**Figure 4**) is like both a plant and an animal cell. If there is lots of sunlight, euglena acts like a plant and makes its own food. With reduced sunlight, euglena acts like an animal and begins feeding upon smaller cells.

Figure 3

Each species of diatom has a unique shape. They all have symmetrical grooves and pores.

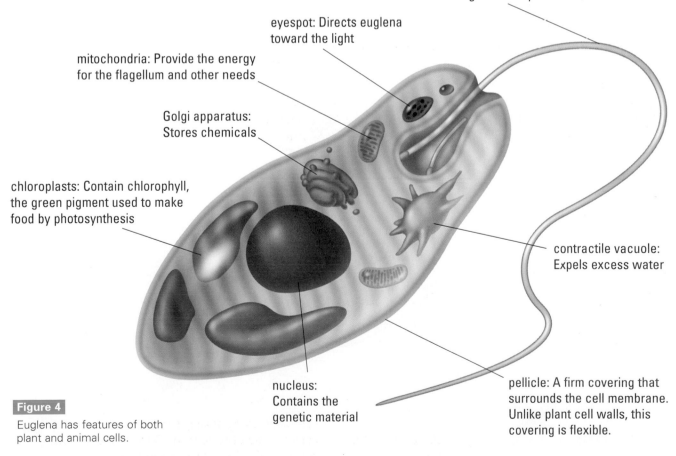

flagellum: Helps the cell to move

eyespot: Directs euglena toward the light

mitochondria: Provide the energy for the flagellum and other needs

Golgi apparatus: Stores chemicals

chloroplasts: Contain chlorophyll, the green pigment used to make food by photosynthesis

contractile vacuole: Expels excess water

nucleus: Contains the genetic material

pellicle: A firm covering that surrounds the cell membrane. Unlike plant cell walls, this covering is flexible.

Figure 4

Euglena has features of both plant and animal cells.

Animal-like Protists

Animal-like protists cannot make their own food and must feed on things that are living or were once alive. They have all of the organelles of an animal cell, and, like euglena, they have a contractile vacuole.

Amoeba

As the amoeba moves, it changes shape (**Figure 5**). These bloblike organisms move by stretching out a branch of cytoplasm, called a pseudopod (false foot). The pseudopod anchors to an object, and the rest of the cell is dragged toward it. This method of movement is also used by animal white blood cells, including the ones in your blood vessels. The crawling motion of the amoeba is also used for feeding.

Paramecium

The paramecium (plural *paramecia*), like the amoeba, uses structures designed for movement to help it feed (**Figure 6**). Tiny hairlike structures, called cilia, beat together to create water currents that move the paramecium. There are also cilia around the paramecium's oral groove. These cilia draw food into the groove. Bacteria and other smaller cells are the main food source for paramecia.

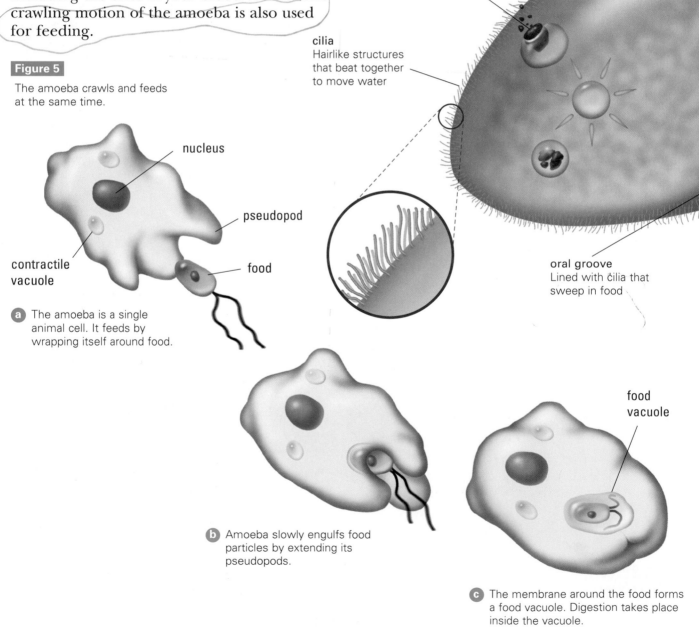

Figure 5

The amoeba crawls and feeds at the same time.

nucleus

pseudopod

contractile vacuole

food

a The amoeba is a single animal cell. It feeds by wrapping itself around food.

anal pore
Expels waste

cilia
Hairlike structures that beat together to move water

oral groove
Lined with cilia that sweep in food

b Amoeba slowly engulfs food particles by extending its pseudopods.

food vacuole

c The membrane around the food forms a food vacuole. Digestion takes place inside the vacuole.

Figure 6

The paramecium is also a single animal cell that must perform most of the functions that your body performs.

macronucleus
Contains genetic material that regulates cell function

micronucleus
Contains genetic information that is exchanged between paramecia during reproduction

food vacuole
Where food is slowly digested

gullet
A cavity at the end of the oral groove. Here the food enters a food vacuole.

contractile vacuole
Pumps out excess water; prevents the paramecium from bursting

Fungus

Fungi (singular *fungus*) include many organisms that are multicellular. Bread mould, mushrooms, and puff balls are well-known fungi. Harmful fungi include those that cause ringworm, Dutch elm disease, and athlete's foot. However, there are some unicellular fungi.

Yeast, the Unicellular Fungus

Yeast is one of the few unicellular fungi (**Figure 7**). There are many different species of yeast. Like animal cells, yeast cells do not have chlorophyll and must rely on other organisms for their source of energy.

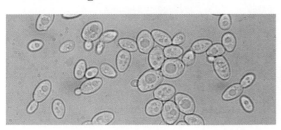

Figure 7
Using a microscope, it is difficult to tell that yeast are living.

Understanding Concepts

1. Why do you think bacter
   considered to be more p
   than other cells that you have studied?

2. Why are diatoms called plantlike protists?

3. Compare euglena to a plant cell. Make a list of similarities and differences.

4. Compare the process of feeding in the paramecium and amoeba.

Making Connections

5. Why do many people associate microorganisms with disease?

6. Using the information that you have gained about osmosis, indicate why euglena, paramecia, and amoebas need contractile vacuoles.

7. Penicillin is an antibiotic that weakens the cell wall of bacteria. The sugars and proteins in the cytoplasm of the bacteria are in higher concentration than they are in their environment. Draw a series of diagrams showing how penicillin kills bacteria.

Exploring

8. What effect do chemicals such as caffeine have on unicellular organisms? State your hypothesis, and design an experiment to test it. With your teacher's approval, conduct your experiment.

Design Challenge

There are cells in the tubes that lead to your lungs that have cilia much like those of paramecium. Human white blood cells, like amoeba, engulf and digest foreign particles. Examine the structures of the unicellular organisms carefully. Would any of these features be useful in your model cell? Consider looking to primitive cells for assistance with your Challenge.

The Need for Cell Division

All large plants and animals, including yourself, are composed of many cells rather than one large cell. Why? Cells can grow, but there is a limit. Eventually every cell reaches a size at which it must divide.

Is Smaller Better?

Think about how far chemical messages travel in a large cell, compared with a small cell. Before the nucleus can tell the organelles in the cytoplasm what to do, it must first receive messages from the cell's surroundings. The bigger the cell is, the longer it takes for messages to reach the nucleus, and for the rest of the cell to receive instructions from the nucleus. Cells must be small for these chemical messages to travel quickly, so the cells can react to changes in their environment. Just one example of why this is important is shown in **Figure 1**.

Cells also need a constant supply of nutrients to work well. Waste products must be removed from the cell. Molecules enter into and pass out of cells through the cell membrane. The more cell membrane there is compared to the volume of the cell, the more efficient the cell is in taking in nutrients and eliminating waste. The amount of cell membrane can be described in terms of the surface area of the cell.

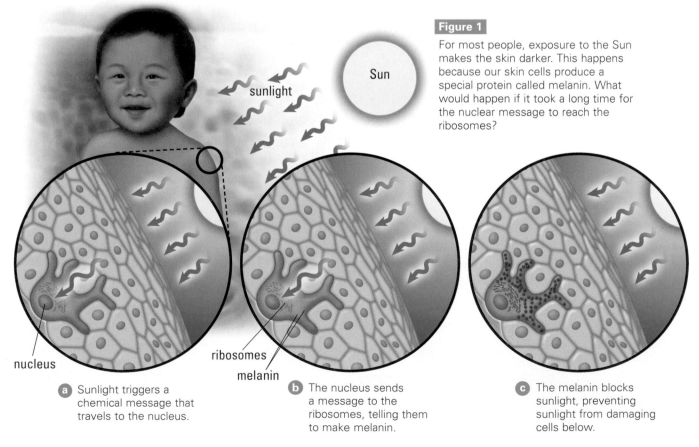

Figure 1

For most people, exposure to the Sun makes the skin darker. This happens because our skin cells produce a special protein called melanin. What would happen if it took a long time for the nuclear message to reach the ribosomes?

Sun

sunlight

nucleus

ribosomes

melanin

a Sunlight triggers a chemical message that travels to the nucleus.

b The nucleus sends a message to the ribosomes, telling them to make melanin.

c The melanin blocks sunlight, preventing sunlight from damaging cells below.

Comparing the Surface Areas of Small and Large C

You will need eight sugar cubes and a ruler to try this comparison.

1. Predict whether many small cells or one large cell would be more effective at exchanging nutrients and wastes. See if you still agree with your prediction after you have completed this activity.

- Measure the length and width of a sugar cube in millimetres. The cube represents a small cell.

- Calculate the surface area of a single sugar cube. To calculate surface area, find the area of each face and then find the sum of those areas.

- To find the surface area of eight sugar cubes, multiply the surface area of the single cube by eight.

- Arrange eight sugar cubes to form a large cube. This block of sugar cubes represents one large cell.

- Measure the length and width of the large cube. Calculate the surface area of the large cube.

- Compare the surface area of the eight individual cubes with that of the large cube. Which is greater?

2. Which has more cell membrane for nutrients and waste materials to pass through: one large cell or eight small cells?

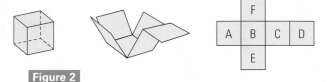

Figure 2
Area of A = length × width
Surface area of cube = 6 × area of A

Some Big, Some Small

Some cells in your body are larger than others. For example, cells in fat tissue are bigger than cells in muscle tissue. Do you know why? If you compare the sizes of cells and their functions, you will find that cells that must do a lot of work are usually smaller than cells that are not as active. The more active a cell is, the more nutrients it needs and the more wastes it produces. Many small cells together are more efficient at exchanging nutrients and waste than one large cell. This is because a group of small cells have a greater surface area than a single large cell.

Understanding Concepts

1. Which size of cell is most efficient at transporting messages from its surroundings to its nucleus: small or large? Explain.

2. Which size of cell would be more efficient at transporting nutrients in and waste materials out—big or small?

3. Explain why highly active cells, such as muscle cells, tend to be small.

Exploring

4. Which cell has the greater surface area if their volumes are the same:

   (a) a cell shaped like a sphere or a cell shaped like a cube?

   (b) a cell with a smooth surface or one with many projections?

Cell Specialization

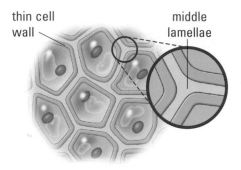

thin cell wall

middle lamellae

(a) Thin-walled plant cells are found in the flexible tissues of the leaf, flower, fruit, and root. Most edible plant roots, such as potatoes and radishes, are composed of these cells.

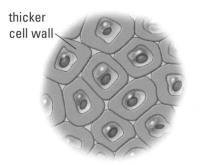

thicker cell wall

(b) Thick-walled plant cells are specialized for support. Their stretchable cell walls are flexible. The tough strings of the celery stalk are made of these cells.

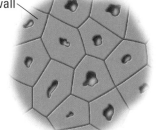

thickest cell wall

(c) Very thick cell walls provide rigid support. The cell wall can get so thick, as the plant matures, that it becomes difficult for nutrients to enter the cell. The cell usually dies, leaving an empty chamber surrounded by a thick wall. Fabrics such as linen are made from these cells.

Figure 1

Plants, like animals, are made of tissues and organs. Each kind of tissue contains a special type of cell.

Imagine how difficult life would be without specialists. Could you build your own television? Grow your own food? Do your own surgery?

Unicellular organisms are not specialists. Each cell must carry out all the functions of life. Multicellular organisms, such as you, benefit from **cell specialization**. We have cells that come in a variety of sizes and shapes, each designed to carry out a special function.

Specialized Plant Cells

The long, thin strings inside a celery stalk, the pit in an apricot, the thin leaves of the lettuce are all evidence that there is a variety of different types of plant cells (**Figure 1**).

The cell wall is one very noticeable feature of plant cells. As plants develop, a primary cell wall is formed around each cell. Once the plant stops growing, an additional secondary cell wall may form inside the primary cell wall. This structure provides added strength.

The spaces between plant cells, referred to as the middle lamellae, contain a sticky, sugary substance called pectin. Pectin acts like cement, sticking plant cells together. The sticky syrup that often forms on the top of a baked apple pie is pectin.

1 Nerve tissue
Nerve cells tend to be long and thin. Many nerve cells are protected by a coating of insulation that prevents short circuits.

3 Blood tissue
(a) Red blood cells carry oxygen in a special protein called hemoglobin. The cells are filled with this protein.
(b) White blood cells protect the body from invaders by engulfing them and digesting them, or by killing them with antibodies.

5 Fat tissue
In fat cells, most of the cytoplasm is occupied by a vacuole that stores fat molecules.

Specialized Animal Cells

The shape of animal cells provides a clue to their function. Many of the features of unicellular organisms can be found in animal cells as you can see in **Figure 2**.

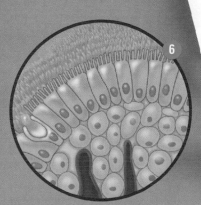

Figure 2

Some specialized cells found in human bodies.

2 The respiratory system
a Particles that attempt to enter your lungs are trapped in mucous and then swept away from the lungs by cells with cilia.
b Cells of the lung are very thin. This allows gases to exchange rapidly between the air and the blood.

4 The stomach
Your stomach contains a powerful acid. Cells of the lining of the stomach are protected from the acid by a layer of mucous. These cells also have many Golgi apparatuses to store the proteins that break down food.

6 The small intestine
Cells that line the small intestine absorb food. Fingerlike projections increase the surface area for absorption.

Understanding Concepts

1. What are the advantages of cell specialization for an organism?
2. Predict what might happen to multicellular plants if a microorganism that digests pectin was accidentally released from a laboratory.
3. What is the advantage of a highly folded cell membrane?
4. What advantage does a thick, flexible plant cell wall provide over a thick, rigid cell wall?
5. Examine the cell shape in **Figure 3**:

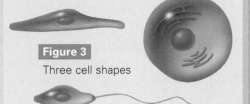

Figure 3

Three cell shapes

   (a) Which cell would be best suited as an egg cell? Give your reasons.
   (b) Which cell would be best suited for movement? Give your reasons.
   (c) Which cell would be best suited as a covering for an organ? Give your reasons.
6. Identify body cells that have a structure similar to that of a unicellular organism.

Reflecting

7. Why are specialized cells dependent on other specialized cells?

Design Challenge

Is the structure of the cell that you are building suited for its special function? What changes should you make in your design now that you know more about specialized cells?

Cell Wars

Many years ago, tens of thousands of people died during epidemics of disease, yet no one knew what caused the disease. Imagine how frightening it was to face an invisible killer! A **disease** is a condition that interferes with the well-being of an organism.

The Invaders

Today we know that many diseases are caused by agents that invade the body and interfere with the normal activities of cells. The invasion is called infection. Some of the invaders are living things, such as bacteria, fungi, or parasitic worms. These invaders either rob cells of their nutrients or produce waste products that poison cells. In either case, the invaders can kill the cell.

(a) Speculate about how the invention of the microscope might have helped doctors to understand what caused diseases.

Viruses

Viruses are often grouped with living invaders; however, viruses are not living things because they are not true cells. A virus contains no nucleus, cytoplasm, organelles, or cell membrane. The virus is a small strand of genetic information covered by a protein coat.

Viruses are only active once they invade a living cell. They take over the cell and turn it into a factory for making more viruses, as shown in **Figure 1**. Viruses are responsible for many diseases, including cold sores, colds, and influenza.

(b) Why are viruses not referred to as living things?

(c) How do viruses spread?

(d) Explain why a virus might exist for years and only become active once it comes into contact with a living cell.

(e) Explain how a living cell can become a virus factory.

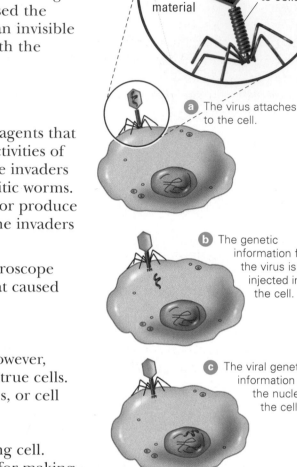

protein coat
protein tail used to attach to cells
genetic material

a The virus attaches to the cell.

b The genetic information from the virus is injected into the cell.

c The viral genetic information enters the nucleus of the cell.

d The genetic information takes the cell over and forces the cell to start making many protein coats and copies of the viral genetic information.

e New viruses are assembled.

f The cell bursts, and a new wave of invading viruses is released.

Figure 1

A virus infects a cell. Viruses have several different shapes. The virus shown here illustrates one body plan.

The Defenders

Your immune system defends you by destroying invaders. One defence is to attack the invaders directly with white blood cells, as shown in **Figure 2**.

Once the invaders are engulfed by the cell, the white blood cell's lysosomes release special chemicals that destroy the invaders, but also destroy the white blood cell. Pus is made of the strands of protein and cell fragments that remain after invaders are attacked by white blood cells. White blood cells attack and kill bacteria, and they also kill body cells that have been damaged by bacteria, viruses, or poisonous chemicals. Only healthy cells remain.

(f) Describe one way the body fights infection and disease.

(g) Speculate about the advantages of removing damaged cells from the body.

Antibodies

Another way your body protects you is by using antibodies. Antibodies are made by a special type of white blood cell. Antibodies are large molecules that lock onto invading organisms.

Invading cells and viruses all have distinctive molecules on their cell membranes or protein coats. These molecules (called markers) have a specific shape. Antibodies are designed to fit the shape of those molecules and lock onto them, as shown in **Figure 3**. Each type of antibody will work on only one type of invader.

(h) Will an antibody produced against the influenza virus lock onto a common cold virus?

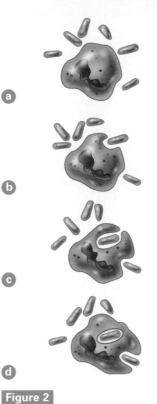

Figure 2

A white blood cell engulfs and digests invading bacteria.

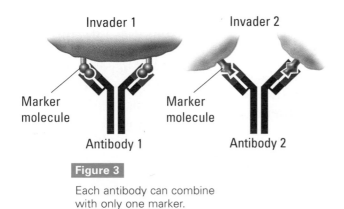

Figure 3

Each antibody can combine with only one marker.

Invader 1   Invader 2

Marker molecule   Marker molecule

Antibody 1   Antibody 2

Understanding Concepts

1. Explain what disease is in your own words.

2. What types of invaders cause infection in humans?

3. Identify two ways in which white blood cells protect the body from disease.

Making Connections

4. How does your body benefit when a white blood cell kills a cell that has been infected by a virus?

5. Vaccines work by introducing dead or weakened invaders into the body. The body will develop antibodies against the weak invaders. If a strong invader of the same kind enters the body later, the antibodies can be used to destroy it before it takes over any cells. Using diagrams, show how a vaccine might protect the body from invaders.

1.17 Inquiry Investigation

SKILLS MENU
- ● Questioning
- ○ Hypothesizing
- ○ Planning
- ● Conducting
- ● Recording
- ● Analyzing
- ○ Communicating

Water Movement in Plants

Water is necessary for plants to convert light energy into chemical energy, in the form of food. As you can see in **Figure 1**, plants must be able to gather water and transport it to their leaves to survive.

Question

(2B) After you have read through this investigation, write a question that you will try to answer.

Hypothesis

Blood is carried through our body in tubes called blood vessels. There must be similar structures in a plant.

Experimental Design

You will examine the movement of water through celery stalks, using food colouring to follow the flow. You will also find out if the presence of leaves has any effect on water movement.

Materials

- apron
- 2 stalks of fresh celery
- paring knife
- 200-mL beaker
- water
- red food colouring
- spoon
- paper towel
- ruler

Be careful when cutting. Always cut away from your body.

Procedure

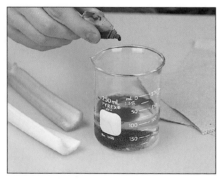  

1 Use the knife to cut 2 celery stalks to the same length.
- Use your fingers to remove the leaves from one of your celery stalks.
- Half-fill a 200-mL beaker with water.
- Add 5 drops of red food colouring to the water and mix well.
- Place both celery stalks in the water.

2 Make a table to record your observations.

(a) Predict which celery stalk will show the greatest movement of water (and dye). Explain your prediction.

3 After 3 h, take the celery stalks from the water. Lay both celery stalks on a paper towel. Use a ruler to measure the length of each stalk from the end to where the leaves begin.

✎ (a) Record the length of each stalk in your table.

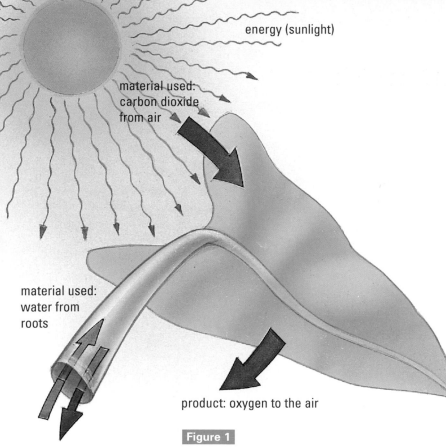

energy (sunlight)

material used: carbon dioxide from air

material used: water from roots

product: oxygen to the air

Figure 1

A plant must move water into its leaves to perform photosynthesis.

product: sugar (food)

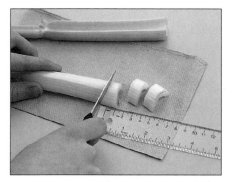

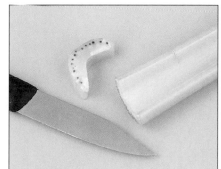

4 Use the knife to carefully cut 1 cm from the end of each stalk. Examine the cut.

(a) Draw a sketch to show where the red dye appears in the stalk.

5 Continue cutting the celery 1 cm at a time until you find no dye in the stalk.

(a) For each cut, record in your table whether dye was visible in the stalk.

(b) Record the total distance the dye moved in each stalk.

(c) Calculate the percentage of the stalk the dye and water moved up:

$$\frac{\text{distance moved (Step 5)}}{\text{length of stalk (Step 3)}} \times 100\%$$

Making Connections

1. A gardening book recommends removing some of the leaves from a plant that has been moved into a new pot. The idea is to help it conserve water until it has grown more roots. Based on your observations, will removing some leaves help the plant? Explain.

Exploring

2. Repeat this investigation, but this time place plastic bags over the top ends of the two celery stalks. Predict the results.

Reflecting

3. Scientists often have different explanations for the same experimental evidence. One explanation of your observations in this investigation is that celery contains vessels that carry water from the roots to the leaves. Create another explanation and write a laboratory report.

Analysis

6 Analyze your results by answering the following.

(a) What effect did the leaves have on water movement?

(b) How does water get from celery's roots to its leaves?

(c) Explain why you started with two celery stalks that were about the same length.

(d) Why is it helpful to calculate a percentage in order to compare the movement of dye in the two stalks?

Cells, Tissues, Organs, and Systems **53**

From the Ground Up

Did you ever forget to water a house plant? It doesn't take very long for a plant to wilt. Water is an essential chemical for plants. But plants outside the home cannot rely on regular watering. The survival of most plants requires an efficient water-absorbing system and a water-transport system.

Water Absorption

As **Figure 1** shows, most plants get water from the soil. Water passes into the plant through root hairs. Root hairs are tiny extensions on the surface of the cells of a root. They greatly increase the surface area of the cell membrane of the root cell. The cell membrane allows water and dissolved nutrients, such as minerals, to enter.

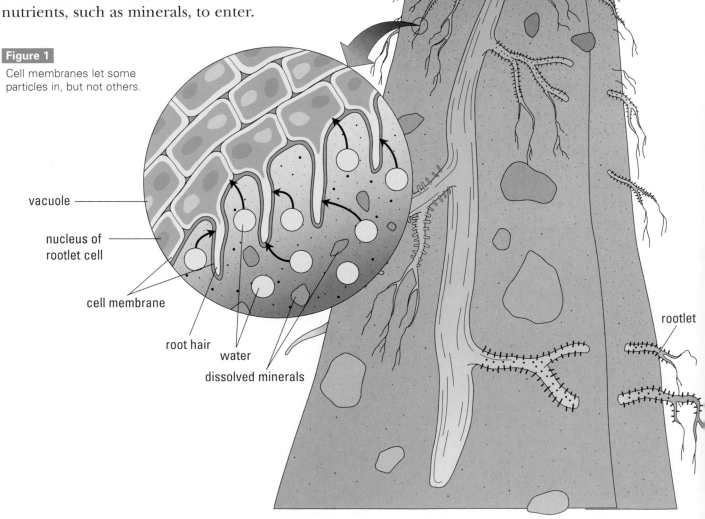

Figure 1

Cell membranes let some particles in, but not others.

rootlet

rootlet

vacuole

nucleus of rootlet cell

cell membrane

root hair

water

dissolved minerals

Tubes for Transport

Water is an essential raw material for photosynthesis. Plants must be able to gather and transport water in order to survive. Just as you have tubes called blood vessels to transport blood inside your body, plants have tubes called **xylem vessels** to transport water. As shown in **Figure 2**, xylem vessels are formed from cell walls left behind as columns of cells die. **Figure 2d** shows developed xylem tubes.

Formation of a xylem vessel

xylem vessel

a As the cell walls thicken, cells begin to die.

b The cell walls between the cells dissolve, leaving only the outer cell walls for support.

c Eventually, a narrow, strawlike tube forms.

d Xylem vessels in a root

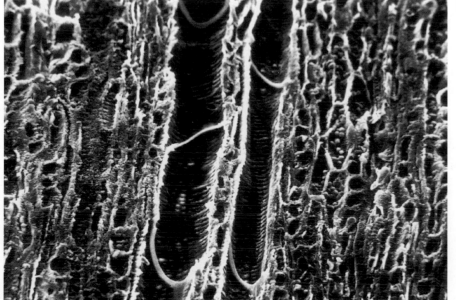

Moving Water Around

Tall trees must lift water as much as 100 m from their roots to their leaves, as you can see in **Figure 3**. How they do this is not fully understood. Many scientists believe there are three forces that help water rise such great distances.

- **Root pressure:** Root cells may actively pull in certain minerals. Water from the soil will then enter the cells by osmosis. The water being drawn into the root produces a pressure that pushes water up the xylem vessels.

- **Capillarity:** Liquids tend to cling to the sides of narrow tubes. This tendency, called capillarity, helps water to move up inside the narrow xylem vessels.

- **Transpiration:** Water molecules are attracted to each other. As water molecules evaporate from the leaves, they pull other water molecules up behind them in a long chain from the xylem vessels. The evaporation of water from the exposed parts of a plant is called transpiration. The force produced is called transpiration pull.

Figure 3

In some plants, like this Douglas fir, water must travel a great distance from the roots to the leaves. How it gets there is still a mystery.

 **Capillary Force**

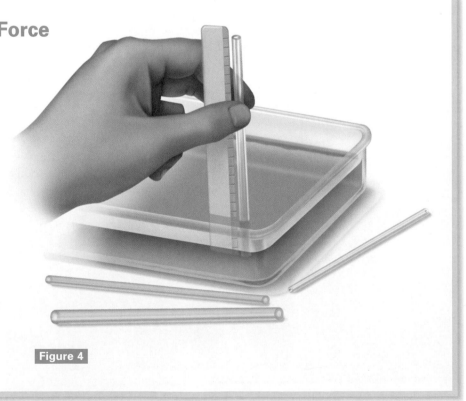

You can demonstrate the power of capillarity with several different diameters of glass tubes. Add a few drops of red or blue food colouring to a tray of water. Stand the glass tubes in the coloured water (see **Figure 4**). Using a ruler, measure the distance the water travels up each tube.

1. In which rod is the liquid highest?

2. How does the diameter of the tube affect the distance water rises?

Figure 4

From the Leaves Down

Plants also have another transport system (**Figure 5**). A series of tubes called **phloem vessels** move sugars from the leaves to the stems and roots for food and storage. Phloem vessels also transport nutrients from the roots up to the leaves, as needed. Unlike the xylem vessels, phloem vessels consist of living cells. As **Figure 6** shows, they look different from each other.

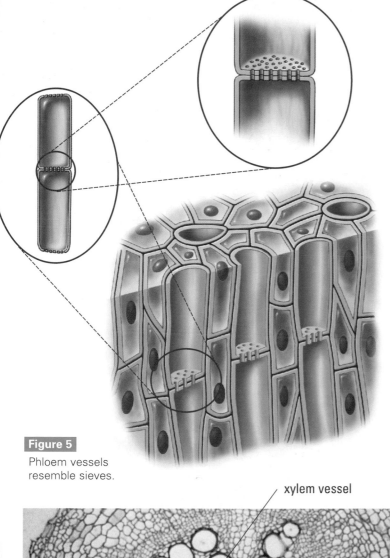

Figure 5

Phloem vessels resemble sieves.

xylem vessel

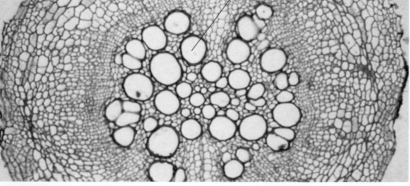

Figure 6

Xylem vessels carry water from the roots to the leaves. These vessels are formed from cell walls left behind as columns of cells die in the plant.

Understanding Concepts

1. Why is the ability to move water important to the survival of plants?

2. What structures in plants help them move:

   (a) water?

   (b) sugars?

3. List and explain in your own words the three forces that may help plants to move water.

4. Make a concept map of fluid transportation in plants.

Making Connections

5. Some insects get their nutrients by sticking a needlelike mouth part into a plant. Which vessel do you believe they are tapping?

Exploring

6. After consulting with your teacher, carefully cut the tip from the stem of a white carnation using a sharp knife. While holding the stem under water, cut the stem lengthwise. Place each section in a separate beaker of water. Add red food colouring to one beaker and blue to the other.

   (a) Predict what will happen in 24 h. State your reasons.

   (b) Compare your prediction and your observations.

Reflecting

7. Make a chart to compare fluid movement in plants to fluid movement in the human circulatory system.

Examining the Leaf

Leaves are like little factories. They use the energy of sunlight to combine water from the soil and carbon dioxide from the air to form sugars and oxygen. Leaves are also exposed to the drying effects of the wind and sun's heat. A great deal can be learned about how a plant survives and where it lives, by looking at its leaves, as you can see in **Figure 1**.

1. Protection: The Cuticle

The cuticle is a coat of wax that covers the leaf. The wax stops water from evaporating from the cells below. The cuticle prevents the leaf from drying out.

2. Protection: The Epidermis

Like human skin, the leaf's epidermis protects the cells below. These cells make the waxy cuticle. Epidermis cells usually have no chloroplasts, so they cannot perform photosynthesis.

3. Photosynthesis: The Palisade

Most of the work of the leaf is done in the palisade, a layer of cells just under the cuticle and epidermis. Palisade cells contain many chloroplasts—the organelles that trap light for photosynthesis.

4. Transport: The Veins

The **vein** is a combination of xylem and phloem vessels. Xylem carries water from the roots to the leaf. Phloem carries the sugar and starch made in the leaf to other plant cells for food and to the roots for storage.

5. Gas Exchange: Inside the Leaf

Under the palisade cells, many leaves have a spongy area with fewer cells and many air spaces. Photosynthesizing cells absorb carbon dioxide from the air spaces and release oxygen into these spaces.

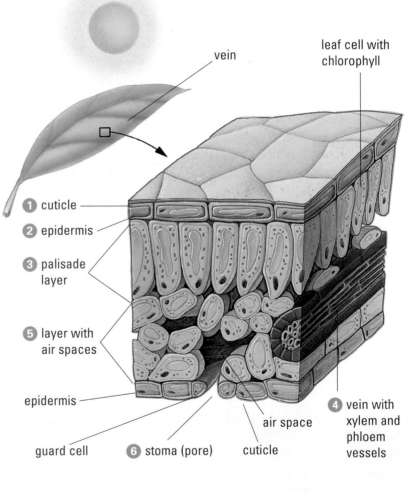

vein

leaf cell with chlorophyll

1 cuticle

2 epidermis

3 palisade layer

5 layer with air spaces

epidermis

guard cell

6 stoma (pore)

air space

cuticle

4 vein with xylem and phloem vessels

Figure 1

A cross-section through a leaf

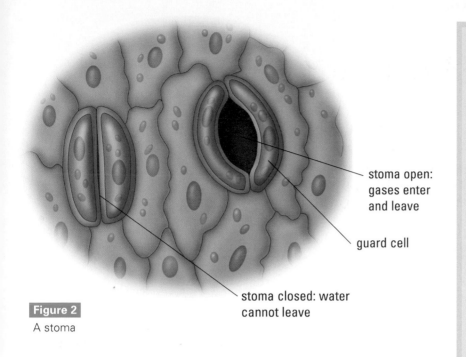

stoma open: gases enter and leave

guard cell

stoma closed: water cannot leave

Figure 2
A stoma

6. Gas Exchange: Inside and Out

Remember that plant cells inside the leaf need carbon dioxide from the air. Also, the oxygen gas made in photosynthesis must leave the leaf. The air spaces allow free movement of these gases. But how do the gases enter and leave the leaf through the waxy cuticle?

As you can see in **Figure 2**, small openings called **stomates** (singular *stoma*) in the surface of the leaf are controlled by a pair of guard cells. The guard cells act like doors. If the air is moist or the leaf has lots of water, the guard cells swell up and open the stomates, so gases can flow in and out. If the air is too dry or the leaf is very low on water, the guard cells relax and the stomates close, protecting cells inside the leaf from drying out.

Adapted to Survive

When you examine the leaves of plants from various environments under a microscope, you will see that they differ greatly from each other. Plants that grow in dry, sunny areas get all the sunlight they need, but they must preserve water. They tend to have thick cuticles on their leaves. They also have only a few stomates, and these are all on the underside of the leaves, protected from heat and wind.

On the other hand, plants that grow in moist, shady areas have lots of water, but not as much sunlight. They must concentrate on photosynthesis. These plants often have thin cuticles and many stomates on both sides of the leaf. This combination lets the palisade cells exchange gases more rapidly, so they can perform more photosynthesis.

Understanding Concepts

1. Match the function from the left column with the structures in a leaf. (Use each structure at least once.)

Function	Structure
(a) allows gases to reach cells	cuticle
(b) transports water from roots to leaves	guard cell
(c) allows gases to move in and out of leaf	xylem vessel
(d) controls movement of gases in and out of leaf	phloem vessel
(e) location of photosynthesis	air space
(f) transports sugars and nutrients	stomates
(g) protects against evaporation	palisade

2. Why is it important to a plant to have air spaces between the cells in the middle of each leaf?

Making Connections

3. Predict how a leaf from an aquatic plant and a leaf from a desert plant would differ. Compare each of the following:
   (a) cuticle
   (b) number of stomates
   (c) location of stomates
   (d) size of air spaces inside the leaf

Observations of a Naturalist

Why do maple trees grow so well in southern Ontario, but not at all in the Yukon? Plants, like plant cells, specialize to grow in specific environments. **Figure 1** shows differences in the plants as you move from north to south in Canada. The kind of plant that you are likely to see growing in any area is determined by the environment and how each plant adapts to it.

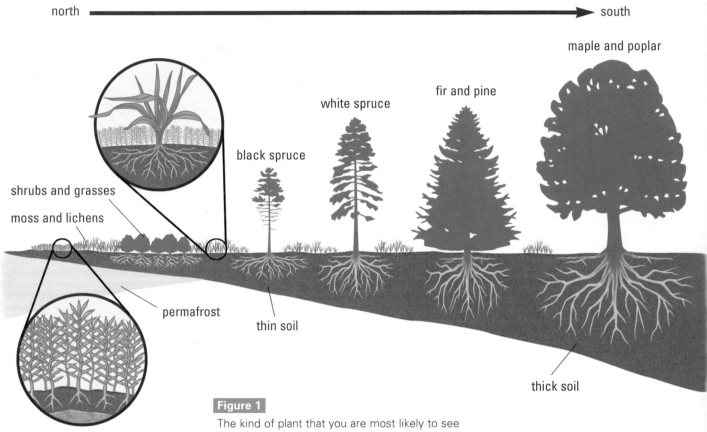

Figure 1
The kind of plant that you are most likely to see changes as you go from north to south.

Environment: The Permafrost Layer

As you move from north to south, there is an important change in the soil, caused by the warmer environment in the south. In southern climates, as summer heat warms the soil, the frost layer disappears. In the north, a layer of ice, called permafrost, remains below the soil all year long.

(a) What happens to the size of the plants as you move south?

(b) How does the size of the plant-root system change as you move south?

(c) How might the permafrost affect plant growth?

(d) Why wouldn't you expect an apple tree to grow in Inuvik?

(e) Speculate about why more soil is found in southern forests than northern forests.

Adaptations: Roots

Each plant is adapted to live in its environment. One adaptation is the type of root system the plant has.

Unlike more advanced plants, mosses do not have true roots, and they do not have xylem and phloem vessels. Water passes from cell to cell by osmosis. This type of fluid movement works because moss plants tend to be only a few cell layers thick. Because mosses do not have a water transport system, they depend on having lots of water in the environment so they can reproduce and photosynthesize.

(f) Why don't mosses grow as tall as spruce trees?

(g) Why would you find a large number of moss plants in a northern ecosystem during the summer months?

Plants that are ideally suited for a location have advantages over other plants that try to grow in that area. Examine the black spruce, white spruce, fir, and maple trees.

(h) Why can't spruce trees compete with maple trees in more southern forests? What advantages do the maple trees have?

Adaptations: Leaves

In the north, the air is very dry in winter and moist in summer. Trees that live there must deal with both conditions. The spruce, fir, and pine trees are equipped with a thick cuticle that covers their needlelike leaves, as you can see in **Figure 2**.

(i) Why are spruce trees more likely to survive in areas with extreme changes in climate?

(j) Why can't the maple tree compete with the black spruce in northern forests?

Figure 2

A waxy cuticle prevents water loss from (a) spruce and (b) pine needles.

Environment: Mountains

Figure 3 shows how the most common plants change from the top to the bottom of a mountain. Compare **Figure 3** with **Figure 1**.

(k) Speculate as to why trees don't grow right to the top of high mountains.

(l) Create a testable hypothesis that explains why trees grow taller as you go from top to bottom down a mountain.

Figure 3

From the top to the bottom of a mountain, different kinds of plants have advantages.

Understanding Concepts

1. What advantage does the maple tree gain with its thick, broad leaves?
2. Why can't moss compete with large trees in southern forests?
3. How does the root system of a plant determine where it will grow best?

Making Connections

4. If you cut into a pine tree, the sap that begins to flow hardens very quickly. What advantage does this give to the tree?

Reflecting

5. Many scientists say the Earth is becoming warmer as a result of global warming. If your area warmed up and winters became less harsh, how might these conditions affect your local plants?

Animal Organ Systems Working Together

All of your cells are organized into tissues, organs, and organ systems. To keep your body healthy, your organ systems must work together. In your circulatory system, for example, blood carrying nutrients and oxygen is pumped to all of the cells of the body. Without circulation, the cells of your skin and digestive system could not survive. In turn, the circulatory system relies on other systems: the respiratory system supplies oxygen; the digestive system, which includes the stomach and intestines, provides nutrients. **Figure 1** shows how four organ systems rely on each other.

(a) Name two other organ systems.

Supplying Nutrients and Removing Wastes

Organ systems can be organized into two main groups. The first group of organ systems supplies nutrients and removes waste (**Figure 1**).

(b) Why does the circulatory system need the respiratory system?

(c) Is the circulatory system important to the digestive system? Why?

(d) Would the circulatory system be able to do its job without the digestive system? Explain.

(e) How does the excretory system help the circulatory system to do its job?

(f) Speculate about what would happen to skin cells if the circulatory system failed to work. Why is a circulatory system necessary for skin cells?

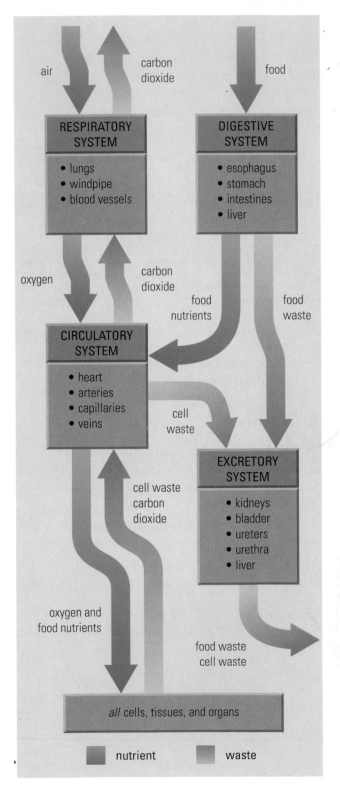

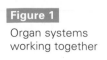

Figure 1
Organ systems working together

Regulating the Body

The second group of organ systems regulates the body, as shown in **Figure 2**.

The endocrine system produces chemical messengers (called **hormones**) that travel to other organs and tell the organs how to adjust to what's going on outside and inside the body. The nervous system detects what's going on outside and inside the body and sends electrical messages throughout the body.

In some situations, the nervous system and endocrine system work together. For example, if a cougar jumps into your path, your eyes (and perhaps your ears and nose) detect the cougar and send an electrical message to your brain through the nervous system. Once you recognize that the cougar is dangerous and you decide to run away, nerves carry electrical signals from your brain to your muscles. The signals cause the muscles to contract, and you begin to run.

Meanwhile, other nerves are carrying messages from your brain to your endocrine glands. Your endocrine glands respond by pumping chemical messengers into your blood. For example, there is a small gland near the top of your kidneys that releases a chemical messenger (called adrenaline) into your blood. When the adrenaline reaches the cells of your heart and your respiratory system, your heart starts beating faster, and your lungs take in more oxygen. The result is that your muscle cells suddenly have more nutrients available to them, and you can run faster.

(g) Which system, the nervous system or the endocrine system, is best suited to detect danger? Explain why.

(h) What is the difference between a response by the nervous system and a response by the endocrine system? Explain.

(i) If you stepped on a tack, how would your nervous system respond? What other organ systems would be signalled? Explain.

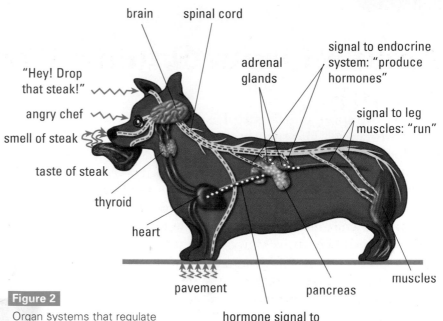

Figure 2
Organ systems that regulate other organ systems

Understanding Concepts

1. Categorize the following organs as either: *Supplying nutrients and removing wastes* or *Regulating the body*.

   heart   artery   kidney
   eyes   brain   stomach

2. How do nerves and muscles work together?

3. Explain why organ systems that regulate or control other body systems are important.

Making Connections

4. How would the health of an animal be affected if disease damaged an organ that:

   (a) delivered nutrients?

   (b) removed wastes?

   (c) informed it about environmental change?

   (d) controlled other organ systems?

Reflecting

5. How does the statement "all for one and one for all" apply to large, multicelled orgamisms?

Fluid Movement in Animals

Life for the sponge in **Figure 1** is very straightforward. The sea water acts as a transport system, carrying nutrients and removing wastes. Simple diffusion across cell membranes accomplishes both tasks.

For larger and more complex animals, specialized cells must work together to move fluids. In animals, a circulatory system is responsible for carrying nutrient-rich fluids to body cells, and the excretory system is responsible for eliminating the wastes.

The Circulatory System

Relying on diffusion to deliver oxygen and nutrients is too limiting for a complex multicellular animal. A circulatory system brings every cell into almost direct contact with oxygen and nutrients. In fact, no cell in your body is farther than two cells away from a blood vessel that carries nutrients. Your circulatory system has 96 000 km of blood vessels to sustain your 60 trillion cells.

Open and Closed Circulatory Systems

In an open circulatory system, like that of the snail in **Figure 2**, blood carrying oxygen and nutrients is pumped into body cavities, where it bathes the cells. When the heart relaxes, blood is drawn back toward the heart through open-ended pores.

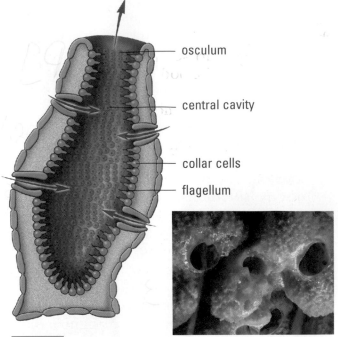

— osculum

— central cavity

— collar cells

— flagellum

Figure 1

Sponges live anchored to the sea floor. They do not need a fluid transport system because they have only two cell layers. Water and nutrients are drawn into the sponge by cells that have a flagellum. Once inside the body, the water and wastes are expelled through the large pore at the top of the body.

In a closed circulatory system, like that of the worm in **Figure 3**, the blood is always contained within blood vessels. The earthworm has five heartlike vessels that pump blood through three major blood vessels. Larger blood vessels branch into smaller vessels that supply blood to the various tissues. Blood vessels that carry blood away from the heart are called **arteries**, and vessels that return blood to the heart are called **veins**.

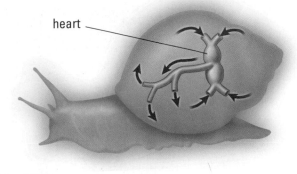

heart

Figure 2

The snail has an open circulatory system.

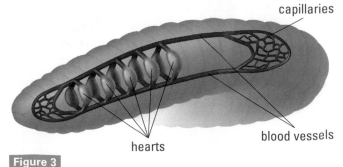

capillaries

blood vessels

hearts

Figure 3

The worm has a closed circulatory system.

Humans' Twin Pumps

The heart of humans (**Figure 4**) and other mammals is not a single pump, but two parallel pumps separated by a wall of muscle. The right side of the heart receives blood low in oxygen from the body, which it delivers to the lungs. The left side of the heart accepts freshly oxygenated blood from the lungs and delivers it to the body cells. The body cells remove oxygen and nutrients. The blood completes its journey by travelling back to the right side of the heart.

Figure 4

The human heart has four chambers: two atria (singular atrium) and two ventricles. The atria are holding chambers for blood entering the heart. The stronger, more muscular ventricles pump the blood to distant tissues.

A One-Way Flow

Valves that operate as one-way doors keep blood flowing in one direction in the human heart. Valves are found in both sides of the heart, as you can see in **Figure 5**. The first set are located between the atria and ventricles. The second set lie between the ventricles and the arteries that carry blood away from the heart.

a Blood is carried to the heart by veins. As the heart relaxes, the atria fill with blood.

b The atria contract and blood is pushed into the ventricles. The ventricles fill with blood.

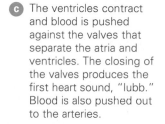

c The ventricles contract and blood is pushed against the valves that separate the atria and ventricles. The closing of the valves produces the first heart sound, "lubb." Blood is also pushed out to the arteries.

d The ventricle relaxes and because little blood remains, the pressure is low. Blood is drawn back toward the ventricle from the arteries. This causes the valves to close and the second heart sound, "dubb."

Figure 5

The human heart is a double pump, with four chambers and four sets of valves.

Try This   A Filter Model

You can create a model of a filtering excretory system.

- Fill a funnel with aquarium charcoal and put a small beaker beneath it. Fill a second beaker with about 25 mL of water and add a few drops of food colouring.

- Pour the coloured water through the funnel and collect it in the small beaker.

- Compare the colour of the filtered water with the original.

1. Predict what would happen if the water was filtered once again.

- Test your prediction.

Excretory System

For unicellular organisms, getting wastes out of the cell is just as important as bringing in nutrients. Without a way to get rid of wastes, a cell would soon die. Multicellular organisms such as worms (**Figure 6**), insects (**Figure 7**), and humans (**Figure 8**) are faced with the same problem, on a much bigger scale. However, not every cell is designed to remove wastes. Specialized cells that work together in the excretory system are designed to remove wastes from the body or to store the wastes until it is appropriate to remove them. The excretory system also has a second function in most animals: it helps to regulate body water. As the contractile vacuole of the paramecium and amoeba prevent these cells from swelling, the excretory system ensures that water balance is maintained.

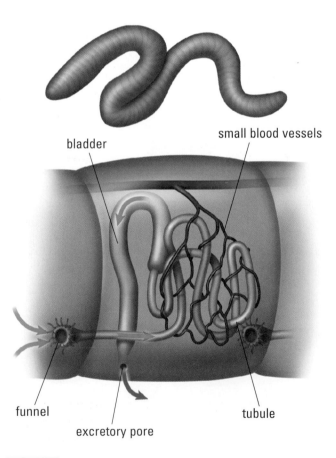

bladder

small blood vessels

funnel

excretory pore

tubule

Figure 6

The earthworm uses a series of tubules to remove wastes from the blood and body cavity. Cells lined with cilia surround a funnel-like opening, and draw fluids from the body cavity into tiny tubules. The wastes are stored as urine and are held in a bladder for a short time. A series of small pores along the body wall are responsible for releasing the wastes from the tubules.

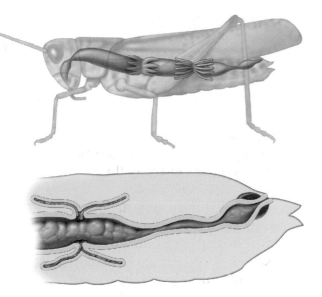

Figure 7

Tubules that run throughout the body cavity of an insect absorb wastes by diffusion. Wastes are released into the gut and eliminated with solid wastes from the anus.

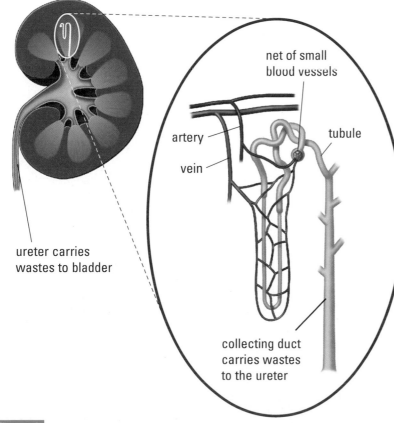

kidney

artery

vein

net of small blood vessels

tubule

ureter carries wastes to bladder

collecting duct carries wastes to the ureter

Figure 8

The human kidney contains millions of tubules. They filter wastes from the blood. High-pressure blood vessels push wastes across a thin membrane at the upper end of the tubules. Wastes are then carried to the bladder, where they are stored.

Understanding Concepts

1. Why do sponges not need a fluid transport system?

2. Why do multicellular animals need:

    (a) an excretory system?

    (b) a circulatory system?

3. What is the difference between a closed and an open circulatory system?

4. Draw a diagram of the movement of blood through the four chambers of the heart.

Making Connections

5. Compare the way plants and animals move fluids.

6. Compare an open and a closed circulatory system. Which one do you think is most efficient? Give your reasons.

7. Why is the muscle surrounding the left ventricle of a human heart larger than the muscle surrounding the right ventricle?

8. A heart murmur is caused by a faulty valve that allows blood to flow back into one of the chambers. Explain why this two-way flow of blood would create problems.

Exploring

9. Improve upon the design of the filtering system in the Try This. You will be allowed to run the fluid through the filter only once. Work with your classmates to set up a scale to rate the efficiency of the filtering system.

Reflecting

10. How could an animal use specialized cells to improve on one of the fluid transport systems described in this section?

Animal Digestive Systems

Unlike plants, animals cannot make their own food. They get energy either from other organisms, or from food products that come from another living thing. They use specialized cells to break food down.

Digestion is the process your body uses to break large food molecules into smaller molecules. Your body uses the smaller molecules for "fuel" and as building blocks for growth and repair. Chemicals that help speed up the process of digestion are often referred to as enzymes.

Digestion in a Sac

Many animals with simple body plans, such as the hydra in **Figure 1**, have a digestive system with a single opening. These saclike cavities both take in food and expel undigested wastes.

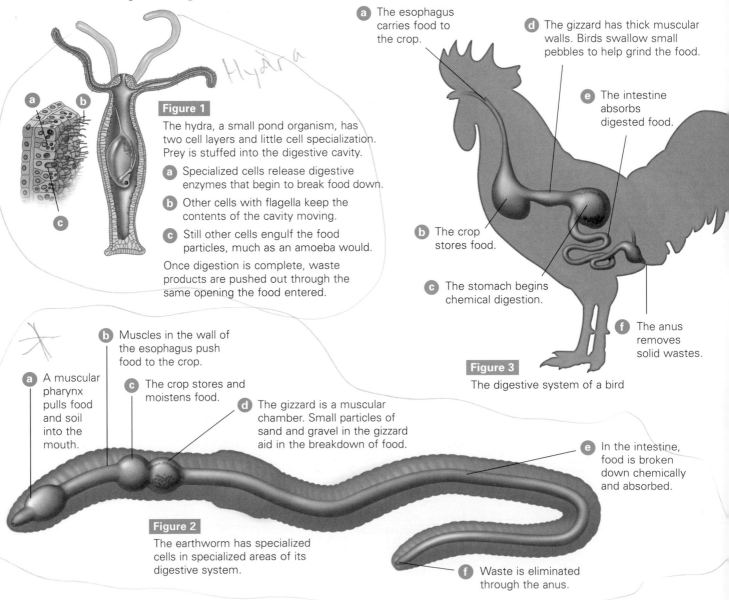

Figure 1

The hydra, a small pond organism, has two cell layers and little cell specialization. Prey is stuffed into the digestive cavity.

a Specialized cells release digestive enzymes that begin to break food down.

b Other cells with flagella keep the contents of the cavity moving.

c Still other cells engulf the food particles, much as an amoeba would.

Once digestion is complete, waste products are pushed out through the same opening the food entered.

a The esophagus carries food to the crop.

d The gizzard has thick muscular walls. Birds swallow small pebbles to help grind the food.

e The intestine absorbs digested food.

b The crop stores food.

c The stomach begins chemical digestion.

f The anus removes solid wastes.

Figure 3

The digestive system of a bird

b Muscles in the wall of the esophagus push food to the crop.

a A muscular pharynx pulls food and soil into the mouth.

c The crop stores and moistens food.

d The gizzard is a muscular chamber. Small particles of sand and gravel in the gizzard aid in the breakdown of food.

e In the intestine, food is broken down chemically and absorbed.

Figure 2

The earthworm has specialized cells in specialized areas of its digestive system.

f Waste is eliminated through the anus.

Digestion Along a Canal

More complex animals, such as the earthworm in **Figure 2**, the bird in **Figure 3**, and the human in **Figure 4**, digest food along a tube or canal that has a separate opening (mouth) and exit (anus). Because food moves along the tube in only one direction, each area of the tube can have a specific functions. For example, one area might have muscle cells to grind food particles into smaller droplets; another area can produce enzymes that help break down large molecules. Other areas can be devoted to storage or to the absorption of digested molecules.

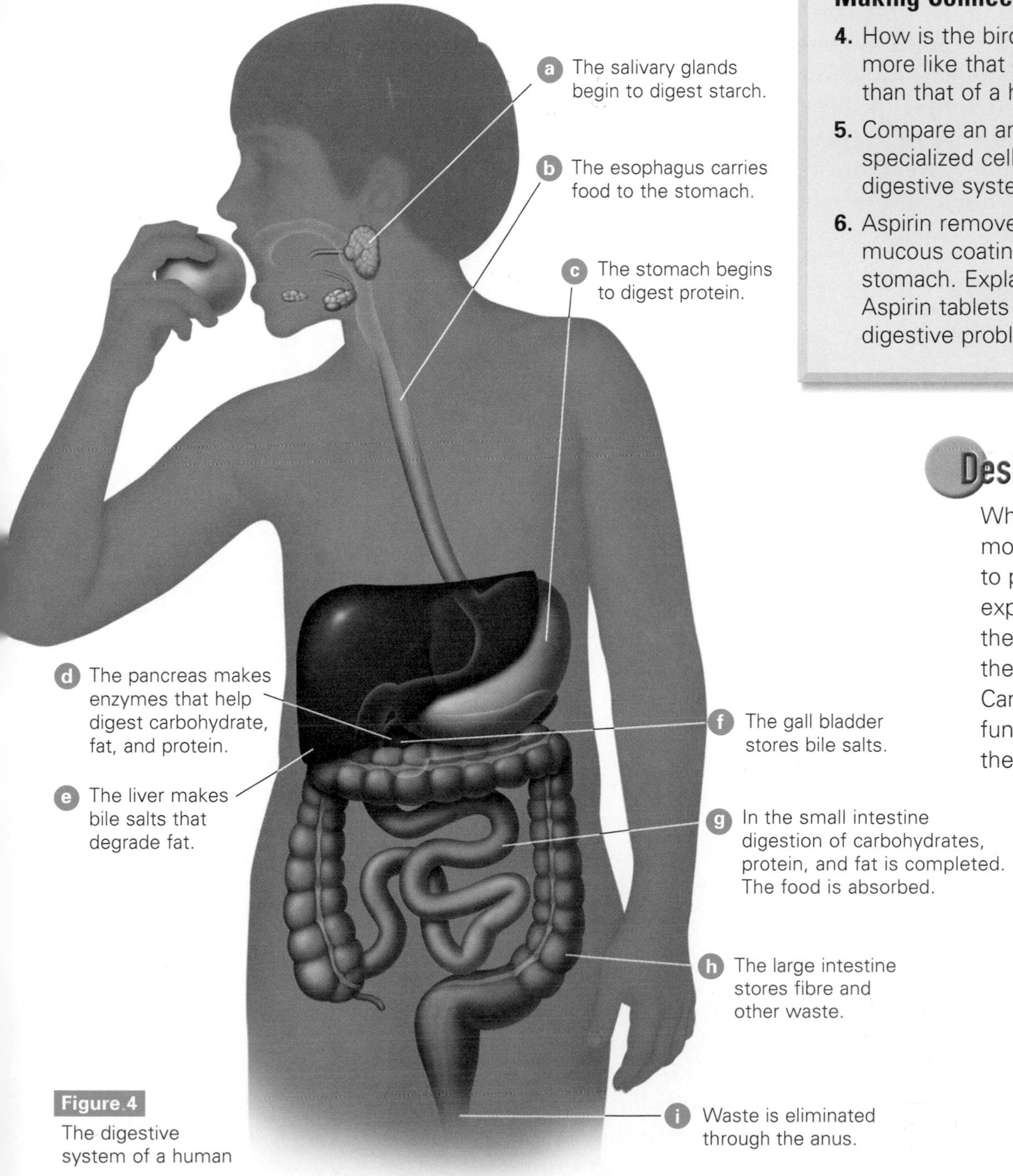

a The salivary glands begin to digest starch.

b The esophagus carries food to the stomach.

c The stomach begins to digest protein.

d The pancreas makes enzymes that help digest carbohydrate, fat, and protein.

e The liver makes bile salts that degrade fat.

f The gall bladder stores bile salts.

g In the small intestine digestion of carbohydrates, protein, and fat is completed. The food is absorbed.

h The large intestine stores fibre and other waste.

i Waste is eliminated through the anus.

Figure 4
The digestive system of a human

Understanding Concepts

1. Explain *digestion* in your own words.

2. What advantage is there in having digestion take place in a tubelike structure rather than a saclike structure?

3. Summarize how human digestion occurs in the mouth, stomach, and small intestine. Show your answer in the form of a chart or diagram.

Making Connections

4. How is the bird's digestion more like that of an earthworm than that of a human?

5. Compare an amoeba with a specialized cell in the human digestive system.

6. Aspirin removes the protective mucous coating that lines the stomach. Explain why taking Aspirin tablets may cause digestive problems.

Design Challenge

What function is your model cell specialized to perform? Could you expect it to perform the functions needed in the digestive system? Can it live without the functions performed by the digestive system?

Factors That Affect Reaction Time

The nervous system is an elaborate communication network. In the brain alone there are more than 100 billion nerve cells. Like all cells, nerve cells contain a nucleus and cytoplasm. But unlike most cells, they have a direct connection to other cells because of the thin projections of their cytoplasm. These connections make the cells a network. **Figure 1** shows two kinds of nerve cell.

Every move you make relies on that network of cells. For example, catching a falling ruler seems fairly simple, but inside your body millions of cells must work together to make it happen. **Figure 2** shows the series of events that must take place as nerve signals travel from your eye to your brain and back to your hand to make the catch.

Materials
- ruler (at least 30 cm long)
- cold water
- large plastic container

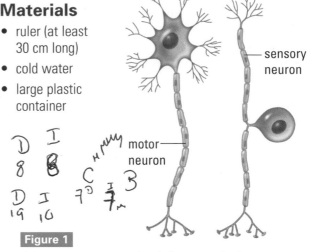

Figure 1

Motor neurons carry signals from your brain to your muscles. Sensory neurons collect information. For example, you have sensory neurons in your skin to detect changes in temperature or pressure.

Question
What factors affect reaction rates?

Hypothesis

(2C) **1** Write a hypothesis for the effects of two factors (temperature and fatigue) on reaction time.

Experimental Design
In this investigation you will measure the distance a ruler drops before it is caught. You will use this distance as a measure of your subject's reaction rate.

(6D) ✎ **2** Read the procedure and make a data table to record the data you will collect.

Procedure

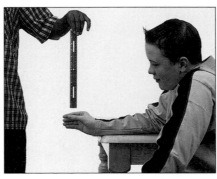

3 Ask your subject to place his or her right forearm flat on the desk. The subject's entire hand should extend over the edge of the desk.
- The index finger and thumb of the subject should be about 2 cm apart.
- Place a 30-cm ruler between the thumb and forefinger of the subject. The upper part of the ruler should be even with the top of the thumb and forefinger.

4 Release the ruler and measure the distance that the ruler falls before being caught between the subject's thumb and forefinger.
- Repeat the procedure twice more for the right hand.
- Repeat the procedure three times for the left hand.

✎ (a) Record your findings.

(b) Why should you do more than one trial for each hand?

SKILLS HANDBOOK: (2C) Predicting and Hypothesizing (6D) Creating Data Tables

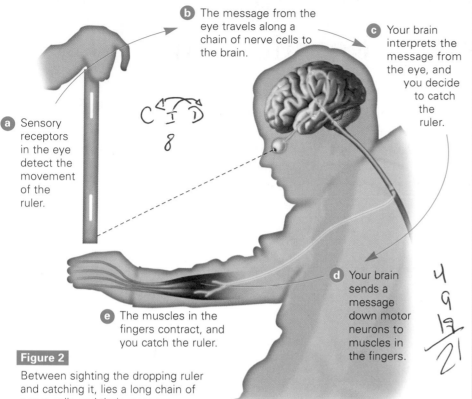

b The message from the eye travels along a chain of nerve cells to the brain.

c Your brain interprets the message from the eye, and you decide to catch the ruler.

a Sensory receptors in the eye detect the movement of the ruler.

d Your brain sends a message down motor neurons to muscles in the fingers.

e The muscles in the fingers contract, and you catch the ruler.

Figure 2

Between sighting the dropping ruler and catching it, lies a long chain of nerve cells and their messages.

4
9
17
21

Making Connections

1. How would you conduct an experiment to determine whether males or females have the faster reaction rate? What variables would you control?

2. If the reaction rate changes as the temperature falls, do impulses move slower or faster along the nerve at low temperatures? What other factors affect the reaction rate?

Exploring

3. In a dimly lit room, have your partner close his or her eyes for 2 min. Rest a piece of cardboard against your partner's face and shine a flashlight into one eye.

(a) What happens to the pupil?

(b) How does your eye respond to changing light intensities?

5 Have your subject vigorously clench his or her hand into a fist and then unclench it, repeatedly for 2 min.
 • Test your subject's reaction rate again immediately after the 2 min.

✎ (a) Record your findings.

6 Ask the subject to immerse his or her hand in cold water for 1 min.
 • Again test the reaction rate.

✎ (a) Record your findings.

Analysis

7 Analyze your results by answering these questions.

(a) How does temperature affect reaction time? In what part of the experiment did you collect evidence to support your conclusion?

(b) How does fatigue affect reaction time? Where did you collect evidence to support your conclusion?

Cells, Tissues, Organs, and Systems **71**

Tinkering with Cells

People in ancient times once imagined creating new plants and animals by crossing different species. They believed that the offspring might have qualities of both parents. For example, if they crossed a rabbit with a turtle, maybe they'd get a shelled animal that could run fast.

Today biologists know that sperm from one animal will not successfully fertilize the egg of another species. However, advances in cell biology have opened the door to the possibility of organisms like the rabirdoo in **Figure 1**.

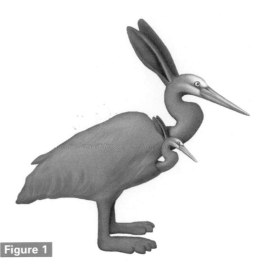

Figure 1

A rabirdoo has the feet and ears of a rabbit, the pouch of a kangaroo, and the feathers and beak of a bird. There is no such animal, but maybe....

The Frog-Bacteria Cross

In 1970, Herbert Boyer and Stanley Cohen were able to transplant genetic information from a frog into a common bacterium, as shown in **Figure 2**. Boyer and Cohen watched in amazement as the genetic information from the frog began telling the bacterial cell what proteins to make, as if it had always been there. Two organisms that would never exchange genetic information in nature had been joined.

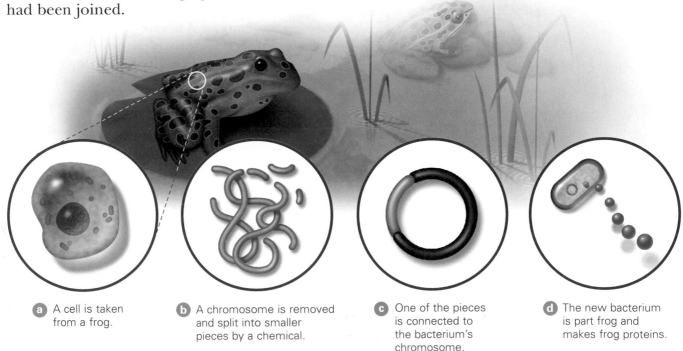

a A cell is taken from a frog.

b A chromosome is removed and split into smaller pieces by a chemical.

c One of the pieces is connected to the bacterium's chromosome.

d The new bacterium is part frog and makes frog proteins.

Figure 2

Genetic information from the cell of a frog is inserted into a bacterial cell.

Understanding Concepts

1. What is the result if sperm from one species is used to fertilize an egg from another species?

2. How can genetic information be transferred from one organism to another?

More Crosses

Scientists haven't restricted themselves to frogs and bacteria. Bacterial genetic information has been transferred into plants, and plant genetic information has been transferred into animals. Human genetic information has also been placed in bacteria and mouse cells. Nonhuman cells with human genetic information can produce hormones like human insulin or, as you can see in **Figure 3**, human growth hormone, which makes human bodies grow larger.

Figure 3

These two mice are the same age, but one of them contains human genetic information—its cells make human growth hormone. Which mouse do you think has been tinkered with?

Debate Combining Living Things

Statement

By combining genetic information from different organisms, scientists are creating new life forms that shouldn't exist. Scientists should not be permitted to alter nature. This kind of research should be banned in Canada.

Point

- The new organisms that are created may not be safe. If they ever get loose, they may be dangerous to other living things or to human beings.

- Companies now apply for patents on the life forms they create. For example, General Electric has a patent on bacteria that eat crude oil. No one should be able to own an organism.

Counterpoint

- New combinations of genetic information provide many benefits. Modified cells make feed for pigs, fuel for cars, and vaccines for humans.

- Biotechnology is a multibillion-dollar industry that employs many people. If research is banned, jobs will be lost, and Canada will fall behind other countries.

What do you think?

(8D) • Consider the statement and the points and counterpoints.

- Discuss the statement, then decide whether you agree or disagree.

(4A) • Search for information on genetic engineering or biotechnology that supports your position. You may find it in newspapers, a library periodical index, a CD-ROM directory, or on the Internet.

- Prepare to defend your position in a class debate.

Design Challenge

SKILLS MENU
- Identify a Problem
- Planning
- Building
- Testing
- Recording
- Evaluating
- Communicating

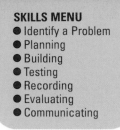

Design and Build a Model or Simulation of Cells

As you have already discovered in this unit, the shape of a cell reveals its function. Designing and building a model or simulation of a cell will allow you to begin thinking about the relationship between a cell's structure and its function.

1 Design and Build a Simulation of a Cell That Carries Oxygen

Problem Situation

Billions of red blood cells carry oxygen to all of the other cells in your body. If your cells do not get oxygen, they die. When people lose blood, their bodies are at risk. Clean, donated blood may not always be available to replace the lost blood. Artificial blood would allow doctors to help their patients.

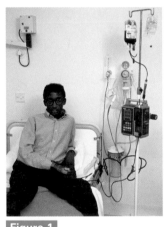

Figure 1
Transfusions replace lost blood.

Design Brief

- Design a simulation that demonstrates how a red blood cell delivers oxygen to other cells.

Design Criteria

- Red blood cells carry oxygen. The model for this cell must also be able to carry oxygen. You can use marbles to represent oxygen.
- Red blood cells move through the twists and turns of our blood vessels. Your model cell must be able to move through a tube with a T-junction. The tube must be only slightly larger than the model cell.

2 Design and Build a Model of Cells That Removes Dirt

Problem Situation

The air contains small particles of dust and dirt. You breathe in these particles. If your lungs didn't have a cleaning mechanism, they would become clogged with dirt, and breathing would become more and more difficult. Fortunately, your respiratory system contains cells that continuously "sweep" trapped dirt up and out of your lungs. Can this idea be modified? The computer is just one example of a modern tool that suffers if dust and dirt intrude.

Design Brief

- Design and build a model to simulate removal of dirt from the lung.

Design Criteria

- A series of at least three fixed but movable components.
- The object (dirt) enters one end of the device and must be moved to the other.

Figure 2
The air is full of dust. How can we get it out of machinery?

3 Design and Build Artificial Skin

Problem Situation

Every year many people are burned in fires. Because burns destroy the skin, treatment of severe burns involves skin grafts (skin transplants). Unfortunately, skin grafts can become infected, or they might be rejected by the patient's body. Unlike skin transplants, artificial skin would not be rejected.

Design Brief

Design and build a model of artificial skin that, like real skin cells, will cover and protect delicate cells below.

Design Criteria

- The model of artificial skin must cover an area of 0.25 m².
- Skin cells must protect cells underneath them. The artificial skin must not be broken if it is scraped with a weight resting on it.
- Skin cells must stretch when we move. The skin must stretch, not break, when pulled at each end.
- Skin cells work with other skin cells. The skin must be made up of at least four cells that are attached to each other.

 When preparing to build or test a design, have your plan approved by your teacher before you begin.

Figure 3

Until their skin grows back, burn victims are open to infection.

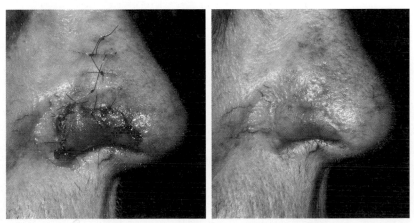

Assessment

Your model will be assessed according to how well you:

Process
- understand the problem
- develop a safe plan
- choose and safely use appropriate materials, tools, and equipment
- test and record results
- evaluate your model, including suggestions for improvement

Communication
- prepare a presentation
- use correct terms
- write clear descriptions of the steps you took in building and testing your model
- explain clearly how your model solves the problem
- make an accurate technical drawing for your model

Product
- meet the design criteria with your model
- use your chosen materials effectively
- construct your model
- solve the identified problem

Unit 1 Summary

In this unit, you have learned that living things are all made of cells—sometimes a single one and often millions of them. Groups of cells are organized into tissues, organs, and systems, which all must work together efficiently.

Reflecting

- Reflect on the ideas and questions presented in the Unit Overview and in Getting Started. How can you connect what you have done and learned in this unit with those ideas and questions?
  (To review, check the sections indicated in this Summary.)
- Revise your answers to the Reflecting questions in ❶, ❷, ❸ and the questions you created in Getting Started. How has your thinking changed?
- What new questions do you have? How will you answer them?

Understanding Concepts

- recognize that living things are composed of cells 1.1, 1.3

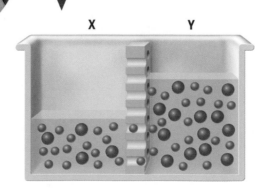

- identify organelles in cells and explain their functions 1.3, 1.6

- describe how advances in microscope technology have allowed us to gather more knowledge about cells 1.5

- describe how unicellular organisms move, feed, and reproduce 1.13

- explain how cells must exchange materials with their environment in order to survive 1.7

- describe the movement of gases and water into and out of cells during diffusion and osmosis 1.8

X   Y

- describe how cells in plants and animals are organized in tissues, organs, and organ systems 1.12, 1.15, 1.18, 1.19

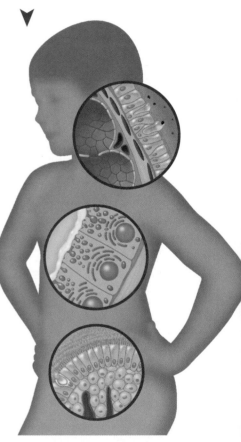

- recognize that cells in multicellular organisms must reproduce to form and repair tissues 1.14

- compare how the structures of different plants are specialized to live in specific environments 1.19, 1.20

Applying Skills

- use a microscope to observe and draw cells 1.2, 1.4

- observe the differences in structure between plant and animal cells 1.4

- design, plan, and carry out an investigation to show the effects of osmosis 1.9, 1.10

- gather data on reaction time and analyze some factors that affect it 1.24

- experiment and observe how water moves in a plant 1.17

- understand and use the following terms:

artery	microorganism
bacteria	mitochondria
cell membrane	multicellular organism
cell specialization	nervous system
cell wall	nucleus
chloroplast	organ systems
chromosomes	organ
circulatory system	organelles
cytoplasm	osmosis
diffusion	phloem vessel
digestion	protists
digestive system	respiratory system
disease	selectively permeable
endocrine system	tissue
endoplasmic reticulum	turgor pressure
excretory system	unicellular organism
field of view	vacuole
Golgi apparatus	vein
hormone	xylem vessel
lysosome	

Making Connections

- describe how organ systems in animals work together to maintain the health of the animal 1.16, 1.21, 1.22, 1.23

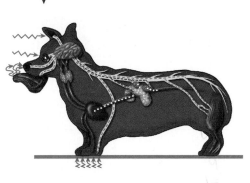

- identify a career that requires knowledge of cells and systems 1.11

- describe how organ systems in animals are organized to supply nutrients and remove waste, and to regulate the body 1.21, 1.23

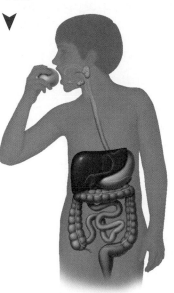

- describe how cell research helps us understand how to keep our bodies healthy 1.16, 1.22, 1.24, 1.25, 1.26

- through research and debate, decide if limits should be placed on cell research 1.25

Unit 1 Review

Understanding Concepts

1. Use the terms listed in the Unit Summary to construct a concept map.

2. What are the two main statements of the modern cell theory?

3. Do large animals have larger cells than small animals? Explain your answer.

4. Copy and complete **Table 1** in your notebook. Put a check mark beside the features that are present in plant and animal cells. This will help you better understand how plant and animal cells are different and how they are alike.

Table 1

Feature	Function	Plant Cell	Animal Cell
cell membrane	?	?	?
cell wall	?	?	?
nucleus	?	?	?
cytoplasm	?	?	?
chloroplast	?	?	?
large vacuoles	?	?	?
mitochondria	?	?	?

5. Copy **Table 2** into your notebook.

Table 2

Organ System	Organs Contained	Tissues Contained

Place the following words into your table. (You will use some words more than once.)

  respiratory, esophagus, fat, intestines, heart, digestive, lungs, circulatory, blood, connective, stomach, muscle, windpipe, nerve, epithelial

6. A plant cell and an animal cell are placed in a concentrated salt solution. Draw each cell to show the effects of the salt and describe the difference.

7. In your notebook, for each of the following, write T if the statement is true. If it is false, rewrite the statement to make it true.

(a) All living things are composed of cells.

(b) The light microscope allows scientists to view cells, molecules, and atoms.

(c) It is easy to tell animal cells from plant cells, because animal cells are always larger.

(d) All cells are surrounded by a cell wall.

(e) The nucleus is the control centre of the cell.

(f) Chloroplasts are found in plant cells, but not animal cells.

(g) A group of cells that are similar in shape and function are called a tissue.

(h) Diffusion occurs when molecules move from an area of low concentration to an area of high concentration.

(i) If an onion cell is placed in a concentrated salt solution, water will move out of the cell.

(j) All bacteria are harmful.

8. In **Figure 1**, the cell membrane is structure(s):
   (a) V   (b) W   (c) X
   (d) V and X   (e) Z and Y

9. In **Figure 1**, the nucleus is structure(s).
   (a) V   (b) X   (c) Y
   (d) V and X   (e) Z and X

10. In **Figure 1**, the plant cell is cell type
   (a) A, because it has chromosomes and a nucleus.
   (b) B, because it has cytoplasm and a nucleus.

Figure 1

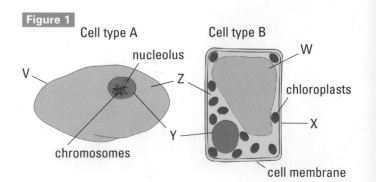

(c) A, because it has a nucleus and cell membrane.

(d) B, because it has chloroplasts and a cell wall.

11. Identify each of the following photographs as either a plant or an animal cell.

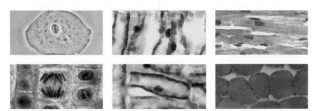

12. Interpret **Figure 2**. Why does the sugar move into the cell? Explain why more sugar is found inside the cell in B. Why has the concentration of sugar decreased in C?

Figure 2

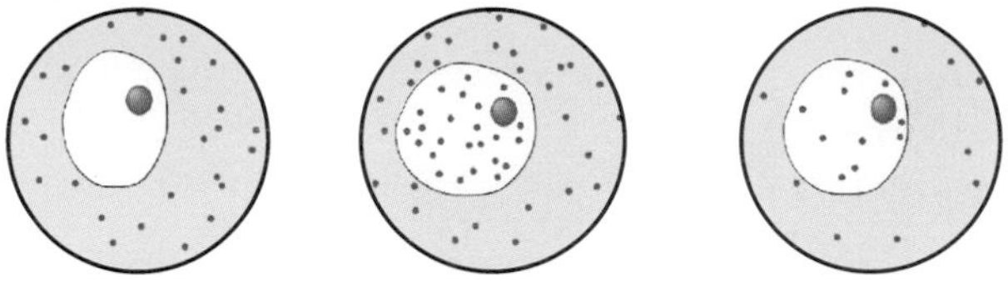

| Cell placed in 5% sugar solution at time = 0 | Time = 30 min greater sugar concentration found inside of cell | Time = 1 h Decreased sugar concentration inside of cell and in solution |

Applying Skills

13. Evidence for diffusion can be gained from which observation in **Figure 3**?

   (a) 3, because the starch moved into the dialysis tubing.

   (b) 3, because the dialysis tubing increased in size.

   (c) 2, because the dialysis tubing is permeable to starch.

   (d) 2, because the dialysis tubing is not permeable to starch.

   (e) 2, because iodine moved into the dialysis tubing.

14. Which conclusion correctly interprets the evidence gathered from the investigation in **Figure 3**?

   (a) Water moves into the dialysis tubing by osmosis; iodine moves into the dialysis tubing by diffusion; and the dialysis tubing is impermeable to starch.

Figure 3

Procedure:

- Dialysis tubing was filled with a 5% starch solution.
- Both ends of the tubing were tied and the dialysis tubing was placed in a beaker of distilled water.
- Five drops of iodine were added to the distilled water.

Observations:

1 The water in the beaker turned a yellowish colour from the iodine.

2 After 2 min, the solution in the dialysis tubing turned a blue-black. The water in the beaker remained yellow.

3 The dialysis tubing increased in size.

   (b) Iodine moves into the dialysis tubing by osmosis; starch moves out of the dialysis tubing by diffusion; and the dialysis tubing is impermeable to water.

   (c) Starch moves into the dialysis tubing by osmosis; iodine moves into the dialysis tubing by diffusion; and the dialysis tubing is impermeable to water.

15. Solve the following puzzle to find the mystery word.   microscope

(a)	the outer covering of an animal cell	CE**l l** (m)E**m b r a n e**
(b)	the organelles called the "powerhouse" of the cell	m(i)T**o c** b(r)**o n d** i A
(c)	the thick outer covering that surrounds a plant cell	(c)**e** l L **w A** b l
(d)	a threadlike structure that carries the genetic material	c b(R)**o m** (o)**s** o m e
(e)	the control centre of the cell	N u**c l e u** (s)
(f)	a green, oval-shaped organelle involved in food production	(c)**h** l(o)**R** o(p)l**a s t**
(g)	a fluid-filled space	**V** a**c u o l** (e)

16. You are observing a single-cell animal under the medium-power objective lens of a microscope. The organism is moving in the direction indicated by the arrow in **Figure 4**. To keep the animal within the field of view, which way should you move the slide? Indicate your answer using a letter.

Figure 4

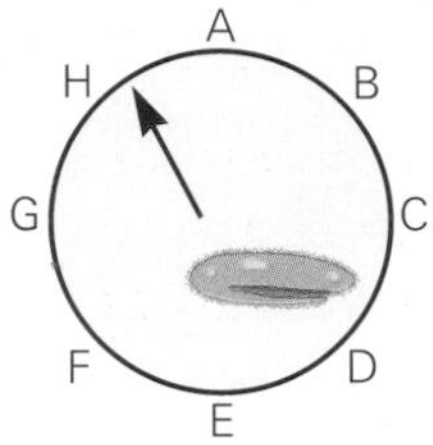

17. The microorganism in **Figure 5** was viewed under high-power magnification. The field diameter is 400 µm. Calculate the size of the organism.

Figure 5

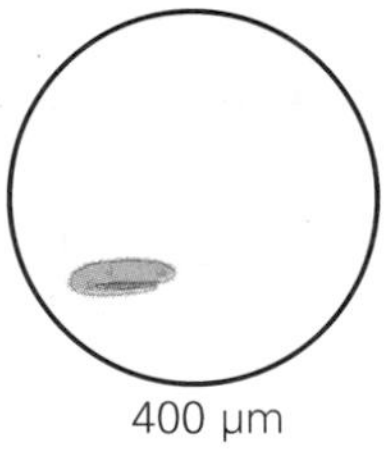

400 µm

18. (a) Calculate the volume of cell A and of cell B in **Figure 6**.

(b) Calculate the surface area of cell A and of cell B.

(c) Determine the ratio of surface area to volume for cell A and for cell B.

(d) Which cell should be better at absorbing nutrients and removing wastes? Explain your answer.

Figure 6

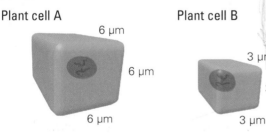

Plant cell A
6 µm
6 µm
6 µm

Plant cell B
3 µm
3 µm
3 µm

19. **Figure 7** shows two carrots used as osmometers (a device used to measure osmosis). Scientists placed a carrot in each beaker. One beaker contained distilled water and the other contained 10% salt. All of the conditions around the beakers were kept as close to identical as possible. Unfortunately, the scientists forgot to record which beaker contained the salt solution.

Figure 7

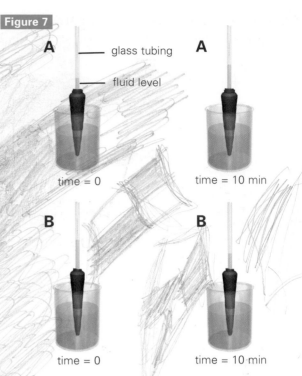

A — glass tubing — fluid level   A

time = 0   time = 10 min

B   B

time = 0   time = 10 min

(a) What problem were the scientists investigating?

(b) Identify the independent and dependent variables in the experiment.

(c) On the basis of your observations, predict which beaker contained the distilled water.

(d) Suggest a method for determining the rate of osmosis for beaker A.

(e) Based on the observations after 10 min, draw a conclusion from the experiment.

20. In **Figure 8** a red blood cell has been placed in distilled water and examined under a microscope. Explain the changes in shape of the red blood cell.

Figure 8

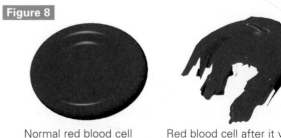

Normal red blood cell   Red blood cell after it was placed in distilled water

21. A scientist wishes to know if large cells are more active than smaller cells. Design a procedure that would allow you to investigate this question.

22. A student used the experimental design in **Figure 9** to examine diffusion in living cells.

Three similar celery stalks placed in solution of dye for 5 min.

25 °C   10 °C   40 °C

Celery is cut into 1-cm pieces with a knife

(a) What question was the student attempting to answer?

(b) State a hypothesis for the experiment.

(c) Identify the independent and dependent variables.

(d) How would you measure the rates of diffusion?

(e) Predict which celery stalk would have the greatest movement of dye. Explain why.

(f) Suggest improvements to the experimental design.

Making Connections

23. Which of the sizes and shapes in **Figure 10** would best suit a muscle cell? Explain your answer.

Figure 10

A   B   C

24. A scientist views cross-sections of leaves from the rain forest and the desert. Explain why she found more air spaces between cells in the middle layer of the rain forest leaves.

25. Athletes lose salt and water as they compete. The hotter it gets, the more they sweat. If they drink only pure water after exercise, their blood cells will swell. If they have worked very hard for a long time, some of their red blood cells might even burst.

(a) Why do the blood cells swell?

(b) Design an experiment to answer the following question: How much solute should be added to the water that an athlete drinks after exercise?

26. In most plants, the stomates (pores of the leaf) are found on the under surface of the leaf.

(a) Why aren't the stomates on the top of the leaf?

(b) Where would you expect to find the stomates on plants that float on water, such as the water lily? Give your reason.

27. Mosses have no xylem or phloem vessels to transport water. Mosses are always very short plants, usually growing only a few centimetres above the ground. Explain why a lack of transport vessels prevents moss from growing tall.

28. Two marigolds grown in different parts of Ontario are shown in **Figure 11**. Both marigolds came from the same package of seeds. Which plant do you believe grew in an area that had more rainfall? Give your reasons.

Figure 11

29. Compare specialized cells of the respiratory tract with paramecia. Identify similar structures and explain how each is used.

30. Compare the food-getting mechanisms of a single-cell amoeba with those of an animal. Describe the advantages of each system.

31. Explain why digestion in a hydra is less efficient than that of an earthworm.

Unit 2

Fluids

Unit 2 Overview

Getting Started: Fluids in Our Lives

2.1   A Close-Up Look at Fluid Flow

2.2   Fluid Flow Around Objects

2.3   Viscosity: A Property of Fluids

2.4   Inquiry Investigation: Liquids Can Be Thick or Thin

2.5   Career Profile: Viscosity and the Chocolate Factory

2.6   Measuring Matter: Mass, Weight, and Volume

2.7   Inquiry Investigation: Relating Mass and Volume

2.8   Density: Another Property of Fluids

2.9   Inquiry Investigation: Some Liquids Just Don't Mix

2.10   Comparing Densities

2.11   The Ups and Downs of Buoyancy

2.12   How and Why Do Things Float?

2.13   Design Investigation: Another Way to Measure the Density of a Liquid

2.14   Case Study: From Bladders to Ballast: Altering Buoyancy

2.15   Explore an Issue: Human Impact on Natural Fluid Systems

2.16   How Does Temperature Affect Viscosity and Density?

2.17   Case Study: Fluids and the Confederation Bridge

2.18   Inquiry Investigation: How Fluids Handle Pressure

2.19   Confined Fluids Under Pressure

2.20   Pressurized Fluid Systems: Hydraulics

2.21   Pressurized Fluid Systems: Pneumatics

2.22   Design Investigation: A Closer Look at Fluid Power

2.23   Fluid Power at Work for Us

Design Challenge: Design and Build a Device That Uses the Properties of Fluids

Unit 2 Summary

Unit 2 Review

Unit 2 Overview

luids cover Earth's surface. You breathe them and drink them. They flow through your body and in your home. Many machines and devices use fluids, from dentists' chairs to propane barbecues. The use and investigation of fluids affect our lives.

What are fluids? How are they used? What advances in technology have been made from understanding fluids?

Properties of Fluids

Air, engine oil, propane, and corn syrup are all fluids. What do they have in common? How are they different? As we investigate fluids, we find that they have different properties that we can describe: viscosity, buoyancy, density, and pressure.

You will be able to:

- predict how temperature affects the flow rate of liquids

- compare the viscosities and densities of various substances, and understand the relationship between the two properties

- describe the difference between mass and weight

- measure the density of liquids with an instrument you have designed and constructed

- explain how buoyancy and gravity are related

- use the particle theory of matter to compare the densities of solids, liquids, and gases, and to describe the effects of temperature on fluids

- compare what happens to different fluids when an external pressure is applied or when the temperature is changed

The Use of Fluids

A fluid's properties may pose some challenges, such as getting the ketchup out of its bottle! But we can also make the properties of fluids work for us. Fluids for example, fuel the airplane below and allow the pilot to move the flaps on the airplane's wings.

You will be able to:

- plan and conduct an investigation to compare the densities of liquids and solids

- explain how the buoyant force on an object can be altered

- explain how the properties of fluids are used in the design of technical innovations

- design and build a model of a device that uses hydraulics or pneumatics

- compare how liquids and gases transmit force in hydraulic and pneumatic systems

▼

▲

Fluids and Living Organisms

Fluids have a wide range of properties. By looking at nature—the shape of a whale and the stickiness of tree sap—we can learn a lot about fluids that will help us to improve design technology. At the same time, investigating fluids and their properties in artificial systems can help us understand the natural world better.

You will be able to:

- compare how fluids function in living things and manufactured devices

- explain how the study of hydraulics and pneumatics increases understanding of fluids in the human body

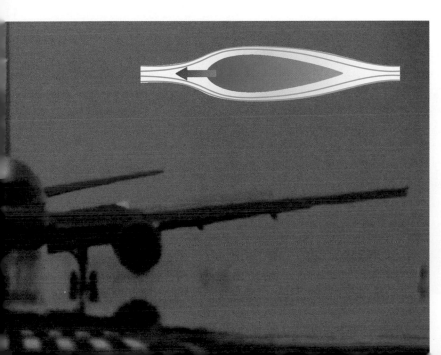

Design Challenge

You will be able to...
demonstrate your learning by completing a Design Challenge.

Devices That Use the Properties of Fluids

You will design and build a model of a device that uses the properties of a fluid to perform a certain function. Your model will help you to understand the relationship between the properties of fluids and their use in machines and devices.

In this unit you will be able to design and build:

1 **A Pneumatically or Hydraulically Operated Safety Hinge**
Design and build a model of a door that opens or closes using pneumatics or hydraulics.

2 **A Boat Navigation Lock**
Design and build a model of a navigation lock that allows boats to travel between waterways of different levels.

3 **A Fish-Tank Cleaner**
Design and build a fish-tank cleaning device that will raise or lower itself in water.

To start your Design Challenge, see page 134.

Record your thoughts and design ideas for the Challenge when you see

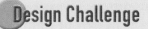

Design Challenge

Getting Started

Fluids in Our Lives

1 Name a fluid. You probably think of one like water, and you are right. Liquids are fluids, but so are gases such as the air we breathe. Although fluids have properties they share with other substances—they take up space and are made of matter—fluids also have unique properties. Liquids can be thick or thin. Some things float in fluids, and others sink.

    In what other ways are we concerned with the movement of fluids? What do you think are some of the properties of fluids?

2 Fluids help to make our lives easier. Engineers harness the energy of water to generate electricity. As air rushes into a vacuum cleaner, it carries dirt and dust along with it.

    A machine called a tree spade enables us to transplant very large trees. The blades are forced open and then down by the movement of oil within cylinders in the spade.

    What other problems can we solve by investigating and using fluids? What kinds of devices and machines do we make that use fluids?

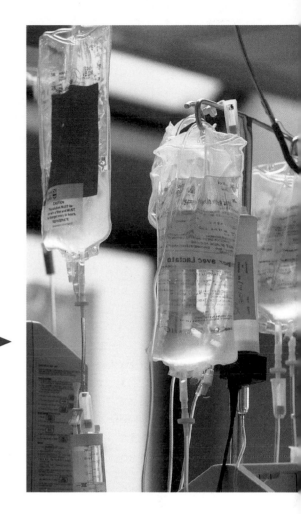

Reflecting

Think about the questions in ❶,❷,❸. What other questions do you have about fluids? As you progress through this unit, reflect on your answers and revise them based on what you have learned.

❸ The health of Earth's fluid systems, including its waterways and atmosphere, is necessary to sustain our lives and the lives of future generations. Fluids such as blood and air keep us alive. Intravenous fluids are delivered to hospital patients when needed. Is the way fluids function in living things the same as the way they function in systems we create? How do changes in fluids affect living things?

Try This Where Are Fluids in Your Life? 9E

Think about the fluids in your life and the devices that use them.

- Work with a small group. Each member should have about 20 pieces of paper, each approximately 6 cm × 6 cm. On each piece of paper, write down any fluid you can think of or any instrument or machine that uses a fluid. Use only one piece of paper for each item.

1. How do you decide what things are fluids and what things aren't?

- When each group member has used up all 20 pieces, combine your group's papers into one pile. Separate the words into categories.

2. What categories are you using?

- Glue the words in their categories onto a poster-sized piece of paper. Use markers to give each category a heading and to draw arrows between words that are connected. You are making a word map. Draw illustrations where appropriate. Write the word *fluids* somewhere on the word map.

3. Compare your group's word map to another's. Are the categories similar? Why might there be differences?

A Close-Up Look at Fluid Flow

Fluids are substances that flow (**Figure 1**). Water flows from the tap when you wash your hands; you see it flowing in a stream. But liquids are not the only substances that flow. What flows past your face when you coast your bicycle down a hill? What carries dandelion seed fluff around the neighbourhood in the spring? Air, which is a gas, also flows. Both gases and liquids are fluids.

Systems involving moving fluids are a concern for people in many professions and fields. (See **Figure 2**.) How will a tower withstand a gusty wind? How will deposits on artery walls affect the flow of blood? Is the inside of a pipe smooth enough to enable natural gas to flow safely? How is an airplane affected by different kinds of airflow? The concern with fluid flow exists both when a fluid is moving and when an object is moving through the fluid. How quickly a fluid flows in a given amount of time is called its **flow rate**.

Systems involving moving fluids are said to be **dynamic**. **Aerodynamics** refers to air (gas) moving around solid objects. **Hydrodynamics** refers to the motion of liquids (usually water) around solid objects.

Figure 1

Flow tests are conducted on fire hydrants to ensure there will be enough water in an emergency.

Try This Determining Flow Rate

You can find the rate at which the water flows from the tap in your classroom or outside the school.

• Calibrate a large bucket at the 10-L mark by measuring water into it using a 1-L container, such as a plastic beaker. Mark the 10-L water level with a black waterproof marker.
• Place a mark on the handle of the tap. Determine how many turns of the tap (how many times the black mark rotates) are required to open the tap fully.

1. When the tap is opened fully, how long does it take to fill the bucket to the 10-L mark?

2. When the tap is opened halfway, how long does it take to fill the bucket to the 10-L mark?

3. How does the result you obtained in question 2 compare to the result in question 1? Is this what you expected to happen? Explain.

• The volume of liquid that flows in a second is called its flow rate. Calculate the flow rate of the tap in litres per second.

Solids That Seem to Flow

A fine powder, consisting of a very large number of tiny solid pieces, can be poured from one container into another. (See **Figure 2**.) But have you ever seen water form a heap, as flour does when you pour it? Can you make a pile of milk, as you can of sand or wheat? The answer, of course, is no: only solids can be piled in a heap. Liquids take the shape of their container and gases expand to fill whatever container they are in.

Figure 2

Here is a material that is not a gas or a liquid but appears to flow. Flour, sand, and wheat all seem to flow. Why are they not considered to be fluids?

Explaining Flow Using the Particle Theory

The **particle theory** of matter provides a model to help us understand the differences between fluids and solids. It also aids in understanding and predicting fluid behaviour.

The particle theory states that
- all matter is composed of particles;
- particles are in constant motion;
- there are forces of attraction among particles.

When particles are close together and moving slowly, the forces of attraction are strong. The particles in a solid are so close together and their forces of attraction are so strong that they cannot flow past one another. In liquids the particles are moving more rapidly, so forces of attraction between them are not as strong. Because the particles are not locked in a fixed arrangement, they move a little farther apart and can slide over one another. This explains why liquids are capable of flowing. In gases the particles are so far apart from each other and the forces of attraction are so weak that the particles can move independently of each other. As a result, gases flow very easily.

Understanding Concepts

1. Using the particle theory, explain why solids do not flow.

Making Connections

2. How is the flow of air used in transportation?

Exploring

3. Investigate how a water-saving
4A shower head works.

Reflecting

4. Take another look at the word map you prepared in the Getting Started Try This activity. Are any of your examples solids that seem to flow? Should they remain on the map?

Design Challenge

You are using a fluid in your Design Challenge. How will you consider the flow of that fluid during the design and testing of your model?

Fluid Flow Around Objects

The shape of an object determines how fluids flow around it. Consider the flow of water in a river. A deep river, with steep banks and no obstacles, flows fast and smoothly. The water travels in straight or almost straight lines. This is known as **laminar flow**. Now imagine a shallow river, with irregular rocks breaking the surface. The water will be broken and choppy—unable to flow in straight lines. This is called **turbulent flow**, which may result in rapids, eddies, and whirlpools.

The same thing occurs with gases in motion. As moving air encounters objects such as buildings or trees, the flow becomes turbulent. **Figure 1** illustrates laminar and turbulent flow.

Shapes that produce a laminar flow have less air or water resistance than shapes that produce a turbulent flow (**Figure 2**). Resistance is referred to as **drag**. For cars and airplanes travelling at high speeds, less drag means better fuel consumption and less wind noise. Shapes that create a laminar flow are said to be **streamlined** or aerodynamic. (See **Figure 3**.)

A fluid moving relative to an object experiences resistance as its particles slam into the object. Water flowing under a bridge meets resistance as it passes the piers. Airplanes encounter the resistance of air when they are flying. Objects falling through the air are slowed down because of air resistance.

Figure 1

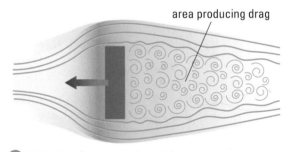

area producing drag

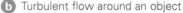

a Laminar flow around an object

b Turbulent flow around an object

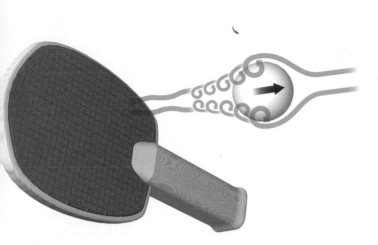

Figure 2

Turbulent and laminar flow can be used to control movement and direction. Sports balls are designed with this in mind. The airflow around this ball becomes turbulent at the top and bottom of the ball. This helps to slow the ball.

Wind Tunnels: A Closer Look at Gas Flow

Canadian Wallace Rupert Turnbull is credited with building Canada's first wind tunnel in 1902. He conducted experiments in the tunnel to test his propeller inventions.

A wind tunnel has a propeller at one end that propels air into it. Smoke is often added to make the flow of air visible.

Wind tunnels are widely used today. (See **Figure 4**.) Engineers use them to test the airflow around wings of aircraft and investigate how ice on wings affects airflow. Vehicles are examined in wind tunnels to determine how streamlined they are. By placing precisely designed scale models of tall buildings, bridges, and towers in wind tunnels, engineers can examine how the structures are affected by high winds.

Figure 4

Figure 3

The bodies of whales and dolphins are streamlined for decreased water resistance. This is achieved by an elongated shape with no narrowing at the neck, no protruding parts, and smooth skin. The tail fluke produces a more laminar flow of water around the body. Notice how a side view of one-half of the tail fluke resembles an aircraft wing.

Understanding Concepts

1. Make a chart with two headings: Laminar Flow and Turbulent Flow. List some examples of each type of flow.

Making Connections

2. Why might a car manufacturer change the shape of side mirrors on a particular model?

3. How would deposits on the walls of arteries affect the flow of blood moving through the body?

4. Would you prefer turbulent flow or laminar flow around a racing bicycle? Which would you like for whitewater rafting?

Exploring

5. Research the importance of air (4A) resistance in your favourite high-speed sport.

Reflecting

6. Why do scientists study airflow?

Viscosity: A Property of Fluids

Have you ever tried to pour ketchup out of a brand new bottle? It takes a lot of force to start the ketchup flowing. (See **Figure 1**.) Very little force is required to start maple syrup flowing, as **Figure 2** shows. That's because maple syrup is much thinner and has less resistance to flowing than ketchup. **Viscosity** is the term for the resistance that a fluid has to flowing and movement. The particle theory helps us to understand that this resistance is due to the forces of attraction among particles. The stronger the attraction among the particles, the greater the resistance of the particles to flowing past one another. Different substances are composed of different particles and have different forces of attraction. This helps to explain why fluids can have different viscosities.

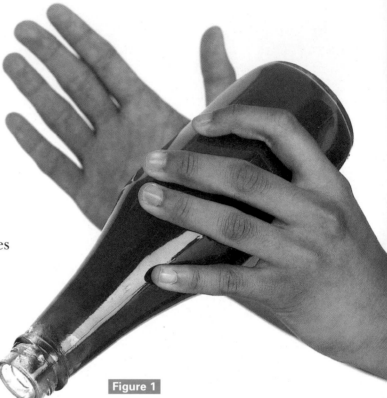

Figure 1

Ketchup is thick and has a high viscosity. Maple syrup is less viscous (has a lower viscosity) than ketchup. Water is a thin, runny liquid with a low viscosity. Maple syrup is more viscous than water, but less viscous than ketchup. Water has less resistance to flowing and movement than maple syrup.

When fluids are stationary, viscosity is not a concern. However, when a fluid is moving, or when something is moving through a fluid, the property of viscosity can be very important.

Figure 2

Measuring Viscosity

We often need to know how quickly or how slowly a fluid flows. If you tipped a water pitcher as quickly as a salad dressing bottle, you might soon find a puddle of water on the table! You handle the two fluids differently because you know that they have different viscosities.

We might use the words *thick* and *thin* to describe viscosity, but these words do not give enough information about this property. We need some way of measuring viscosity quantitatively. One method involves timing how quickly a solid, such as a pearl-sized ball, falls through a column of the liquid. Another method times how long it takes a liquid at a certain temperature to flow into a small pot.

An instrument that measures viscosity is called a **viscometer**.

Design Challenge

How viscous is the fluid you are using in your Design Challenge? What effect does its viscosity have on your design?

Understanding Concepts

1. Molasses has a high viscosity. Explain what this statement means.

2. How does the thickness of a fluid compare to its viscosity? Give an example.

Making Connections

3. Research an industry in which (4A) viscosity testing is important. Present your findings as a poster.

Exploring

4. Research how soap affects the viscosity of water.

5. Plan an investigation to help you (2E) rank the following fluids in order, from least viscous to most viscous: shampoo, melted chocolate, cooking oil, air, and cola.

Reflecting

6. What does the viscosity of a fluid tell you about its flow rate?

Try This — Let's Examine Moving Fluids

Figure 3

Figure 4

- Fill a small, clear plastic bottle with a tight-fitting lid with corn syrup, leaving a 3-cm space at the top. Fill another with water, leaving a 3-cm space at the top. Add a small, identical amount of paper confetti to each bottle. Fasten the lids securely (**Figure 3**).

As each bottle moves, carefully observe the confetti.

1. How does the movement of the confetti in the two liquids compare?

- Using a board at least 110 cm long, build a ramp with a low incline. (See **Figure 4**.) Roll the bottles, one at a time, down the ramp. Observe the movement of the confetti.

2. Sketch your observations.

3. What conclusions can you make about the movement of the two liquids?

4. Why do you think you were told to add confetti to the bottles? What might the confetti represent?

Liquids Can Be Thick or Thin

Have you ever put the corn syrup bottle in the fridge instead of the cupboard? What happens when you try to pour the syrup? You have a problem! How could you make it easier to pour? What happens to the syrup when it lands on your hot pancakes? All these questions involve viscosity and temperature. Are these two properties related?

Question

Does temperature affect the viscosity of oil? (See **Figure 1**.) If so, how? How can this change be measured?

Hypothesis

2C Predict the change in viscosity as heat is added to or removed from a sample of oil.

Experimental Design

In this investigation you will explore what happens to viscosity when a fluid is heated or cooled. You will use a homemade viscometer to measure the flow rate of oil at three temperatures. Flow rate is a measure of viscosity.

1 Copy the observation chart in **Table 1**.

Materials

- apron
- safety goggles
- water
- 150-mL foam cup
- beaker
- wax pencil
- retort stand
- ring clamp (for foam cup)
- small metal skewer
- ruler
- stopwatch
- 500-mL beaker
- 80 mL of cooking oil at three temperatures: 20–24°C, 5–8°C, and 45–50°C
- thermometer
- tissues
- hot plate

Procedure

2 Using 70 mL of water as a guide, mark the 70-mL line on your beaker.
- Empty the container and wipe it dry.

3 Use the skewer to poke a hole in the bottom of the foam cup.
- Attach the ring clamp 30 cm from the table top. Sit the foam cup in the ring.
- Put the beaker underneath the cup.

4 Measure the temperature of the 20–24°C oil.

✎ (a) Record the actual temperature in your chart.

- Wipe the thermometer.
- Tightly cover the hole in the cup with a finger and pour the sample into it.
- Remove your finger and immediately start timing.

5 Stop when the oil reaches the mark on the beaker.

✎ (a) Record this time, calculate, and record the flow rate. Use the formula.

$$\text{flow rate} = \frac{\text{volume of fluid (mL)}}{\text{time (s)}}$$

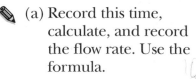

- Allow the cup to drain. Empty the beaker according to your teacher's instructions. Wipe out both containers.

Figure 1

Table 1
Flow Rate of Oil

Oil Temp.	20–24°C	5–8°C	45–50°C
Time	?	?	?
Flow Rate	?	?	?
Appearance	?	?	?

Making Connections

1. From your graph, predict what flow rates you would expect for oil at 12°C and at 100°C. Explain your reasoning.

   🛑 Do NOT try heating oil to 100°C.

2. How would you solve the corn syrup problem mentioned in the introduction to this Investigation?

3. What household products could require viscosity testing during manufacturing?

Reflecting

4. Why were you given 80 mL of oil, but asked to record the time for 70 mL to flow?

6 Repeat steps 4 and 5 with the 5–8°C and 45–50°C oil samples.

   (a) Describe the appearance of the oil at these temperatures.

7 Make a graph of your
(7C) results. Put temperature on the x-axis and flow rate on the y-axis. Give your graph a title.

Analysis

8 Analyze your results by answering the following questions.

   (a) At which temperature is the oil most viscous? Give a qualitative and quantitative description of the oil that supports your answer.

   (b) At which temperature did the oil have the highest flow rate? What does this tell you about the viscosity of the oil at that temperature?

   (c) What relationship exists between the temperature of the oil and its flow rate?

   (d) Why did you wipe out the beaker after step 5 each time?

9 Write a formal lab report
(8A) for this investigation.

🛑 Be careful when heating oil. The oil must be heated in a hot water bath. Do not heat the oil past 50°C. Follow your teacher's instructions.

Remain standing as you perform this investigation.

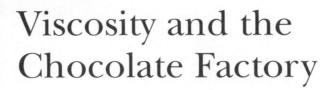

Viscosity and the Chocolate Factory

Randy Droniuk is a food scientist. His career is the envy of chocolate lovers everywhere. Randy is one of the many people working every day in a factory to ensure the quality of chocolate products are delicious. He runs tests during the chocolate-making process, and he researches how to improve the process. "I enjoy the variety of work involved in my job," says Randy. "It is really nice to work on anything that involves a better quality product for our customer. I also love to eat chocolate. My favourite is dark chocolate."

To test and research the chocolate-making process, Randy needs to understand the property of viscosity and how it applies to liquid chocolate. "Viscosity testing is very important in this industry. We want to ensure your favourite chocolate bar is of the same high quality from batch to batch. Both temperature and ingredients greatly influence viscosity. By running regular tests, we can produce a dependable product."

Figure 1

Some chocolate bars are made in moulds. Liquid chocolate, at approximately 30°C, is poured into moulds that resemble ice cube trays. A vibrator settles the chocolate into the moulds. Filled moulds are cooled slowly, and the chocolate solidifies. The moulds are turned over and out falls a chocolate bar ready to be packaged.

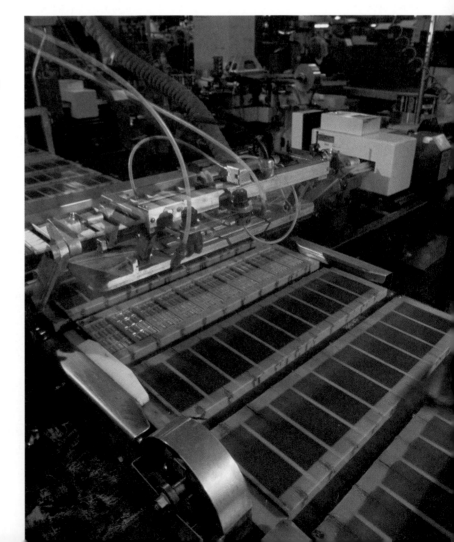

The Importance of Viscosity

Not all chocolate bars are the same. Neither is the chocolate that goes into the many different varieties of these treats.

Scientists in a chocolate factory measure the flow rates of liquid chocolate. A different viscosity is required for moulded or solid bars than for bars that have many ingredients. Imagine what would happen if the chocolate that surrounds the other ingredients was too runny. Too much would run off and the centre would not be properly coated. What if the chocolate pouring into the moulds was too viscous? The mould might not fill before the conveyor belt moved it along, or the chocolate might not flow throughout the entire mould, leaving air bubbles or gaps. Viscosity is a very important measurement in the production of chocolate bars.

Factors Affecting the Viscosity of Chocolate

An interesting aspect of Randy's job involves investigating how chocolate is ground down to the right smoothness. The pieces must be just the right size to ensure the chocolate product is smooth to taste. The size of pieces and the temperature of the chocolate affect its viscosity. When a lower viscosity is desired, scientists can add more fat to the chocolate. Fat, such as cocoa butter, coats the fine solid pieces in the chocolate so it flows more freely. Careful adjustments are made to obtain the right combination of smoothness, fat content, and temperature in liquid chocolate. This ensures its viscosity is perfect for each application.

Figure 2
This specialized viscometer is measuring the viscosity of chocolate. A spindle rotates inside a sample of chocolate. If the chocolate has a high viscosity, there will be more resistance to the turning of the spindle. Viscosity tests are normally run on chocolate that has been heated to 40°C.

 **Hot Chocolate**

Look at how different the viscosity of chocolate can be for two different types of products. You will need chocolate from chocolate baking chips and from a moulded, solid milk-chocolate bar.

In separate glass measuring containers, carefully heat a small sample of each chocolate to 40°C. Measure the temperature of each sample to confirm they are the same.

 Because chocolate burns easily, use a microwave oven at a medium setting to melt the chocolate.

- Stir each sample of liquid chocolate with a separate spoon.

1. Does one sample seem thicker and more viscous than the other? If so, which one?

- Fill each spoon with the liquid chocolate and hold it above the sample. Slowly pour the chocolate off the spoon onto a plate.

2. Which sample is slower to start pouring?

3. Which sample more quickly forms a pool of chocolate with a flat surface?

- Consider how these two types of chocolate are intended to be used.

4. How does this explain why their viscosity is different?

5. Why is it necessary to heat each sample to the same temperature before testing its viscosity?

Measuring Matter: Mass, Weight, and Volume

Using fluids—both liquids and gases—requires an understanding of their behaviour. You need to know how they behave when they are still, when they are moving, when something is moving in them, when they are pushed, or when they are pulled. Learning about these things requires the ability to measure matter.

Mass and Weight

"How much does it weigh?" "Let's check the weight of the candy." You hear expressions like these almost daily. Usually, when people use the term weight, they are referring to the measurement of mass. Mass and weight are not the same thing.

Mass is the amount of matter in an object and is used to measure many things, from food to mail. An object's mass stays constant everywhere in the universe. Mass is measured in grams (g), or units derived from grams, such as milligrams (mg) and kilograms (kg).

An object's **weight** is a measurement of the force of gravity pulling on the object. It is measured in newtons (N), named after Sir Isaac Newton. Because gravity is not the same everywhere in the universe, an object's weight varies according to where that object is in the universe. (See **Figure 1**.)

Because gravity is approximately the same everywhere on Earth's surface, people often use the words mass and weight interchangeably. Remember that mass and weight are different.

Volume

In addition to having mass and weight, matter occupies space. **Volume** is a measure of the amount of space occupied by matter. It is measured in cubic metres (m^3), litres (L), cubic centimetres (cm^3), or millilitres (mL).

Capacity is related to volume. It is a measure of the amount of space available inside something. People measure the volume or capacity of things such as fish aquariums, medical syringes, and ships' cargo holds.

Different types and quantities of matter are measured in different ways. Here are some techniques that you might use in your class.

Measuring Liquids

Liquids are measured by observing how much of a container they fill. A tall, narrow container (such as a graduated cylinder) gives the most accurate measurement. Look at the container from the side, with your eye level with the surface of the liquid. You might notice a slight curve at the edges of the surface where the liquid touches the

Figure 1

The downward pull (force of gravity) on an object on the surface of Earth is approximately 6 times as large as on the Moon. Because of this difference in gravity, objects on the Moon weigh 1/6 what they do on Earth. The *weight* of the object changes, but the mass is the same in both locations.

container. This "curved" surface is called the meniscus. Read the volume at the lowest place on the meniscus. Liquids are generally measured in litres (L) or millilitres (mL).

Measuring Volume of Solids — Rectangular Solids

Rectangular solids may be measured with a ruler, and their volume calculated using the formula

$$volume = length \times width \times height$$

Solids are usually measured in cubic metres (m^3) or cubic centimetres (cm^3), but may sometimes be given in litres (L) or millilitres (mL). Interestingly, 1 cm^3 is the same as 1 mL, so 1000 cm^3 equals 1 L.

Measuring Volume of Solids — Small Irregular Solids

The volume of a small irregular solid must be measured by **displacement**. In this technique, you choose a container (such as a graduated cylinder) that your small object will fit inside. Then pour water into the empty container until it is about half full. Record the volume

of water in the container, then carefully add the object. Record the volume of the water plus the object. Calculate the volume of the object using the formula:

volume of object = (volume of water + object) − (volume of water)

Measuring Volume of Solids — Large Irregular Solids

To measure the volume of a large irregular solid, you will need an overflow can and a graduated cylinder (**Figure 2**). This measurement is best done over a sink. Fill the overflow can with water until water starts to run out of the spout. Wait until the water stops dripping, then place the graduated cylinder under the spout. Carefully lower the object into the water and observe what happens.

Figure 2
A volume of water equal to the volume of the solid will pour out of the spout and into the measuring cylinder.

Try This Measuring Volume

Your teacher will provide you with several samples of matter and equipment to measure volume. Estimate the volume of each sample.

1. Record your estimates in a chart.
• Select the appropriate equipment for measuring the volume of one of the samples.
• Following the guidelines given above, find the volume of your sample.
• Share your results with the rest of your class.

2. Record the volumes of all the samples in your chart.

3. Which samples were you able to estimate quite accurately? Which were harder to estimate?

Understanding Concepts

1. Describe the relationship between mass and weight. Give an example of this relationship.

2. Imagine you have travelled to a planet that has twice the force of gravity of Earth. You have taken a solid with a mass of 1 kg with you. Describe its mass, weight, and volume on this planet, compared with that on Earth.

Design Challenge

What measurements will you need to make of the fluid in your Design Challenge?

Relating Mass and Volume

How are volume and mass related to each other? If you double the volume of a substance, how will the mass change? Would the same volume of a different substance have the same mass? Which is heavier: a kilogram of feathers or a kilogram of lead? The answer seems obvious, but there is an important difference between feathers and lead. Equal masses of these substances have very different volumes.

Question

What does mass have to do with the amount of space (volume) a liquid occupies?

Hypothesis

1 Write a hypothesis about how you think the mass and volume of a
2C liquid are related.

Experimental Design

In this investigation, you will measure volume and mass, plot them on the same graph, and draw conclusions about the relationship between them.

2 For each liquid, construct an observation chart with 3 columns, as in **Table 1**.

Materials

- apron
- safety goggles
- distilled water
- corn syrup
- saturated solution of salt water
- triple beam balance
- 150-mL or larger graduated cylinder
- small plastic pipette
- 150-mL beaker with a pour spout
- tissues

Procedure

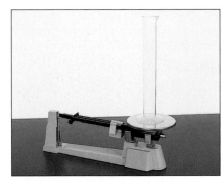

3 Measure the mass of an empty graduated cylinder.

✎ (a) Record this figure.

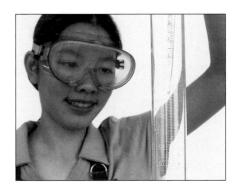

4 Obtain a sample of one of the three liquids from your teacher.
- Add 10 mL of the liquid to the graduated cylinder.

✎ (a) Record the mass of the cylinder and the liquid.

✎ (b) Calculate and record the mass of the liquid.

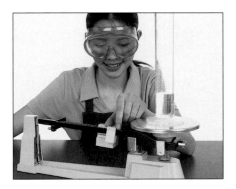

5 Continue to add the liquid, in 10-mL amounts, until you have a total of 100 mL in the cylinder.

(a) Calculate the mass of each new volume of liquid.

(b) Calculate the mass-to-volume ratio for the 20-mL and 60-mL volumes.

- Clean the cylinder.

Table 1

Volume of Liquid Added	Mass of Cylinder and Liquid	Mass of Additional Liquid
?	?	?
?	?	?

Figure 1

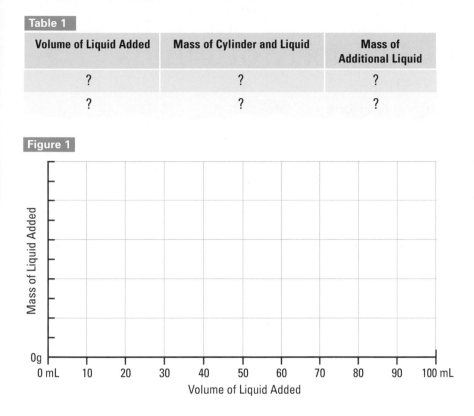

Mass of Liquid Added

0g

0 mL   10   20   30   40   50   60   70   80   90   100 mL

Volume of Liquid Added

Making Connections

1. The line on your graph should go through the origin. Explain why.

Exploring

2. Make a prediction: add a line to your graph to show the relationship between mass and volume for copper. With your teacher's permission, repeat the investigation using copper pennies. You will have to find the volume of a copper penny. How well do your results match your prediction?

Reflecting

3. All water does not have the same composition. Why is it important to use distilled water in this investigation?

6 Make a line graph of your
7C results. Put the volume of liquid added on the *x*-axis, and the mass of the liquid on the *y*-axis (**Figure 1**).
- Draw the line of best fit through the points.

7 Repeat steps 4 and 5 with the other liquids.
- Add new data to the graph.
- Make a legend to distinguish the liquids.

Analysis

8 Analyze your results by answering the following questions.

(a) Why did you measure the mass of the graduated cylinder at the beginning of the experiment and not after the liquid was poured out?

(b) Calculate the mass of 1 mL of each liquid, by calculating the mass of 1 mL of liquid from each 20-mL amount that was added, then taking the average.

(c) How do the mass-to-volume ratios for the 20-mL and 60-mL volumes of each liquid compare to your answers to (b)?

(d) Your line graph illustrates the relationship between the mass and volume of three liquids. State this relationship in a way that answers the question at the beginning of this investigation.

Density: Another Property of Fluids

We have all seen the devastating effects of a spill from an oil tanker. (See **Figure 1**.) Cleaning up would be much more difficult if oil did not float on top of water. But why does oil float? We could say that oil is lighter than water, but what would that mean? A litre of oil is certainly not lighter than a glass of water.

Before we can compare fluids using the words "light or heavy," we must examine the same volume of each fluid. Thus, a litre of oil is lighter (has less mass) than a litre of water. When we compare the masses of the same volume of different substances, we are comparing their densities. Oil floats on water because it is less dense than water.

Figure 1

Calculating the Density of a Substance

Density is the mass of a substance per unit volume of that substance. It is expressed as grams per cubic centimetre (g/cm^3), kilograms per cubic metre (kg/m^3), or grams per millilitre (g/mL).

Density is calculated by dividing the mass of an amount of substance by its volume. The formula looks like this:

$$Density = \frac{Mass}{Volume} \quad or \quad D = \frac{M}{V}$$

For example, the cube of water in **Figure 2** has a volume of $1 \ m^3$ and a mass of 1000 kg.

$$Density = \frac{1000 \ kg}{1 m^3} = 1000 \ kg/m^3$$

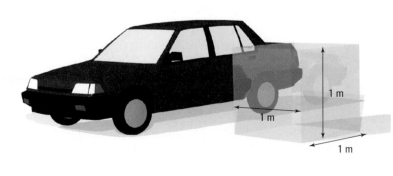

Figure 2

One cubic metre ($1 \ m^3$) of water is as heavy as a small car.

Table 1	Densities of Common Substances	
	Density	
Fluids	**g/cm^3 (g/mL)**	**kg/m^3**
hydrogen	0.000 089	0.089
helium	0.000 179	0.179
air	0.001 29	1.29
oxygen	0.001 43	1.43
carbon dioxide	0.001 98	1.98
gasoline	0.69	
isopropanol (rubbing alcohol)	0.79	
vegetable oil	0.92	
distilled water	1.00	
seawater	1.03	
glycerol	1.26	
mercury (a metal)	13.55	
Solids		
wood (balsa)	0.12	
wood (pine)	0.5	
wood (birch)	0.66	
ice	0.92	
sugar	1.59	
salt	2.16	
aluminum	2.7	
limestone	3.2	
iron	7.87	
nickel	8.90	
silver	10.5	
lead	11.34	
gold	19.32	

Figure 3

These balloons float because they are filled with helium.

Density Is a Property of Fluids and Solids

In Investigation 2.7, you calculated the density (mass-to-volume ratio) of water, corn syrup, and salt water. You found that this ratio was constant for each fluid. Each gas also has its own density. Helium gas will float on top of air (**Figure 3**), just as oil floats on top of water. This happens because helium is less dense than air.

Solids also have their own unique densities. Those that float in water have a density of less than 1.00 g/mL. Solids that sink in water have a density of more than 1.00 g/mL.

The densities of two substances can be used to predict which will float and which will sink.

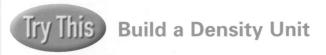 **Build a Density Unit**

This activity lets you take a closer look at the density of water.
- Design a cube that is 1cm² on each side. Leave the top of the cube open. Make it out of a light plastic, such as an overhead transparency. Be careful with your measurements. Accuracy is important. Fasten the cube together using cellophane tape. Fill the cube with water.

1. How much water will fit into this 1-cm³ container?

2. What is the mass of this amount of water?

3. Calculate the density of water.

4. Compare your calculated value with the value in **Table 1**. Explain any difference.

Understanding Concepts

1. Compare the densities of the three liquids in Investigation 2.7.

2. **(a)** What substance in **Table 1** is the most dense?

   (b) What substance is the least dense?

   (c) Give one use for each of these substances.

3. **(a)** List all of the solids that will float on water.

   (b) List all of the solids that will float on liquid mercury.

   (c) List all of the gases that will float on air.

Making Connections

4. Propane gas, which is used in many barbecues, is denser than air. It is also flammable. Propane appliances are often used in areas without electricity. Explain why a leak from a propane appliance is very dangerous.

Exploring

5. With your teacher's approval, (2E) design and conduct an investigation to find the density of a $1 Canadian coin from its mass and volume. Could density be used to identify counterfeit coins? Explain.

6. Make a 1000-cm³ container. What will be the dimensions of the length, width, and height? How much water will this container hold? What is the mass of this amount of water?

 **Design Challenge**

Why is the density of water an important consideration when designing a submersible device or a boat lock?

2.9 Inquiry Investigation

SKILLS MENU
○ Questioning   ● Conducting   ● Analyzing
● Hypothesizing   ● Recording   ● Communicating
● Planning

Some Liquids Just Don't Mix

If you've made homemade salad dressing with vinegar and oil, you've likely noticed how one of these liquids tends to float on top of the other.

Question
Can different liquids float on top of each other?

Hypothesis

1 What will happen when corn syrup, vinegar, and cooking oil are
2C placed in the same container? Predict whether a piece of cork and a plastic block will float or sink in the container. Write a hypothesis explaining your predictions.

Experimental Design
You will observe what happens when some common liquids are poured into the same container. You will also observe the relative densities of two solids: a cork and a plastic block.

2 Construct an observation sheet for this investigation, after reading the Procedure.

Materials
- apron
- safety goggles
- corn syrup
- white vinegar
- cooking oil
- piece of cork
- small plastic block
- 50-mL graduated cylinders, 2
- 15-mL measuring spoon
- paper towel
- triple beam balance
- food colouring

Procedure

3 Slowly pour 15 mL of any of the three liquids down the sides of one of the graduated cylinders.
- Rinse and dry the measuring spoon.

✎ (a) Draw a diagram of your observations.

4 Repeat step 3 with the other liquids.

5 Using the second graduated cylinder and the triple beam balance, calculate the densities of vinegar, cooking oil, and corn syrup.

✎ (a) Show your density calculations on your observation sheet.

✎ (b) Write the density of each liquid beside its layer in the diagram.

6 Slide the cork and the plastic block into the column of liquid. Observe where they settle in the column.

✎ (a) Draw and label their positions in the diagram.

Analysis

7 Analyze your results by answering the following questions.

(a) How do your observations of the liquids compare with your prediction?

(b) Were the results affected by the order in which you poured the liquids?

(c) How do the positions of the solids compare with your prediction?

(d) Write a brief explanation of the results you obtained referring to the properties of fluids.

(e) There are really four fluids in your density column. What is the fourth fluid?

(f) Compare the densities of the liquids to their position in the container. Are your results consistent with the density values? Explain.

Making Connections

1. What common food is made of the same three fluids, plus a little seasoning?

Exploring

2. Add 10 drops of 15% table cream to the column of liquids. Draw a diagram of your observations.

3. Estimate the densities of the cork and the plastic.

Reflecting

4. (a) Of the three liquids, which one took the longest to pour? Which poured most quickly?

   (b) Propose a hypothesis 2C relating two different properties of fluids.

5. Could food colouring added to the vinegar affect the density calculation of the vinegar? Explain.

Comparing Densities

You have already learned that every pure substance has its own characteristic density. Usually, solids have greater densities than liquids, and liquids have greater densities than gases. The particle theory can help us to understand this: the particles in solids are tightly packed together, held by the attractive forces between particles. There is relatively little space between the particles (**Figure 1**), so the substance tends to be dense. Liquids have a little more space between the particles, so are slightly less dense. Gases have very large spaces between the particles, so have the lowest density. When a solid is heated until it melts, it expands slightly and becomes less dense. So how can we say that each substance has its own characteristic density?

We need to understand that, unless we are told otherwise, the density given is for a substance in its most common state at room temperature. Copper, for example, is solid, and oxygen is a gas. There are a couple of exceptions to the "solids are most dense" rule. Mercury, a metal that is liquid at room temperature, is more dense than many solids and over 13 times as dense as water.

Water, also, is something of a special case. At some temperatures, liquid water is more dense than solid ice!

Using Pure Water as a Standard

Water is the most abundant liquid on Earth. We use the density of pure water as a standard by which the densities of all other fluids and solids are measured.

In the Try This activity in 2.8, you discovered (within experimental error) that the cubic centimetre you made holds 1 mL of water and that 1 mL of pure water has a mass of 1 g. The density of water is $1g/mL$ or $1g/cm^3$. This value is used to compare the densities of all other fluids and solids.

Table 1 in 2.8 lists the densities of some common substances. Comparing densities allows us to determine which substances will float on top of other substances. For example, carbon dioxide gas, a byproduct of respiration, is more dense than air. As a result, air floats on top of carbon dioxide, but both air and carbon dioxide sink below helium gas.

As you discovered in Investigation 2.9, more dense substances sink below less dense ones. Hydrogen is extremely explosive so firefighters need to know whether a hydrogen leak is likely to stay near the ground or float up, possibly getting trapped under a roof. Look at **Table 1** again and compare the density of hydrogen with that of air. Where do the firefighters need to worry about the escaped hydrogen?

Figure 1

This diagram shows how the particles of a substance gain energy and start to move as they are heated. We are looking at a fixed volume of the substance. You can see that the density and mass decrease as the temperature increases.

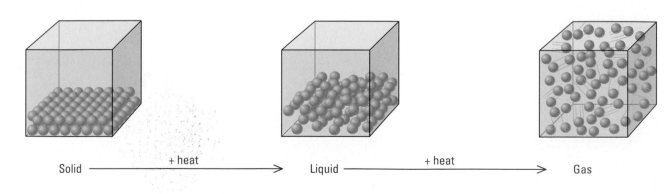

Solid ——— + heat ———> Liquid ——— + heat ———> Gas

Figure 2
Approximately 90% of an iceberg is under the surface of the water. Only about 10% shows above, which is why icebergs are so hazardous to ships.

Understanding Concepts

1. Make a general statement comparing the densities of solids, liquids, and gases.

Making Connections

2. Suppose alcohol, glycerol, water, and gasoline are placed in a tall container. Draw and label a diagram showing the order you would expect to find them.

3. Calculate the percentage of a piece of birch that will float above the surface of vegetable oil.

Exploring

4. (a) Great airships called dirgibles used to carry passengers between continents. The *Hindenburg* was the largest dirgible built and was filled with hydrogen gas. Research and report on what happened to the *Hindenburg*.

(b) What were the advantages and disadvantages of using hydrogen gas in a dirigble?

What Portion of an Iceberg Is Submerged?

What happens when you add an ice cube to a glass of water? Not all the ice floats on the surface—some of the ice is below the surface (submerged). This also happens with icebergs. (See **Figure 2**.) By comparing the density of ice to the density of seawater, you can calculate how much of an iceberg is submerged:

$$\frac{\text{Density of ice}}{\text{Density of seawater}} \times 100 = \frac{0.92}{1.03} \times 100$$
$$= 89\%$$

Figure 4

Reflecting

5. Isn't ice supposed to float? Explain why the ice cubes in **Figure 4** have sunk to the bottom of the liquid.

Figure 3

Fluids **107**

The Ups and Downs of Buoyancy

What happens when you jump into water? The water pushes aside (displaces) to make room for you. (See **Figure 1.**) All fluids, gases as well as liquids, behave this way when an object is placed in them. A helium-filled balloon pushes aside air like a swimmer pushes aside water.

The fluid also pushes back in all directions on the object. The upward part of the force exerted by fluids is called **buoyancy**. Buoyancy is a property of all fluids.

Buoyancy is not the only force acting on an object in a fluid. The force of gravity (weight) also acts on an object. The effect of both forces operating together is described in the next section.

Figure 1

The volume of fluid displaced is equal to the volume of the object in the fluid.

Try This Comparing Buoyancy and Gravity Forces

How are the buoyant force and the force of gravity related? What role do these forces play in getting an object to float?

- Weigh a lump of modelling clay (approximately 300 g), using the newton spring scale. You will need to tie a piece of string (about 0.5 m long) around the clay, leaving a loop to attach the scale. Record this weight as "weight in air."

Figure 2

- Fill a pail with tap water and lower the lump of modelling clay into the water. Submerge it completely but do not let it touch the bottom or sides of the pail. Record its weight when it is submerged in the water. Do not submerge the spring scale. (See **Figure 2**.) Record this as "weight in water."

1. What do you notice about the weight in air and the weight in water? What might the difference between these two values represent?

2. What is the buoyant force acting on the clay?
   - Use this calculation and the words "force of gravity" to explain why the lump sank.
   - Modify the shape of your lump of clay until it floats.
   - When the clay floats, find the weight of the new shape in air.

3. What do you notice about this weight?
   - Let this new clay shape float.

4. Would you be able to find the weight in water now? Explain.
   - Add marbles, one at a time, until the clay shape is one marble away from sinking. Record the total mass of marbles that your shape will hold.

5. What design similarities exist among all of the class's floating clay structures?

6. Does each floating clay shape hold the same mass of marbles? How does the shape that holds the most marbles compare to the shape that holds the least?

Archimedes' Principle

About 250 B.C., the king of Syracuse, on the island of Sicily, suspected that his goldsmith had secretly kept some of the gold meant for the royal crown and replaced it with a cheaper metal. The king asked Archimedes, a Greek mathematician, to determine whether the crown was made of pure gold.

Here's how Archimedes solved the problem. He found that the crown appeared to weigh less in water than a bar of pure gold with the same mass. This meant there was a greater buoyant force on the crown. Archimedes realized that the crown displaced more water than the gold bar. (See **Figure 3**.) Since the volume of each object was equal to the volume of water it displaced, the volume of the crown was greater than that of the gold bar. Therefore the crown had a lower density and was not made of pure gold.

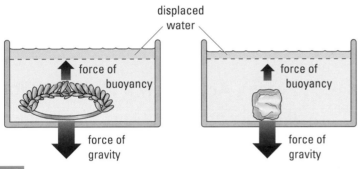

displaced water

force of buoyancy

force of gravity

force of buoyancy

force of gravity

Figure 3

The buoyant force equals the weight of the fluid that the immersed object displaces.

The key idea that Archimedes realized is still known as **Archimedes' principle**: The buoyant force on an object immersed in a fluid is equal to the weight of the fluid that the object displaces. According to legend, Archimedes thought of the idea while taking a bath. He was so happy that he leapt up and ran through the streets crying "Eureka!" (which means "I have found it!").

Understanding Concepts

1. Why did the king's goldsmith mix a less dense material with the gold from the crown?

Making Connections

2. **(a)** How would the buoyant force acting on the floating clay shape change if it were immersed in seawater?

   (b) How would this affect the amount of weight it could carry?

Exploring

3. Measure the amount of water that was displaced with the clay lump and the floating clay shape. How do these amounts compare?

Reflecting

4. How can you modify a dense solid substance to make it float in a less dense fluid?

5. Think back to Investigation 2.9. Explain the behaviour of the cork and plastic block, using the terms "buoyant force" and "density."

Design Challenge

How might your knowledge of buoyancy assist you in the Challenge of designing a submersible device or a boat lock? Explain.

Figure 4

Logs are buoyant: they float on water.

How and Why Do Things Float?

Figure 1

Hundreds of 2-L plastic bottles are given a second life as part of a dock flotation system. The sealed bottles are stacked in the float drum (inset) and add volume without much weight. Reusing the bottles reduces waste in landfills.

Remember the Try This activity in 2.11? You took a dense material (clay) and made it float. Shipbuilders do this all the time. They take steel, which has a density eight times that of water, and make it into a floating boat. Just as you changed the shape of the clay, ship engineers design the hull of a steel ship to contain a large volume of air. The overall density (total mass divided by total volume) of the whole ship, including the hollow hull, is less than the density of water. Like the pop-bottle floating dock in **Figure 1**, the ship is buoyant. It floats.

Figure 2

Forces Acting on a Floating Object

If the upward buoyant force on an immersed object is greater than the downward force of gravity (weight of the object), the object will rise. If the buoyant force is less than the object's weight, it will sink. If the two forces are equal, the object will not move up or down. (See **Figure 2**.)

But Archimedes' principle says that the buoyant force on the object equals the weight of the fluid it pushes aside. So the object will rise or sink depending on whether it weighs less or more than the fluid it displaces. Since they have equal volumes, the object will rise or sink depending on whether it is less or more dense than the displaced fluid.

It is interesting to note that buoyancy depends on gravity, because buoyancy is a result of the weights of various substances. Without gravity there would be no buoyancy. We say that the object has **positive buoyancy**, **negative buoyancy**, or **neutral buoyancy** according to whether it rises, sinks, or remains level in the fluid. (See **Figure 3**.)

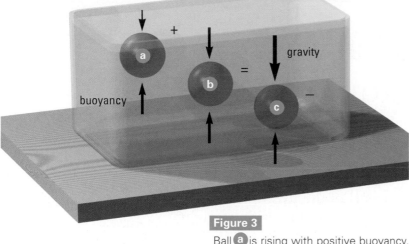

Figure 3

Ball ⓐ is rising with positive buoyancy. Ball ⓑ is stationary with neutral buoyancy. Ball ⓒ is sinking with negative buoyancy.

Buoyancy in Air

The buoyant force acts on objects immersed in a gas the same way it acts on objects immersed in a liquid. The densities of gases and liquids are very different. Air is almost 800 times less dense than water. That is why you would need an enormous helium balloon to rise through the air, but only a small life jacket to float on top of the water. To support your weight, the balloon must displace a much greater volume of less dense fluid.

Safe Floating Levels

The load lines on a ship are called Plimsoll lines. These lines, or numbers, show a safe floating level when the ship is fully loaded. (See **Figure 4**.) They are named after Samuel Plimsoll, a British politician. Around 1870, he helped develop a law that every British ship should have these load lines. Before this law, many owners overloaded their ships, and many ships sank. By the end of the 1800s, every ship in the world was using Plimsoll lines.

Understanding Concepts

1. If you were to do the Try This in 2.11 again, using cooking oil instead of tap water, how would the buoyant force change?

2. Explain, using scientific terms, why overloading a ship might cause it to sink.

Making Connections

3. Give examples of three real-life situations that match the diagrams in **Figure 3**.

Figure 5

4. Why do floating candles (**Figure 5**) float higher in the water as they burn?

Exploring

5. A hard-boiled egg in water is negatively buoyant—it sinks. Using salt, alter the buoyant force of tap water until the egg becomes positively buoyant (floats). How much salt do you use?

Design Challenge

How can you apply this additional knowledge of buoyancy to enable a submersible device to be positively or negatively buoyant?

Figure 4

Plimsoll lines on the hull of a ship indicate the depth to which it may be legally loaded.

Another Way to Measure the Density of a Liquid

In Investigation 2.9, you compared fluid densities without making precise measurements. An instrument that measures the density of liquids is called a **hydrometer**. It is designed to float at different heights in liquids of different densities. The upper part of the hydrometer is marked with a scale. Most hydrometers are long and thin, with a weight at the bottom end.

Problem

In the production of maple syrup (**Figure 1**), there isn't enough time to measure the mass of a volume of boiling sap and then calculate its density. A faster method is needed.

Design Brief

Design and build a hydrometer. Determine the effectiveness of your homemade hydrometer by comparing it to a commercial model.

Design Criteria

Design a hydrometer that floats at different heights in different liquids, indicating the density of each liquid. The instrument must float upright. Your design should use only the materials made available to you.

• The instrument must be calibrated (a readable, linear scale must be present on the instrument), using water as the standard.

Materials

• apron
• safety goggles
• wooden dowel 17 mm in diameter
• fine, permanent marker
• bucket filled with water
• short, galvanized screw
• galvanized nut
• screwdriver
• centimetre ruler
• drill with 6-mm drill bit
• mitre box
• junior hacksaw
• saturated salt solution
• water
• pickling vinegar
• commercial hydrometer
• tall, thin cylinder

Build

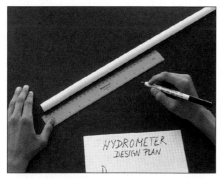

1 Design your hydrometer.
• After your teacher has approved your design, build your hydrometer.

Test

2 Test your hydrometer and modify it as necessary.

✎ (a) Record your modifications.

3 Use the commercial hydrometer to measure densities of the liquids above.
• Wipe off the hydrometer between liquids.

✎ (a) Record your observations.

Analyzing

1. When will a hydrometer float higher? When will it become more immersed?

2. What limitations might exist with your homemade instrument because it is constructed out of wood?

3. Rank the liquids by density, from least to greatest.

4. How effective is your hydrometer in measuring liquids with similar densities?

Making Connections

5. How could a hydrometer be used during the manufacture of maple syrup?

6. What happens to sap that is boiled too long?

Exploring

7. Make sugar solutions with concentrations of 200 g/L, 300 g/L, and 400 g/L. Measure the density of each solution with the commercial hydrometer. How does measured density relate to the mass of sugar dissolved in each solution?

Reflecting

8. Explain the meaning of the following hydrometer readings: 1.03, 0.87, and 1.00.

Figure 1
The sap used to produce maple syrup is cooked in huge evaporating pans.

 Use tools and materials properly. If you are not certain how to use equipment safely, ask your teacher.

Evaluate

5 Evaluate your hydrometer by assessing how well it met the design criteria.

(a) Did your hydrometer float at different heights in different liquids?

(b) Did you use only the materials made available to you?

(c) Is your hydrometer calibrated to indicate the density of liquids?

(d) If you had to modify your hydrometer, why did you have to make those modifications?

4 Calibrate your hydrometer by floating it in the three liquids.
- Mark the height for each, and write the densities on the instrument.

(a) Draw and label your completed hydrometer.

 **Design Challenge**

Is density an important measurement to consider when designing your Challenge? Explain.

From Bladders to Ballast: Altering Buoyancy

Fish and some aquatic plants (**Figure 1**) have adaptations that alter their buoyancy in water. Design features of ships, submarines, hot air balloons, and scuba equipment also alter their buoyancy, allowing them to move vertically in water or air. Natural and engineered methods of altering buoyancy have many similarities.

Nature's Method

Fish control their depth in water using swim bladders containing air. (See **Figure 2**.) They can get more gas into their swim bladders either by gulping air in at the surface of the water or by releasing dissolved gases from their blood.

(a) By expanding and contracting their swim bladders, fish can change their level in water. How does this enable fish to become more or less buoyant?

(b) Speculate why fish need to descend or rise to different water levels.

(c) How would an adaptation such as air bladders benefit seaweed?

Figure 1
Bladders filled with air enable rockweed to stay upright underwater.

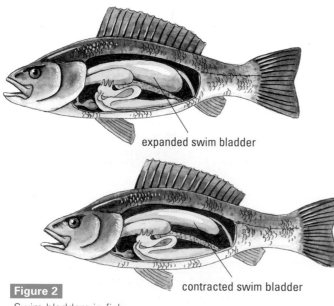

expanded swim bladder

contracted swim bladder

Figure 2
Swim bladders in fish

The Human Method

The human body has an overall density very close to that of water. When immersed in water, a relaxed swimmer with filled lungs is positively buoyant. Wearing a wet suit further increases buoyancy. Divers wear weight belts to give them more density and less buoyancy. (See **Figure 3**.)

A scuba diver might also use a buoyancy compensator vest to alter her buoyancy in the water. If she wants to sink down, she releases air from the vest, thus making herself more dense. The vest also enables the diver to stop descending and become neutrally buoyant. To swim back to the surface, the diver can blow air into the vest to decrease her density and increase her buoyancy.

(d) In what ways are fish bladders and buoyancy compensator vests similar?

Controlling Ballast

Ballast is any material carried on ships, submarines, hot air balloons, or dirigibles (air ships) that acts as weight and alters buoyancy. The ballast helps the vessel to be stable and to travel at the appropriate level in the fluid. Tanks of water often provide the ballast for ships and submarines. In a hot air balloon or dirigible, ballast may be sand or water.

A fully loaded ship floats lower in the water and is more stable than an empty one. When a ship unloads its cargo, water is taken in as ballast to maintain stability in the water. When the ship takes on a new cargo, it pumps out the water it was using as ballast.

Hot air balloons and dirigibles are immersed in air. They use ballast to control their buoyancy. The weight of the fuel and passengers is calculated before deciding how much ballast is needed. Once in flight, the crew can increase buoyancy in one of two ways. It can increase the volume of gas in the balloon part by heating the air or adding more helium. Alternatively, it could release some of the ballast. To decrease buoyancy, the crew either has to reduce the volume of gas (by letting it cool or releasing some of it) or pick up more ballast (perhaps by scooping water from a lake in a bucket on a long rope).

If the ballast tanks are filled with water, a submarine will descend. (See **Figure 4**.) When the submarine reaches the desired level, some water in the ballast tanks is pumped out, to be replaced with air. This continues until the submarine stops sinking and becomes neutrally buoyant. To make the submarine surface, or float at a higher level, more water in the ballast tanks is replaced with air.

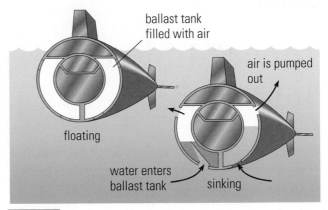

Changing the amount of water in its ballast tanks makes a submarine sink or rise.

Figure 4

(e) Do ships in the Great Lakes need more or less ballast than ocean-going ships? Give reasons for your answer.

(f) What could the crew of a hot air balloon do to raise the balloon above some trees?

(g) What factors affect how much water is carried in a submarine's ballast tanks?

(h) Where might the air come from to replace the water that is pumped out of a submarine's ballast tanks?

Making Connections

1. If the force of gravity (weight) on a scuba diver is 600 N, what should the buoyant force be if the diver wants to
   (a) descend?
   (b) rise to the surface?

2. You are asked to add ballast to a helium-filled balloon until it will float in the centre of the room.
   (a) What could you use as ballast?
   (b) What happens if you add or remove some of this ballast?

Design Challenge

If you want a device to move up or down in water or air, the buoyant force needs to be altered. How might the information on these two pages assist you in designing your Challenge?

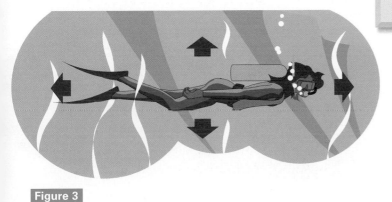

Figure 3

Human Impact on Natural Fluid Systems

Earth is surrounded by fluids, both liquids and gases. These fluids are the water we drink and the air we breathe. Sustaining the health of these systems is essential. Healthy fluid systems are necessary for the survival of natural ecosystems as well as for human health. At the same time, many economic activities (fishing, shipping, and tourism) depend on Earth's fluid systems. We must manage Earth's fluid systems in a way that benefits the environment, the economy, and society. Despite their importance, these fluid systems have been abused and neglected.

Ballast Beware

Each year, many different cargos from around the world arrive by ship in Canadian harbours. These ships carry almost anything you can imagine, from raw materials such as grain and oil to electronic products and automobiles. In each port where they unload cargo, these ships take in water for ballast. When they load cargo in the next port, they pump out the water.

The problem is that the dumped ballast contains more than just water. It can contain living things from other parts of the world that are not normally found in Canadian waters. These are referred to as exotic species. Exotic species include species of plants (especially algae), fish, and microscopic organisms. (See **Figure 1**.)

When conditions are favourable, exotic species can multiply rapidly in their new environment. Usually there are no natural predators, so growth can go unchecked for years—until a predator develops or a method of control is found.

Exotic species of fish brought to the Great Lakes in ballast water include the ruff and the goby. They compete with native populations of fish for food and shelter, upsetting the balance of the ecosystem. This is a concern because fish are an important source of food, recreation, and income for Canadians.

Ballast water may also contain oil or other pollutants. After some oil tankers empty their shipments of crude oil, they take on seawater as ballast in the same tanks that held the oil. When the tankers are filled again, this contaminated ballast is pumped into the local waters.

Zebra Mussels in Canadian Waters

In 1985 or 1986, ballast water from a European freighter accidentally brought zebra mussels to the Great Lakes. They were first discovered in Lake St. Clair and Lake Erie and have now spread to inland lakes and rivers throughout Ontario and Quebec. The effects of zebra mussels have been widespread. They reduce the food supply available to fish by feeding on plankton. They clog water intake pipes and screens of factories and water treatment plants, affecting the water flow rate. (See **Figure 2**.) If less water enters the intake pipes, not enough water is available for use. Because zebra mussels are filter feeders, they contain high concentrations of toxins. Any animal that feeds on them will ingest these toxins, which are then passed up the food chain. Millions of dollars are spent annually on zebra mussel control.

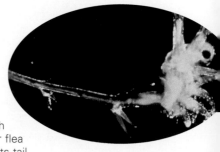

Figure 1

The spiny water flea, a tiny crustacean, arrived in Canada in ballast water around 1993. It feeds on plankton, an important food source for native small fish. Many native fish cannot eat the spiny water flea because of the spines on its tail.

Figure 2

Adult zebra mussels attach themselves to hard surfaces. Here they clog a water intake pipe.

Presentation **Ballast Water Management** ⑧ᴅ

Statement

Action should be taken to stop the pollution of Canadian waterways by contaminated ballast water.

Sample Opinions

From a utilities official

Ballast water pollution has introduced zebra mussels into our lakes and rivers. This water is used for electricity generation and for drinking water. The zebra mussels are blocking the water intake pipes. It's a disaster for utility companies. The technology and labour needed to remove the mussels from our intake pipes is very expensive. This cost is passed on to everyone who uses electricity or water. Who knows what further damage may be caused by the introduction of other exotic species?

From a port official

Ships are designed to float at a certain depth, so they have to carry ballast when they have no cargo and empty the ballast when they load up. Shipping is a very competitive industry. If Canadian ports make too great a demand on shipping companies to control their ballast water, they'll go to other ports. Thousands of Canadian jobs could be lost, and the cost of shipping to and from Canada will increase. Canadian consumers and exporters will have to pay more.

From the captain of a Great Lakes fishing boat

The damage has already been done. Many species of fish have already been almost wiped out: out-competed or eaten by exotic species from ballast tanks. If there's to be any hope of the fish stocks recovering, we must stop exotic species from getting into our waterways. But ships have to have ballast. Maybe there's some way of cleaning the ballast water.

From a cottager

The water in our lake is much cleaner than it used to be. That may be because of the zebra mussels: they're all over our dock's piers. But we can't catch the same kinds of fish that used to be in the lake. I think they're been eaten by the introduced species. I prefer the way the lake used to be. Let's stop ballast pollution.

What Do You Think?

- Read the sample opinions and evaluate each one. Record the main points under appropriate headings in a chart. Add other points of your own under these headings.
- Design a solution to the problem and prepare a proposal outlining your solution.
- Present your proposal to the class. In your presentation, explain how your solution would reduce the human impact on the environment.

How Does Temperature Affect Viscosity and Density?

Have you noticed that it's easier to run after a good warm-up? Fluids run more easily when they're warm, too. Viscosity, density, and buoyancy all change with changes in temperature.

First, let's discuss fluids other than water. Have you heard the expression "slower than molasses in January"? This describes the increase in resistance to flow that fluids experience when the temperature drops. As heat is taken away from a fluid, its particles slow down and come closer together. This causes the fluid to contract—its volume decreases. Thus the fluid's density will increase. (Remember, $D = M/V$. Since M stays the same and V gets smaller, then M/V will get bigger.) Viscosity will also be affected. When the particles slow down and come closer together, the forces of attraction between them will increase and so make it harder for them to flow past each other. Thus, viscosity increases at lower temperatures.

As you would expect, the opposite occurs when the temperature rises. When heat is added to a fluid, its density and resistance to flow decrease.

The reaction of air to temperature change explains the behaviour of hot air balloons. As air is heated and released inside the balloon, the balloon rises. This happens because hot air is less dense than the surrounding air, so it rises to float above the cooler air. As the air inside the balloon cools, it becomes denser, and the balloon descends. Periodic bursts of heat keep the balloon aloft.

Water: A Special Case

Water behaves differently from other fluids when the temperature changes. You may have noticed during a dive into a lake that the top layer of water feels warmer than the lower layers. During the summer, warmer water, because it is less dense, floats on top of cooler water. But as the temperature of water drops below 4°C, water becomes less dense again! **Table 1** illustrates this.

Table 1	
Temperature of Pure Water	**Density (g/cm³)**
100°C	0.958
20°C (room temperature)	0.998
4°C	1.000
0°C	0.92

Ice floats because it is less dense than liquid water. Water is most dense at 4°C.

This unique property of water keeps lakes from freezing solid in the winter. As the water cools, it sinks to the bottom. The deepest part of the lake will be at 4°C: a liquid. This enables aquatic life to survive. The ice on top of a lake insulates the water beneath. (See **Figure 1**.) Only shallow ponds freeze solid in the winter.

The viscosity of water also changes with temperature. Water at 0°C is approximately seven times more viscous than water at 100°C.

Figure 1

Water becomes lighter as it freezes. At 4°C, it is most dense and falls below cooler, frozen water.

Water at 0°C

Water below 4°C

Explaining the Effect of Temperature Changes Using the Particle Theory

In a solid, particles are closely packed together and held in a rigid structure by forces of attraction between them. The particles can move, but only by vibrating in the same place. When a solid is heated, the particles gain more energy and vibrate faster. As more heat is added, this speed of vibration becomes so fast that the force of attraction cannot hold the particles together. The rigid structure of the solid falls apart, melting occurs, and a liquid is formed. In a liquid, the particles are slightly less tightly packed together (less dense) than in a solid.

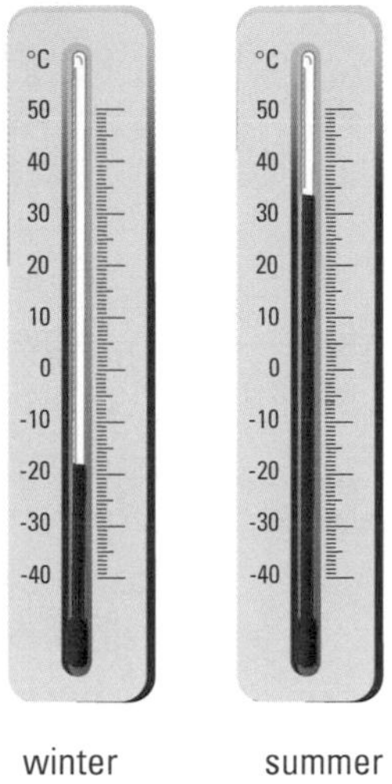

Figure 2

As the temperature of a liquid increases, the spaces between its particles become greater, and the volume of the liquid increases. When placed in a glass tube, alcohol increases or decreases in volume as the temperature fluctuates. That's how thermometers work.

As more heat is added to a liquid, the particles move even faster. The forces of attraction between them are broken, and the particles are able to move in all directions, leaving larger spaces in between. The particles take up more space or volume (**Figure 2**), making the density lower. Particles eventually escape from the liquid, and a gas is formed. (See **Figure 3**.)

The reverse process occurs when heat is taken away from a gas or a liquid as its temperature decreases.

As the density of a fluid decreases with a rise in temperature, so does the force of buoyancy that the fluid exerts on an immersed object. Why is that? Because the displaced fluid weighs less at a higher temperature. The viscosity of the fluid also decreases as the attraction between its molecules weakens.

Table 2

	Volume	Density	Viscosity	Buoyancy
Temperature ↑	?	↓	?	?
Temperature ↓	?	?	?	?

Figure 3

Firefighters often use water in the form of a fine spray. This fine spray absorbs heat from the fire faster than a solid stream of water would. As heat is absorbed, steam is produced. Steam occupies a larger volume and displaces the air that is fuelling the fire.

Understanding Concepts

1. Copy **Table 2** and complete it by adding up or down arrows to indicate how each property changes with temperature.

2. Use the words *mass*, *volume*, and *density* to distinguish between gases, liquids, and solids in terms of the particle theory of matter.

3. Use the particle theory to explain the effects of temperature changes on the cooking oil in Investigation 2.4.

4. How does water behave differently than other fluids when the temperature changes?

Making Connections

5. In many aircraft, oxygen masks are stored in compartments above the passengers. The oxygen for these masks is stored as a liquid. When it is needed, it is warmed up until it is a gas. Explain why oxygen is stored as a liquid rather than a gas in this situation.

6. Will ships float lower or higher in tropical waters? Explain your answer using the words *buoyancy* and *density*.

7. Suggest two examples of a substance changing its temperature in the natural world. What happens to its viscosity and density in each case?

Exploring

8. Lava, brought to the surface when a volcano erupts, changes in viscosity as it cools. Research how lava is produced. Explain the viscosity changes it undergoes.

Design Challenge

How will temperature changes affect the fluid in your Challenge?

Fluids and the Confederation Bridge

Imagine the challenge of building a structure over 12 km long, across a storm-tossed stretch of ocean. The structure has to last 100 years and be safe for motorists to drive on. That was the task facing the engineers on the Confederation Bridge project. The connection from Prince Edward Island to New Brunswick opened on May 31, 1997. The 12.9-km bridge crosses the Northumberland Strait and is the world's longest bridge to cross ice-covered waters.

Some of the challenges facing the bridge designers are described below. In order to solve these challenges, engineers required a knowledge and understanding of the properties of fluids and how forces and motion affect fluids.

Barges

During the building of the bridge, much construction took place from rectangular floating vessels called barges. Many activities were carried out from the barges, including positioning the pier bases and cementing them to the bedrock, and transporting

The *Svanen*, a barge with a floating crane, was used to carry and install the bridge sections.

supplies to workers. One barge was even equipped with a helicopter landing pad.

So building of the bridge could continue during the long winter season, sections for the bridge had to be first built on land and then floated out to their final position. Each bridge section consisted of a pier and girders and weighed about 7500 t.

(a) What forces must an engineer consider when designing a barge?

(b) Why is it crucial that barges float and be stable during all of the activities that are carried out from them?

(c) What could the engineers do to ensure a barge was stable before use?

Water and Ice

Water constantly exerts force on the bridge piers. Some days enormous waves crash into the piers. This pushing force increases as the water freezes and ice slams into the piers.

The ice in the Northumberland Strait was a major concern for the engineers designing the Confederation Bridge piers. A model of this situation was constructed. In an enormous basin, several centimetres of ice were produced. A model of a pier attached to a bridge was pushed through the ice and across the basin. The speed at which the pier was pushed was carefully controlled to mimic actual water current conditions. Engineers recorded the investigation on videotape and took measurements throughout the testing. The

Figure 2

Exploring

1. Research the design and building of the Confederation Bridge.

   (a) What structure was added to the base of each pier to break up ice sheets drifting down the Northumberland Strait during the winter?

   (b) How was the *Svanen* brought to Canada? What are some interesting facts about this amazing vessel?

results were used to determine the forces the piers must be able to withstand.

(d) Is the force of the water on the piers the same at the water surface as it is 30 m below the surface?

(e) Why did engineers construct a model of the piers?

Winds

High winds posed another challenge to the bridge designers. They considered how air would flow around the bridge and how winds would affect the bridge itself. How the winds would affect the vehicles using the bridge was also a major concern, and barrier walls on each side of the roadway were designed to minimize this effect.

(f) Suggest some design features that might reduce the amount of air turbulence around the bridge.

Concrete

The concrete used in the design of the bridge also concerned the engineers. To make a pier that could withstand collisions from ice and possibly ships, a special high-strength, low-water concrete was used. The concrete had to be pumped through pipes and poured into forms to make the pier shapes. The engineers changed the viscosity of the concrete by adding special products. This allowed the concrete to remain liquid longer.

(g) Why did engineers add special products to the concrete used in the bridge?

(h) Why was it necessary that the concrete fill the entire form it was poured into?

Figure 4

An apparatus that looks like the Canadarm was used to pour concrete.

Figure 3

2.18 Inquiry Investigation

SKILLS MENU
- Questioning
- Conducting
- Analyzing
- Hypothesizing
- Recording
- Communicating
- Planning

How Fluids Handle Pressure

"I'm under so much pressure!" How often have you heard that phrase? An upcoming test or too much to do in a short period of time can make people say they're under a lot of pressure. Fluids can be under a different sort of pressure. What happens to fluids under pressure? What effects can we observe?

Materials
- apron
- safety goggles
- 20-mL syringes, 2
- 5-mL syringes, 2
- 3-cm lengths of 6-mm tubing, 3
- 40-cm length of 6-mm tubing
- straight connector
- T-connector

 Use equipment only as instructed. Be careful when working with syringes under pressure.

Question

2B **1** After reading through this investigation, write a question that you will be trying to answer.

Hypothesis

2C **2** Write a hypothesis for this investigation.

Experimental Design

In this investigation, you will investigate the effects of exerting pressure on air and water in closed systems.

3 Copy **Table 1** and complete it.

Procedure

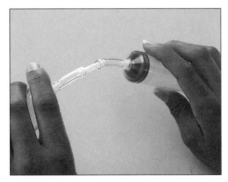

4 Connect both 20-mL syringes with a 3-cm piece of tubing.

(a) Can you pull one plunger back? If not, what do you have to do to one plunger before connecting the tubing?

(b) As you depress one plunger, what happens to the other one?

(c) Try moving one plunger and holding the other one still. What happens?

(d) What fluid are you investigating here?

5 Repeat step 4 using the 40-cm piece of tubing.

(a) Do you notice anything different happening when you move one plunger?

6 Use a straight connector and two short pieces of tubing to join both 20-mL syringes.

(a) What is different about the movement of the plungers compared to the setup in step 4?

SKILLS HANDBOOK: **2B** Asking a Question **2C** Predicting and Hypothesizing **3D** Planning a Prototype

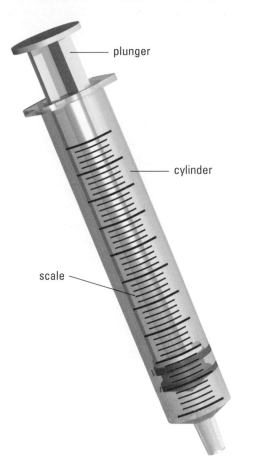

plunger

cylinder

scale

Table 1	Investigating Water and Air Pressure		
Investigation	Setup Used		What Happened?
1. Air pressure	(a) large syringe + 3 cm tubing + large syringe		?
	(b) large syringe + 40 cm tubing + large syringe		?
2. Water pressure	(a)	?	?
	(b)	?	?

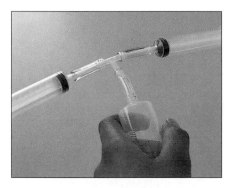

7 Join one 20-mL syringe to both 5-mL syringes using the T-connector and three short pieces of tubing.

(a) Record the volume of air that starts in the large syringe.

(b) As you depress the plunger of the large syringe, what happens?

(c) Write your prediction for what you think would happen if you were to use water in steps 4 to 7.

8 Repeat steps 4 to 7 with the system full of water. You must ensure that there are no bubbles present.

Analysis

9 Analyze your results by answering the following questions.

(a) What would happen if the tubing on the syringes, or the plunger in the syringe, did not make a tight seal?

(b) What differences did you observe between the two different fluids when you applied pressure to them?

(c) Write a report explaining your results.

Making Connections

1. Design a syringe setup to **3D** raise an object attached to one plunger. Draw a sketch of your design.

2. Needles are attached to syringes when injections are given to people or animals. How do health care personnel get air out of the syringe?

Exploring

3. Use what you have learned about syringes to explain the benefit of having two lungs instead of one.

Design Challenge

How has this investigation on pressure helped you in designing your Challenge?

Confined Fluids Under Pressure

What are confined fluids? They are any fluids in a closed system. Confined fluids can move around within the system, but they cannot enter or leave the system. The blood moving through your body is a confined fluid (providing you don't cut yourself!) and so is the air in an air mattress (**Figure 1**). When fluids are confined, they have some very interesting effects.

Figure 1

In Investigation 2.18, you discovered that moving one syringe causes another syringe to move. In other words, applying a force to one part of a fluid system results in movement in another part of the system. The force was transmitted through the fluid to another moveable part, some distance away. This is one effect of a pressurized fluid system: forces can be applied in one place and have an effect somewhere else—even in another direction. The brakes in a car are an example of this. The driver presses down on the brake pedal, which pushes fluid through the brake lines toward the wheels, where the brake pads are forced against the moving wheels (**Figure 2**).

You might have noticed a difference in the effects of water and air in Investigation 2.18. Did you notice that there was a short delay, or bounce, in the air-filled system, whereas the water-filled system reacted immediately? Why might this be? Can you explain it using the particle theory? Think of the particles in liquids and gases, and the spaces between them.

Pushing the brake pedal forces a piston against the hydraulic brake fluid in the main cylinder.

The brake fluid is forced out of the cylinder into the brake lines toward the wheels.

Figure 2
The braking system in a car is a hydraulic system.

The brake pads are forced against the moving wheels.

Using the Particle Theory

We can use the particle theory of matter to understand what happens to confined fluids when an external force is applied to them. Remember that in a liquid, the spaces between the particles are already very small. When an external force is applied, only a small decrease takes place in the liquid's volume.

In a gas, the particles are far apart from each other. In order for the force to be transmitted from one particle to another, the volume the gas occupies must be reduced. This is referred to as compression. When an external force is applied to a gas, the force will push the particles closer together. This is why there is a delay in the air-filled system. It takes time to compress the air. Gases are very **compressible**. The change in volume of a liquid under pressure is so small that liquids are only very slightly compressible. We can say that liquids are almost incompressible.

There is another effect that can occur when a force is applied to a gas or a liquid. Its state can be changed. By increasing the pressure on a gas, the particles can be pushed close enough together that the gas will change to a liquid. For example, propane is normally a gas, but in a barbecue tank, under pressure, it is a liquid (**Figure 3**). Similarly, a liquid may be compressed until it changes into a solid.

Figure 3
Barbecue tanks contain liquid propane. Putting propane under pressure and storing it as a liquid allows propane tanks to hold more.

Understanding Concepts

1. Using the particle theory and this new information on pressure, explain the results you obtained with syringes in Investigation 2.18.

2. What evidence from the syringe investigation supports the particle theory?

3. The first paragraph on these pages mentions the "interesting effects" of fluids under pressure. What are these effects?

Making Connections

4. Compare liquids and gases in terms of their compressibility.
(6C) Draw a diagram to help your comparison.

5. Cars use a liquid brake fluid to transmit a force from the brake pedal to the brake pads. If air were used instead of a liquid, how different might pushing on the brake pedal feel? Explain.

Exploring

6. The whale is a mammal that has
(4A) adapted to aquatic life. Some whales dive to depths greater than 2000 m, deeper than most submarines can dive. Research how the respiratory system of a whale allows it to perform deep dives despite the enormous pressure of the water.

Reflecting

7. Why would you want to put a fluid under pressure?

Design Challenge

Describe how you will put a fluid under pressure in your Design Challenge.

Pressurized Fluid Systems: Hydraulics

Hydraulics is the word we give to confined, pressurized systems that use moving liquids. Hydraulic systems use liquids under pressure to move many things. Huge amounts of soil at a construction site can be moved with hydraulic machinery such as backhoes and excavators.

What Makes Up a Hydraulic System?

The liquid put into a hydraulic system is called the **hydraulic fluid**. The hydraulic fluid in the system in **Figure 1** is oil. Oil from the tank is sent along a conductor (a hose, tube, or pipe) to a pump where it is pushed into a **cylinder**. The cylinder resembles a giant syringe. The oil pushes up the **piston** in the cylinder like a plunger moving inside a syringe. This upward movement of the piston can be used to do work by moving something else.

A valve placed between the pump and the cylinder controls the flow of oil. This allows the piston to be moved a little or a lot. A second valve, placed between the cylinder and the tank, can be opened to allow the oil to flow back into the storage tank, pushed by the weight of the piston as it moves back down. The fluid is circulated through the system and is not used up.

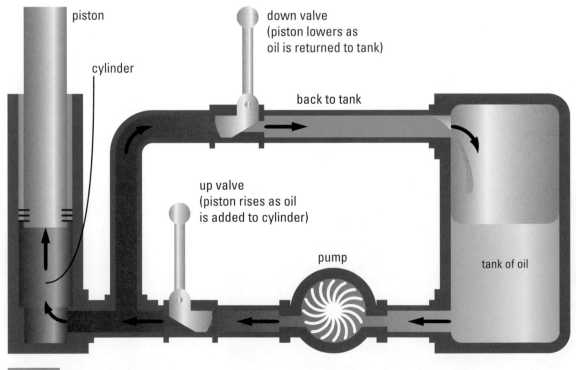

Figure 1

This hydraulic system could be used to raise and lower a snowplow blade or a car hoist.

Pumps and Valves

A pump is used to create a flow of fluid. Pumps often make fluids flow against gravity. They are found in car engines (**Figure 2**), gasoline pumps at gas stations, dishwashers, and many other machines.

Valves control the flow of fluid. There are many different types, but they all have a similar function: to keep a fluid flowing in the desired direction. When you turn on a water tap, you are opening up a valve. There are numerous places where valves are found, including tires, soccer balls, and the human heart. Can you think of any others?

The Heart: A Pressurized Fluid System

Your heart is also a pump. (See **Figure 3.**) It beats over 100 000 times a day to push blood through the veins and arteries that make up your circulatory system. There are four chambers in the heart: right atrium, right ventricle, left atrium, and left ventricle. The chambers in the upper part of the heart are separated from those below by valves. The valves allow blood to flow in only one direction. Knowledge of how fluid flows flow through valves was used to design artificial heart valves.

Blood pressure ensures that all of your organs receive blood. Physicians measure blood pressure with an instrument called a sphygmomanometer.

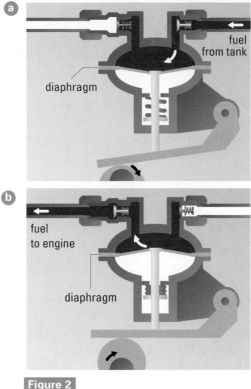

Figure 2

a In a car fuel pump, the diaphragm pulls down allowing fuel to enter the pump chamber.

b Fuel is pushed into the engine when the diaphragm pushes up.

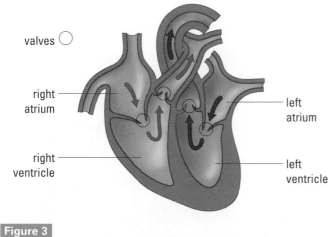

Figure 3

The heart is essentially a pump with valves that pushes blood around your body.

Design Challenge

What conductors will you use to move the fluid in your Design Challenge?

Understanding Concepts

1. List two industries that use hydraulic power.

2. What makes the fluid flow in a pressurized system? What controls this flow?

Making Connections

3. **(a)** What conductors can be used in a hydraulic system?

   (b) What conductors serve this function in the human circulatory system?

   (c) What conductors are found in a tree? What is the fluid that is being moved?

4. Compare and contrast a car fuel pump with a human heart using a Venn diagram.

Reflecting

5. How has knowledge of hydraulics aided our understanding of the human circulatory system?

Pressurized Fluid Systems: Pneumatics

Pneumatics is the name given to confined, pressurized systems that use moving air or other gases such as carbon dioxide. Like hydraulic systems, pneumatic systems possess a great deal of power that can be used to move an object.

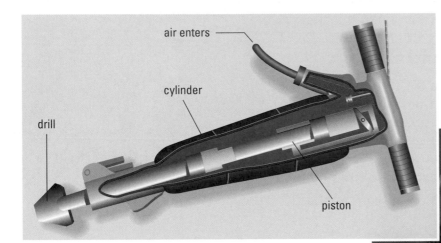

air enters

cylinder

drill

piston

The jackhammer is a pneumatic drill. Compressed air moves a piston up and down, which moves the drill. These portable machines are often used to break apart concrete.

What Makes Up a Pneumatic System?

A pneumatic system is very similar to a hydraulic system (**Figure 1**). An air compressor provides the supply of air in a pneumatic system. The air compressor serves a similar purpose to the pump in a hydraulic system.

Pneumatics operate machinery such as air conditioning systems in aircraft and ejection seats in fighter planes. Pneumatic wrenches are used to remove or tighten nuts during a tire change. **Figure 2** shows a pneumatic drill in operation.

Figure 2

Pneumatic drills hammer away at concrete to break it up, ready for removal.

The Lungs: A Pneumatic System

Your lungs operate like a pump. They draw in air laden with oxygen and push out air and extra carbon dioxide (see **Figure 3**). They could not function without the diaphragm. The diaphragm works in a similar way to the plunger in a syringe. When the diaphragm pulls away from the lungs, the volume of the lungs increases, and the pressure inside lowers. The air outside your body is then at a higher pressure than the air in your lungs. This causes air to rush in. To expel gas, the diaphragm pushes up, the pressure inside the lungs increases, and you exhale. About 1L of air always remains in your lungs to prevent them from collapsing.

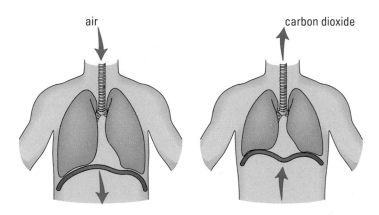

air

carbon dioxide

Figure 3

When we breathe in the diaphragm contracts; when we breathe out, the diaphragm relaxes.

Understanding Concepts

1. Using your diagrams and observation notes from the Try This, write a sentence summarizing the effects of a valve in a pneumatic or hydraulic system.

Making Connections

2. How does the gas on top of the liquid in an aerosol can cause the liquid to come out of the spray nozzle?

3. Compare and contrast a car fuel pump with a human lung using a Venn diagram.

Exploring

4. How does chewing gum relieve pressure inside your ears?

5. Research how natural gas is
(4A) distributed in your community.

Design Challenge

For the safety hinge challenge, predict what would be different about the way a pneumatic and a hydraulic hinge would operate. Give reasons to support your prediction.

Try This Exploring Valves

Figure 4

 Be careful when working with fluids under pressure.

Find out how using a valve alters a pneumatic system.
- Add a valve to the pneumatic system you used in steps 4 to 7 of Investigation 2.18. The valve could go anywhere in the system.
- Draw your system.
- Move each of the plungers in turn and record your observations.
- Move the valve to another position in the system and repeat the procedure.
- Continue until you have tested all possible positions for the valve.

A Closer Look at Fluid Power

There are many kinds of fluid power systems all around us. At an airport, for example, fluid systems are used for passenger movement and baggage handling as well as control of aircraft systems such as doors, wheels, rudder and flaps (**Figure 1**). At the hairdresser's, the client's chair is moved up and down by fluid pressure (**Figure 2**). Even very large, heavy objects can be moved with the assistance of fluid-filled systems (**Figure 3**).

(3B) Problem
Reread the introductory paragraph. Think of a need for a fluid power lift. You have been hired by a management company to design this lift.

Design Brief
Design a hydraulic or pneumatic system that will raise or lower objects. Build a model of your design for test purposes and to present to the management company.

Design Criteria
- The model must raise a mass of 500 g to a specified height of 6 cm, remain stationary for at least 30 s, then descend in a controlled manner.
- The model must use only the materials listed.

Materials
- apron
- safety goggles
- support stand
- screw-on clamp
- 20-mL syringe, 2
- 5-mL syringe
- 2 one-way valves
- 40 cm of clear 6-mm tubing, plus several shorter pieces
- water
- plastic container or beaker with a pour spout
- 500-g ball of modelling clay
- sponge

Build

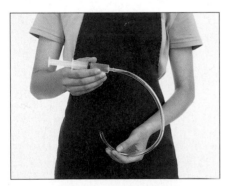

(3D) **1** Design your model lift.
- After your teacher has
(3E) approved your design, build your model.

(a) Record challenges or problems that arise during the design and construction of your model.

(b) Draw your completed model. Include the following labels on your diagram: cylinder, piston, and conductor.

Test

2 How well does your model meet the design criteria?

(3F) (a) If not all of the design criteria are met, what changes do you need to make to your design?

- Make the necessary changes.

Water-filled syringes can be quite dangerous when under pressure. Check your connections carefully first.

Figure 1

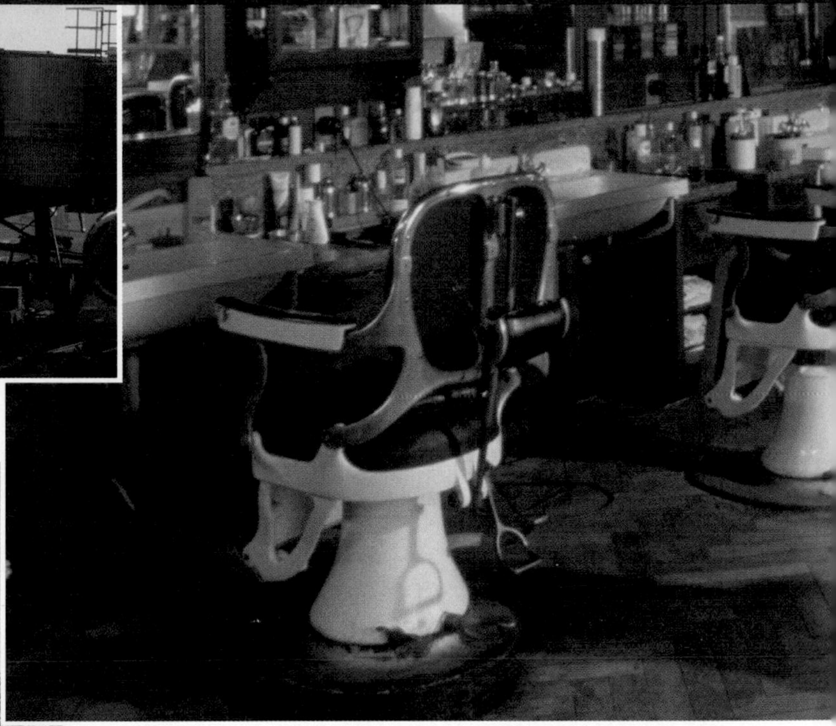

Figure 2

Figure 3

At the Big Chute Marine Railway on the Trent-Severn Waterway, hydraulic cylinders operate slings that support boats as they are carried over a 17.7-m height of land.

Evaluate

3 Evaluate your results by answering the following questions.

(a) When is the fluid in your system being compressed?

(b) Why must no air be present in a system filled with water?

(c) How would you notice if your air-filled system were leaking?

Design Challenge

How has designing and building a model fluid power system assisted you in designing your Challenge?

Making Connections

1. What difference might you notice if your hydraulic model were filled with oil?

Exploring

2. How would you modify your model to lift a load twice as heavy?

3. In your fluid system, clay was used as the object to be lifted. What changes would you need to make to your system to lift a stiff, rectangular object?

4. Set up your lift as a hydraulic system. Exchange the syringe providing the effort force with a smaller syringe. Describe the change in the effort now required to lift the load on the larger syringe.

Reflecting

5. What are two benefits of hydraulic and pneumatic lifts?

Fluid Power at Work for Us

Hydraulic and pneumatic systems are versatile. They can be used to do very heavy or extremely delicate work. Tiny hand-held drills operated by pneumatics are used for medical surgery. Hydraulics and pneumatic robots prevent human injury by performing dangerous jobs on assembly lines. Fluid power machines save industries money, doing heavy tasks quickly and efficiently that would take many people long hours to perform. Hydraulic or pneumatic systems are combined with electrical systems and solid mechanical systems (pulleys and levers) in an amazing variety of ways to meet the needs of society.

Working to Entertain Us

From special effects that include huge moving beasts (**Figure 1**) to amusement park rides (**Figure 2**), fluid power systems work to frighten and thrill us.

Figure 2

A pneumatic system is used to slow or stop roller coasters.

Figure 1

Animated movie figures come to life because of hydraulic systems.

Hydraulics to the Rescue

There are many kinds of Jaws of Life tools. (See **Figure 3**.) Some can cut with a force as high as 169 kN. Others are used to pry things apart. These hydraulic devices are at work opening the sides of cars and slicing guardrails at the roadside to get accident victims to the hospital quickly.

Figure 3

The Jaws of Life tool is a hydraulic cutting-and-prying machine. It uses a hydraulic fluid made especially for accident scenes where the risk of fire or explosion is high. The fluid is fire resistant and does not conduct electricity.

Training Uses

Hydraulic systems are used to create motion in flight and driving simulators. (See **Figure 4**.) Operators sit inside a model of the real vehicle and respond to computer-generated situations as if they were real. Hydraulic cylinders move the whole simulator back and forth and from side to side. Because this is a simulation, dangerous manoeuvres can be tried without anyone getting hurt. Hydraulics is at work to give us the best-trained pilots and drivers.

Figure 4

Moving Earth Beneath Our Feet

Figure 5 illustrates a section of a Tunnel Boring Machine (TBM) at work building a Toronto subway tunnel. The machine has two functions: it bores through the earth to form the tunnel, and it erects the lining of the tunnel.

To form the tunnel, 14 hydraulic motors rotate the cutting head that excavates the ground. While the cutting head digs, 24 hydraulic-thrust cylinders push the machine forward. The excavated soil passes through hydraulically operated doors to a screw-type conveyor. A second conveyor belt takes this soil to waiting rail cars, which haul the dirt away.

As the tunnel is being formed, the lining is built. The concrete tunnel lining is pre-built in segments, which are put in position by a machine and bolted together using pneumatic wrenches.

Boring 1m of tunnel an hour, the fluid power systems in this modern machine are underground working for us.

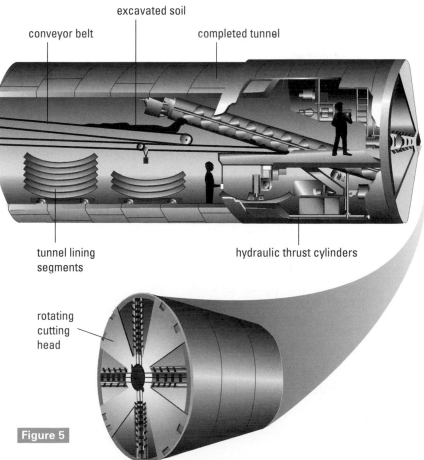

conveyor belt   excavated soil   completed tunnel

tunnel lining segments

hydraulic thrust cylinders

rotating cutting head

Figure 5

Design Challenge

SKILLS MENU
- Identify a Problem
- Planning
- Building
- Testing
- Recording
- Evaluating
- Communicating

Design and Build a Device That Uses the Properties of Fluids

Fluids are a vital part of our natural world. For centuries we have been trying to learn more about the principles of fluids. As our understanding has increased, so too has our use of fluids. Today, the applications of these fluid principles are numerous and have had a great impact on society. By designing and building a fluid device, you will gain a better understanding of the use of fluids.

1 A Safety Hinge

This door operates by pneumatic fluid power.

Problem situation

You are helping some friends build a tree house. The access ladder reaches up from the ground to a trapdoor in the floor of the platform. It is awkward to hold the trapdoor open as you climb through. You wish it would stay open, in an upright position, to allow you to climb in. You'd also like it to close gently, rather than slam down.

Design brief

- Design and build a safety hinge that operates using hydraulics or pneumatics.

Design criteria

- The door must open and close safely.
- After opening, the door must stay open for 15 s.

2 A Boat Navigation Lock

Problem situation

You are working with a team of engineers who are building a waterway between two lakes so that recreational boaters can travel from one to the other. The lakes are close together, but one is 5 m higher than the other. You don't want a rushing river between the two lakes, so you need some way to move the boats from one level canal to the other: you need a "lock."

Design brief

- Design and build a model of a lock that allows boats to travel both ways between waterways of different levels.

Design criteria

- The model lock must move a toy boat from one water level to the other, at least 5 cm higher or lower.

In 1998, the lock at Sault Ste. Marie, Ontario, was reopened after being closed for 11 years. The lock was originally built in the late 1800s to link the St. Lawrence Seaway with Lake Superior. Today, it is used as a recreational lock.

Assessment

3 | A Fish-Tank Cleaner

Problem situation

Your Saturday job at the pet store involves scraping the green algae off the insides of the fish tanks. This is a messy job, and you wish there was some way of doing it that didn't involve getting up to your elbows in water. You decide to use your knowledge of buoyancy to build something that will help you.

Design brief

- Design and build a fish-tank cleaning device that will raise or lower itself in water.

Design criteria

- The fish-tank cleaner must be equipped with a scraper that cleans the walls of the fish tank.
- It must go up and down in the water as a result of its changing buoyancy.

 When preparing to build or test a design, have your plan approved by your teacher before you begin.

Unit 2 Summary

Now that you have completed the unit, can you do the following? If not, review the sections indicated.

Reflecting

- Reflect on the ideas and questions presented in the Unit Overview and in the Getting Started. How can you connect what you have done and learned in this unit with those ideas and questions? (To review, check the sections indicated in this Summary.)
- Revise your answers to the Reflecting questions in ❶, ❷, ❸ and the questions you created in the Getting Started. How has your thinking changed?
- What new questions do you have? How will you answer them?

Understanding Concepts

- explain, using examples, how fluid flow can be classified 2.2
- describe each of the three properties of fluids (viscosity, density, and buoyancy) you have investigated 2.3, 2.8, 2.12
- identify situations where understanding each property is important 2.5, 2.11, 2.12, 2.13, 2.14, 2.15, 2.16, 2.17
- describe how the forces of buoyancy and gravity act on objects immersed in fluids 2.11, 2.12

- distinguish between fluids and solids, using the particle theory of matter, and explain how changes in temperature affect their densities 2.1, 2.16
- define the terms hydraulics and pneumatics 2.20, 2.21

Applying Skills

- predict and measure the effect of temperature on the flow rate of fluids 2.4, 2.16

- calculate the mass-to-volume ratio of a substance 2.6, 2.7

- compare densities of fluids and solids to explain why some substances float on top of other substances 2.9, 2.10

- design, build, calibrate, and use a hydrometer 2.13

- describe what happens to fluids when they are under pressure 2.18, 2.22

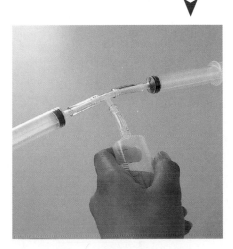

- design and build a hydraulic or pneumatic system. 2.22

- understand and use the following terms:

aerodynamics
Archimedes' principle
ballast
buoyancy
compressible
cylinder
density
displacement
drag
dynamic
flow rate
hydraulic fluid
hydraulics
hydrodynamics
hydrometer
laminar flow
mass
negative buoyancy
neutral buoyancy
particle theory
piston
pneumatics
positive buoyancy
pressure
streamlined
turbulent flow
viscometer
viscosity
volume
weight

Making Connections

- describe situations where the use and investigation of fluids have affected our lives 2.7, 2.12, 2.14, 2.15, 2.19, 2.20, 2.21, 2.22, 2.23

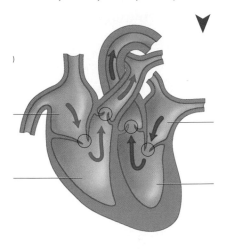

- explain how changes in fluids' viscosity and density can be useful 2.3, 2.4, 2.5, 2.10, 2.12, 2.14, 2.16

- identify a career that requires an understanding of the properties of fluids 2.5, 2.12, 2.17

- describe real life situations where scientists use their knowledge and understanding of fluids to solve challenges 2.5, 2.17

- discuss the versatility of hydraulic and pneumatic systems 2.23

Unit 2 Review

Understanding Concepts

1. Make a list of five fluids that can be found in each of these places:
   (a) the human body
   (b) a kitchen
   (c) a garage

2. Make a list of ten machines or devices that use fluid power systems.

3. Identify five industries where the properties of fluids play an important role. For each industry, provide an example of fluid use.

4. Using the pictures and statements provided in the Unit Summary, develop a concept map of the *Fluids* unit.

5. The following statements contain information about mass or weight. In your notebook, write the letters "a" to "f." Next to each letter, write the word "mass" if that letter's statement refers to the measurement of mass. Use the word "weight" if the statement refers to a weight measurement.
   (a) This measures the amount of matter in an object.
   (b) This measures the force of gravity acting on an object.
   (c) This measurement varies according to the location of the object in the universe.
   (d) Unless something is added to or taken away from the object, this measurement of an object remains the same everywhere in the universe.
   (e) This pulling force is measured in newtons.
   (f) This measurement is not a force.

6. Density is a property of fluids and solids.
   (a) What is the meaning of the term density?
   (b) Why is the density of a substance compared to the density of water?

7. (a) Create a poem about bouyancy, showing that you understand what it means.
   (b) Using the term "buoyant force," explain why a life jacket keeps a person afloat. (See **Figure 1**.)

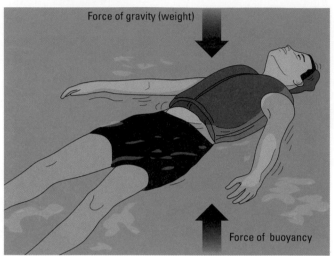
Force of gravity (weight)

Force of buoyancy

Figure 1

8. Compare how a submarine, fish, and scuba diver control their depth in the water.

9. Using the particle theory, explain the effects of temperature changes on solids, liquids, and gases. Draw diagrams to support your explanation.

10. Fill in the blanks in the following sentences with the correct words, whose letters are found scrambled in parentheses.
    (a) The _____?_____ of a fluid is an indicator of its viscosity. (lwof eatr)
    (b) When the flow of fluid around an object is smooth and uniform, it is referred to as _____?_____ flow. (ranamil)
    (c) The _____?_____ of measurement for density is g/cm3 or kg/m3. (itnu)
    (d) Because the volume of a liquid under pressure changes very little, the liquid is said to be virtually _____?_____. (biipmnosesrcel)
    (e) Helium balloons float in air because their _____?_____ is less than that of air. (yesidtn)

(f) Mechanical systems that use fluids to transmit force and move objects are called hydraulic or ____?____ depending on the fluid used. (mtacipeun)

(g) The buoyant force ____?____ the force of gravity. (spspooe)

(h) The force that measures the amount of gravity acting on a mass is ____?____. (tewhig)

(i) A living thing not normally found in the area where it is living and reproducing is said to be an ____?____. (toecix eesscip)

(j) Streamlined shapes produce less drag or ____?____ when they are moving through fluids. (cratesiens)

(k) The first letter from the first word in each blank above spells the answer to the following question: What do you get when confined fluids operate under pressure?

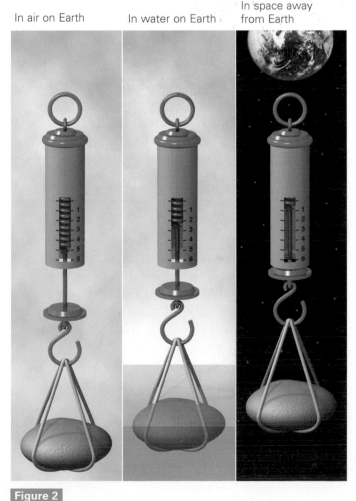

In air on Earth   In water on Earth   In space away from Earth

Figure 2

11. Look at the three sketches in **Figure 2** and answer the following questions:

(a) What measurement is being taken of the rock in air, water, and space?

(b) How does the mass of the rock change at the three locations?

(c) How does the weight of the rock compare among the three locations?

(d) How does the buoyant force acting on the rock differ in air and water?

(e) In what location is the force of gravity the smallest?

(f) Does the force of gravity acting on the rock differ between the air and water locations? Explain.

Applying Skills

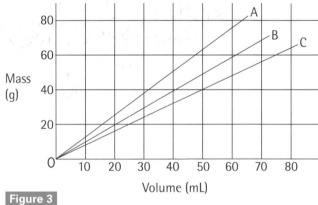

Figure 3

12. The graph in **Figure 3** illustrates the relationship between mass and volume for three liquids, A, B, and C. Using the information in this graph, answer the following questions:

(a) Which liquid has the highest density?

(b) Which liquid has the lowest density?

(c) Suppose you took these three liquids and poured them slowly, one at a time, into a tall container. Draw a diagram of where you would find each liquid in the container.

(d) Calculate the density of liquid B. What could be the identity of this liquid?

13. Your teacher has asked you to design an investigation in which you use an eyedropper to measure the flow rate of the three liquids in question 12.

   (a) Describe how you would do this investigation.

   (b) What variables will you have to keep constant as you test each liquid?

   (c) What sources of experimental error might you encounter?

   (d) From the information in the graph for question 13, which substance might you think has the highest flow rate?

   (e) Could your prediction in (d) be proven incorrect when you perform the investigation? Explain.

14. The reading on a hydrometer standing upright in a liquid is 1.24.

   (a) Explain what this measurement represents.

   (b) Would this liquid float on water? Explain.

   (c) Draw a diagram of the above liquid containing the hydrometer, beside the same hydrometer in a less dense liquid.

15. Which diagram in **Figure 4** represents the particles in a solid? In a liquid? In a gas?

Figure 4

Making Connections

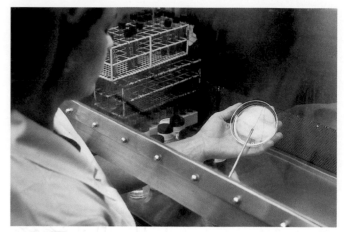

Figure 5

16. Laminar airflow provides a cleaner environment for this microbiologist working with microorganisms (**Figure 5**).

   (a) Draw a picture that shows the invisible airflow inside the hood where the microbiologist is working.

   (b) How does laminar airflow compare to turbulent flow?

   (c) Describe two situations when laminar airflow around an object would be desirable.

17. In order to lubricate a car engine, engine oil must remain viscous. The "W" in motor oil stands for weight. 10W30 motor oil has the viscosity of lighter oil when it is cold, and the viscosity of heavier oil when it is hot. Why is it important that motor oil has these characteristics in Canada's climate?

18. Jacques Cartier returned to France after his explorations in North America with samples of what he thought were gold and diamonds. These samples turned out to be "fool's gold" and quartz. Explain how you could use Archimedes' principle to show that Cartier's samples were not the real thing.

19. Suppose your class is having a pool party (**Figure 6**). What will happen to the level of the water if each person enters the pool at the same time? How could you calculate this change in water level?

Figure 6

20. Two bodies of water, the Dead Sea and Great Salt Lake, are much saltier than oceans. Using the data from the table of densities in 2.8, explain why it is easy for a person to float in these locations.

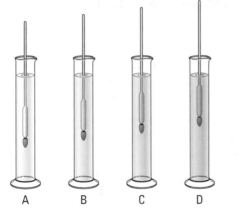
A   B   C   D

21. During the production of a batch of maple syrup, a hydrometer is placed in four test samples taken at different times throughout the evaporation process. Refer to the illustrations above.

   (a) Rank the liquids in order by density from least dense to most dense.

   (b) Which sample was collected earliest in the evaporating process?

   (c) Which sample was collected latest in the evaporating process?

   (d) Which sample would taste the sweetest?

22. Divers (and firefighters) carry a supply of air to breathe. Apply your knowledge from investigating fluids to explain how divers can remain under water for long periods of time with only a small tank of air.

Figure 7

23. Bicycle pumps push air into tires. What is the purpose of the valve on the end of the hose? (See **Figure 7**.)

Figure 8

24. Look at the picture of a car jack raising a car (**Figure 8**). Sketch the hydraulic cylinder inside the car jack.

25. A warning on an aerosol can states, "Caution, container may explode if heated." Explain, using the particle theory of matter, why such a warning is necessary.

26. Describe how the air pressure changes inside a soccer ball when it is kicked.

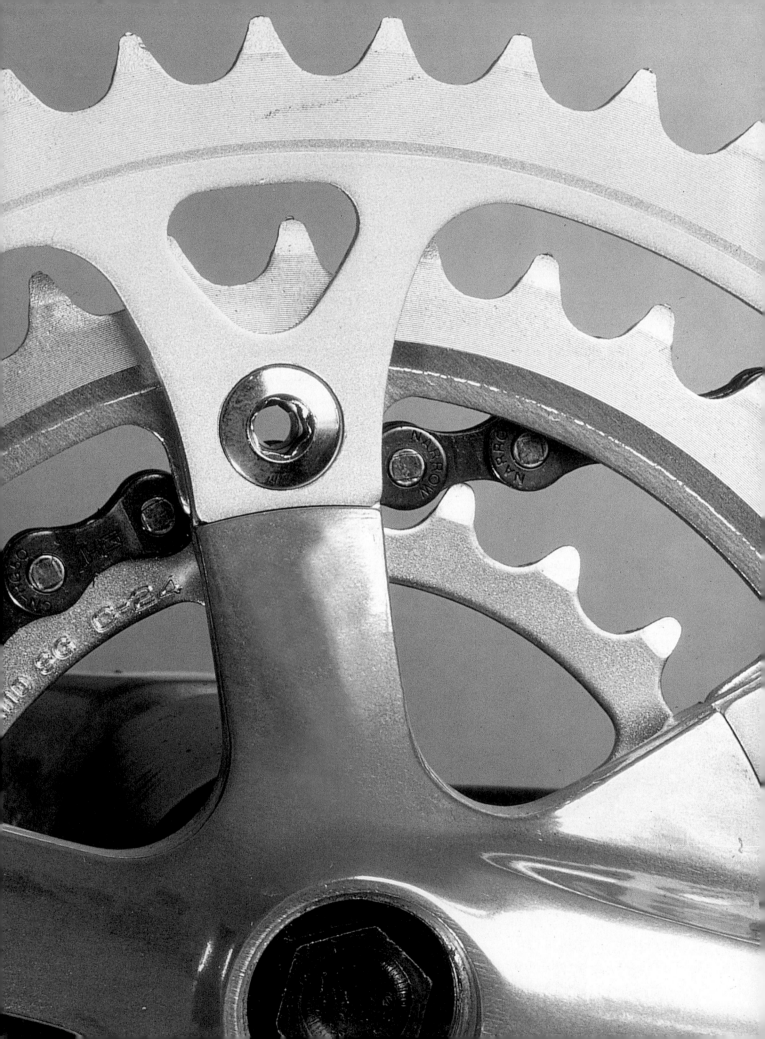

Mechanical Advantage and Efficiency

Unit 3 Overview

Getting Started: Using Machines to Get Things Done

3.1   Designing Machines

3.2   Levers: How They Work

3.3   Design Investigation: Raise It Up

3.4   Simulating Human Movement

3.5   Pulleys, Wheel and Axle, and Gears

3.6   Case Study: Mechanisms in Giant Machines

3.7   Moving Efficiently

3.8   Friction and Mechanical Advantage

3.9   Design Investigation: Moving the Couch

3.10   Career Profile: Testing Force and Endurance

3.11   Inquiry Investigation: Testing Shoes

3.12   Force, Area and Pressure

3.13   Pressure on Liquids and Gases

3.14   Inquiry Investigation: Squeezing Liquids and Gases

3.15   Pressure in Fluid Systems

3.16   Design Investigation: A Hydraulic Solution for a Pain in the Neck

3.17   Case Study: A Student-Friendly Classroom

3.18   Designing for People with Special Needs

3.19   Case Study: Mountain Bike or Road Bike?

3.20   The Life of a Product

3.21   Explore an Issue: A World Without Cars?

Design Challenge: Design and Build a Mechanical Model or Device

Unit 3 Summary

Unit 3 Review

Getting Started

Using Machines to Get Things Done

1 Mechanisms, which are made from simple machines like levers and pulleys, are built into both large and small devices. These devices allow people to pull, push, or lift objects, often without applying much force. How can you tell which mechanisms will be most effective? How do you measure or predict how much force will be needed to operate the machine? What effect does friction have on the efficiency of a mechanism?

2 Mechanical, hydraulic (liquid), and pneumatic (gas) systems are everywhere, but we rarely notice them. From garbage trucks to dentists' drills, these systems can change the direction or speed of movement or multiply or transfer force to lift or push things. How do these systems work? How can we make them more useful and more efficient?

3 Machines and other products must be designed and made with the consumer and the environment in mind. How can the designers know that the product will be easy to use, safe, and reliable? In the chain from design to disposal, where will the product affect the environment? How can that impact be reduced?

Reflecting

Think about the questions in **1**,**2**,**3**. What other questions do you have about mechanical advantage and efficiency? As you progress through this unit, reflect on your answers and revise them based on what you have learned.

Try This The Can Opener: A Simple Device

We use can openers almost every day without much thought. But try opening a can without one!

• Take a close look at a hand-powered can opener.

1. Can openers open cans in a two-step process. What are the two steps?

2. For each step, explain what happens when a force is applied. Draw diagrams showing the direction of the force in each step.

• Try to use the can opener by pressing on the handles near its joint.

3. (a) Is it easier or harder to use?

(b) Would it be easier or harder if the handles were longer? Why?

• Try to turn the handle with your fingers at the centre of the handle.

4. Is it easier or harder to wind the handle?

5. What is the purpose of the round, toothed part of the can opener?

6. Do you think the metal of the can opener is stronger than the metal of the can? What evidence do you have that supports your conclusion?

7. What modifications might make a can opener easier to use?

Levers: How They Work

When you swing a baseball bat or use a shovel you are using a lever. A lever is a rigid bar that pivots at a point called a fulcrum. Levers can multiply a small force into a large force. When you are digging a hole with a shovel, the input (effort) force is multiplied into a larger output (load) force, and you are able to move a heavy load of soil.

Types of Levers

Levers are found in all sorts of tools and in complex machines such as cranes and robots. Despite this variety, there are only three types of levers: Class 1, Class 2, and Class 3. Each classification is based on the relative positions of the effort, fulcrum, and load. Choosing which type of lever to use in a design depends on the input motion and force and what output motion and force is desired.

A Class 1 lever can move a heavy load with a small force. In a Class 1 lever, the fulcrum is between the load force and the effort force. The **load force** is the force exerted by the load, and the **effort force** is the force required to move the load. An example of a Class 1 lever is a screwdriver being used to pry off the lid of a paint can. (See **Figure 1**.)

A Class 2 lever always moves a large load using a small effort force. Unlike in a Class 1 lever, here the fulcrum is at one end. The load acts between the effort and the fulcrum. A wheelbarrow (**Figure 2**) is an example of Class 2 levers.

Unlike Class 1 and 2 levers, Class 3 levers always make things harder to lift or move instead of easier. In a Class 3 lever the fulcrum is at one end and the effort is exerted between the load and the fulcrum. As a result, the load arm is always longer than the effort arm. A fishing rod (**Figure 3**) and a tennis racket are examples of Class 3 levers.

The chief advantage of Class 3 levers is that although a large effort is needed, the longer load arm can magnify movements.

Figure 1

The effort force required to open the lid of this paint can is smaller than the load force.

load force

fulcru

effort force = 250 N

Figure 2

In a Class 2 lever, the effort arm (the distance from the effort to the fulcrum) is longer than the load arm (the distance from the load to the fulcrum).

fulcrum

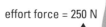

load force = 750 N

load arm

effort arm

ort force

Mechanical Advantage

When designing machines it is helpful to know what benefi[t] mechanism provides compared to another. The usefulness of a mechanism can be expressed in quantitative terms. **Mechanical advantage** is the number of times by which a machine can increase or decrease the effort force. If you know the effort force and the load force, you can determine the mechanical advantage of the mechanism by calculating the following ratio:

$$\text{Mechanical Advantage (MA)} = \frac{\text{load force (N)}}{\text{effort force (N)}}$$

Mechanical advantage has no units. If the mechanical advantage of a machine is 1, the effort force is equal to the load force, and there is no advantage gained. If the mechanical advantage is less than 1, a large effort force is required to move a smaller load (as in Class 3 levers). Machines with a mechanical advantage greater than 1, as in Class 1 and Class 2 levers, allow larger loads to be moved with less effort.

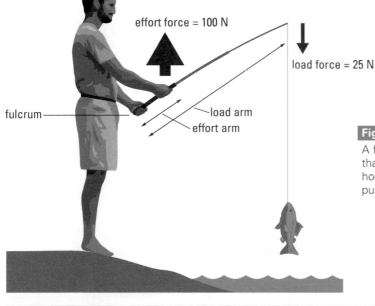

effort force = 100 N

load force = 25 N

fulcrum

load arm
effort arm

Figure 3

A fishing rod magnifies small wrist movements so that a person fishing can easily fling the fishing hook and line. However, a large force is needed to pull the fish out of the water.

Try This Levering Advantage

- You can use the back of a chair, a metre stick, a newton scale, and a weight tied on a string to construct Class 1, 2, and 3 levers.

- Make an example of each class of lever. For each lever, use the newton scale to measure the effort force needed to lift the load.

- Draw a diagram of each lever. Label the fulcrum, load force, and effort force to lift the load.

1. For each lever, calculate the mechanical advantage.

- For each lever, try to improve the mechanical advantage.

2. What is the maximum mechanical advantage for each lever?

Mechanical Advantage and Levers

With levers the mechanical advantage is affected by the distance of the point of application of the load and effort forces from the fulcrum. This relationship is described in the following equation:

$$\text{Mechanical Advantage (MA)} = \frac{\text{length of effort arm}}{\text{length of load arm}}$$

This means that the mechanical advantage increases as the length of the effort arm increases, and also as the length of the load arm decreases.

You now have two ways to calculate mechanical advantage: you can use the measured lengths of the arms of the lever, or the measured magnitude of the forces, as shown in **Figure 4**.

In the real world, however, the two will not be equal. In **Figure 4** we simplified a little: in real life, friction would act on the painter's hand and the screwdriver as they move down, between the screwdriver and the can at the fulcrum, and on the screwdriver and the lid of the can as they move up. The mechanical advantage calculated using the length of the lever arms is useful *only for prediction without friction*. In application, the effort force that is needed will always be greater than the effort force you predict (based on the length of the lever arms) because it takes extra effort to overcome friction. To calculate the real mechanical advantage, you must measure forces.

load force = 80 N

load arm = 1 cm

effort arm = 20 cm

effort force = 4 N   fulcrum

$$MA = \frac{\text{length of effort arm}}{\text{length of load arm}}$$

$$= \frac{20 \text{ cm}}{1 \text{ cm}}$$

$$= 20$$

$$MA = \frac{\text{load force}}{\text{effort force}}$$

$$= \frac{80 \text{ N}}{4 \text{ N}}$$

$$= 20$$

Figure 4

Here the mechanical advantage is large (20), because the effort arm is much longer than the load arm.

Velocity Ratio

If the mechanical advantage of a Class 3 lever is always less than 1, how can mechanisms using Class 3 levers still be useful? A tennis racket is an example of a Class 3 lever (**Figure 5**). Even though a large effort force is required to hit the ball, only a small wrist motion at the handle creates a large motion at the other end of the racket.

Therefore, if you compare the distance that the effort force moves with the distance the load force moves, you will see that, in a Class 3 lever, the load force moves farther than the effort force in the same length of time. The ratio of these two distances is called the **velocity ratio**. This is written as:

$$\text{Velocity Ratio} = \frac{\text{distance effort force moves}}{\text{distance load force moves}}$$

Like mechanical advantage, velocity ratio has no units.

For Class 3 levers, the velocity ratio is always less than 1. For Class 1 and 2 levers, the velocity ratio is larger than 1.

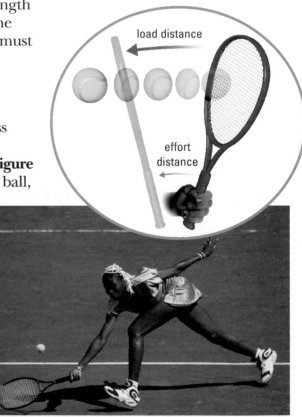

load distance

effort distance

Figure 5

Because the racket is a Class 3 lever, it takes a lot of effort to hit the ball over the net. However, the racket also multiplies small movements of the wrist, allowing the player to easily control the flight of the ball.

Effient Lever Mechanisms

Lers are inexpensive and easy to use in the degn of mechanisms, but how efficient are th/ in being able to move large loads for shrt distances? How can we determine how efcient a machine is?

You can calculate the efficiency of a nechanism by using the following ratio:

$$\text{Percentage efficiency} = \frac{\text{Mechanical Advantage}}{\text{Velocity Ratio}} \times 100$$

Without friction the percentage efficiency of levers is always 100%. However, in reality friction reduces the mechanical advantage of a lever, resulting in an efficiency that is less than 100%.

Connecting Levers Together

Many machines and other devices use a combination of levers called a linkage to transmit force and motion. A **linkage** is two or more levers connected together. The choice of where each fulcrum is placed affects the movement of the connecting lever(s). A given input motion and force can be transferred into the desired output motion and force. (See **Figure 6**.)

Figure 6

Linked levers can be found in a wide variety of mechanisms.

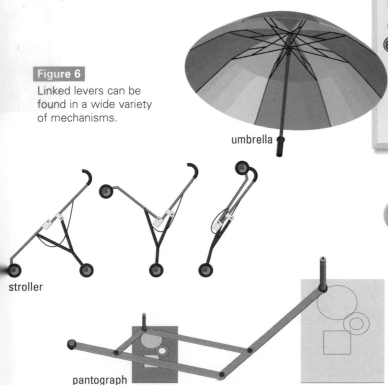

umbrella

stroller

pantograph

Understanding Concepts

1. (a) Draw diagrams of Class 1, 2, and 3 le showing the fulcrum, load force, and force for each.

   (b) Give an explanation of each type.

   (c) Explain how Class 1 and 2 levers can make it easier and more efficient to move things.

2. (a) Define mechanical advantage.

   (b) What is the mechanical advantage of a lever in which the effort force required to move an object is 1/10 of the load force?

3. (a) Define velocity ratio.

   (b) How can you use mechanical advantage and velocity ratio to determine the efficiency of a lever?

Making Connections

4. (a) What type of lever is your arm? Your jaw?

   (b) Explain, using the length of effort arm, where the most powerful teeth in your mouth are located.

5. Mary is raking up wet, heavy leaves and moves her hands down the handle to make it shorter.

   (a) What type of lever is a rake?

   (b) Why will moving her hands make the raking easier?

Exploring

6. Many household products involve levers. Choose one that uses a lever and draw a diagram to show how it works by indicating the effort and load forces, the lengths of its effort and load arms, its power source, if any, and its materials. Be prepared to share your findings with the class.

Design Challenge

In designing your windmill-operated water well or can crusher, is it important to establish what the approximate mechanical advantage will be? If so, how will you decide what it should be?

Design Investigation

SKILLS MENU
○ Identify a Problem ● Testing ● Evalua[te]
● Planning ● Recording ● Comm[unic]ating
● Building

Raise It Up

You have seen that linkage systems are part of many everyday products. One problem, when including levers in any machine or system, is getting them to fit into a limited amount of space, for example, inside a piano (**Figure 1**).

Problem
How can you create a compact system of linked levers to raise a weight a certain height?

Design Brief
Design and build a compact linkage system (using any classes of levers) that will raise a weight, using only the materials available.

Design Criteria
- The linkage system must raise a 0.25-N weight a height of 20 cm.
- The system must include at least two levers.
- All parts of the system must stay within the size of a "box" 0.5 m long, 0.5 m wide, and 0.5 m high.

Materials
- 30 (drilled as needed) popsicle sticks
- glue
- apron
- 10 paper fasteners
- 0.25-N (25-g) mass
- thin rope or twine
- metre stick
- newton spring scale

Build

1 Using a detailed technical drawing, design a linkage system according to the above criteria. On your diagram, indicate materials, size, classes of lever, and how they will work.
(3C) **(6C)**

2 With your teacher's approval, build the system according to your design.
(5E)
   (a) Does your linkage system fit within the size limits?

Test

3 Measure your system to ensure it meets the size limit.
- If it does not, redesign the system so it does.

4 Test your system to see if it raises the 0.25-N weight the minimum height.
- If your system does not pass the test, examine the system and consider how to redesign it.
- Redraw your diagram.
- Rebuild your linkage system, measure it, and test it until it works.

Evaluate

5 Evaluate your results by answering the following questions.

   (a) What other materials might have made the linkage system easier to build?

   (b) Which type of lever takes up more space, a Class 1 lever or a Class 2 lever?

   (c) How could you improve the mechanical advantage of your system?

Figure 1

a An upright piano takes up much less floor space than a grand piano.

b To achieve this, its series of three levers are arranged in a compact space. The first lever is the piano key, which pushes a second lever, which in turn moves a third lever that strikes a string, producing a sound.

6 Using the spring scale, measure how much force is needed to raise the 0.25-N weight.

✎ (a) Record the effort force.

✎ (b) Calculate and record the mechanical advantage of your system.

7 Present your linkage system to the class, explaining your strategies during the design process, any problems you encountered, and your solutions to those problems. Present a diagram showing any improvements you could make to your system.

Design Challenge

Do you think that a multiple-lever system is a practical choice for your can crusher Challenge?

Making Connections

1. Levers are frequently used in sports.

(a) Think of three sports in which a lever is the main tool that players use.

(b) Where is the fulcrum on each lever?

(c) Have the designs or materials changed in any of them over time? Why?

Reflecting

2. Technical drawings can be drawn from different views to show different parts of a system.

6C (a) Draw the system of linked levers you designed from a different view.

(b) Does this diagram help to illustrate any feature better than your first diagram did?

(c) Why would different diagrams of the same product be important?

Simulating Human Movement

Robots: Sophisticated Machines

Robots are one of the most important types of machines being used today. They are sophisticated systems that are controlled by computer and can replace humans in many different situations. Robots are the ideal replacement for certain jobs that need to be done in cold, hot, noisy, or dangerous places (**Figure 1**). They can even retrieve potentially explosive devices.

Most robots copy the movements of the human arm. (See **Figure 2**.) A robotic arm is a series of subsystems that, when combined, performs a specific task. Robotic arms use an electronic system to direct their movement, a hydraulic system to lift and move heavy things, and a mechanical system to grasp objects.

Because it is so difficult to copy all of a human arm's complicated movements, robots are most efficient at doing repetitive tasks such as assembly-line work. Instead of a hand, robots are often fitted with a drill, screwdriver, or spray gun, and can repeat the same task quickly and exactly, without the strain or injuries that humans often get through repetitive movements.

Although basic human arm movements can be copied, it is more difficult to build a robot that has the same delicate precision as human hands and fingers. This is because humans have an extremely sensitive sense of touch, which is controlled by the brain. Also, humans are helped by their sense of sight. Most robots lack any sensors and simply have a computer program that instructs levers where to move.

The challenge is to build a robot with enough electronic sensors at its "fingertips" so that they will supply the robot's computer, or "brain," with detailed information about the type of object being handled (**Figure 3**).

Figure 1
Robots can replace workers in dangerous places that may have high levels of radioactivity, poisonous fumes, or a high risk of infection.

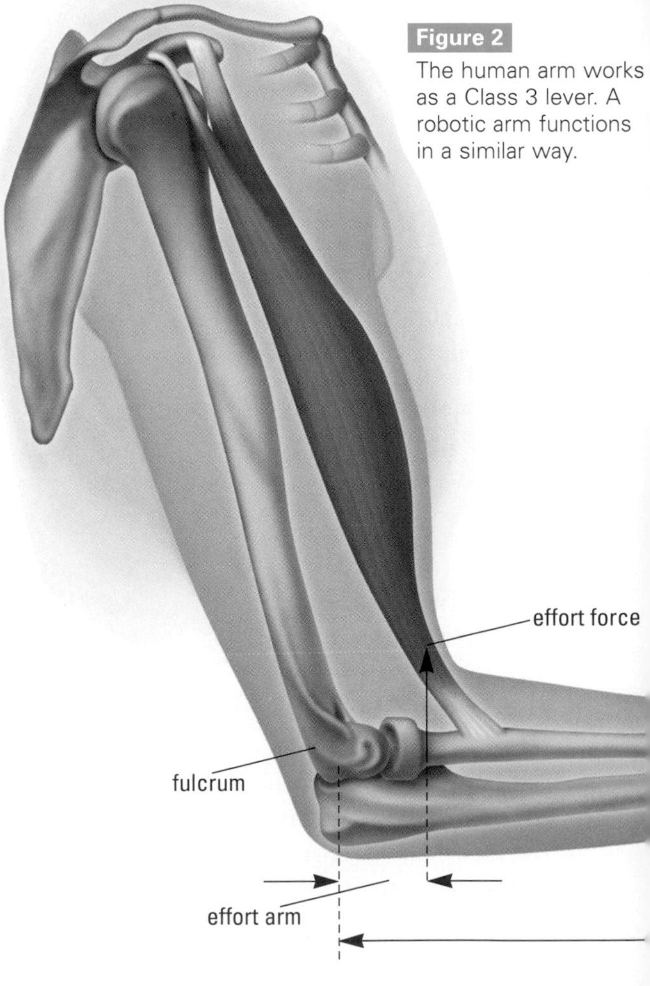

Figure 2
The human arm works as a Class 3 lever. A robotic arm functions in a similar way.

effort force

fulcrum

effort arm

Figure 3
Designers use hundreds of tiny electronic sensors in the robot's "fingers" so it can pick up an egg without crushing it.

Artificial Arms

In some ways an artificial arm is simpler than a robotic arm because the person operating the artificial arm "knows" what to do. But opening and closing an artificial hand still involves complicated computerization and mechanical design.

The most sophisticated models detect the tiny electronic signals transmitted through the human nervous system. This is done by connecting electrodes in the mechanical arm to the nerve endings on the person's arm. Wires then carry signals from the brain to motors in the arm, enabling the person to control the artificial hand (**Figure 4**).

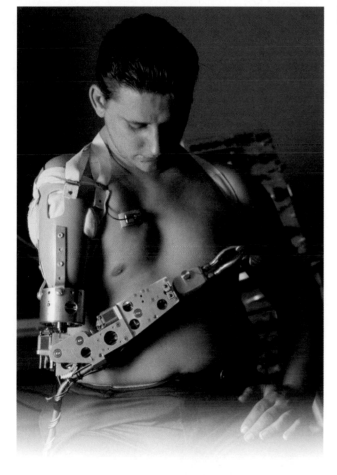

Figure 4

This artificial arm is connected electronically to the nerves so the person can control the arm using natural electronic impulses from his brain.

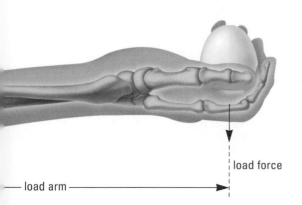

load force

load arm

Understanding Concepts

1. (a) What part of the human body do most robots copy? Why?

(b) What type of simple machine is this?

2. What aspect of humans is difficult to copy in a robot?

3. What types of jobs do robots do best? Explain.

Making Connections

4. In outer space, the Canadian-made Canadarm is a large, mechanized arm and "hand," operated by computer technology, that astronauts use to move objects outside the space shuttle.

(a) What is the advantage of using the Canadarm instead of the astronauts themselves?

(b) Are there disadvantages to using a robotic arm for work in outer space?

Exploring

5. Artificial intelligence refers to
(8D) computers and robots that can "think" and "learn" like human beings. However, many scientists say that the human brain is impossible to copy because it is so complicated. Using the Internet or the library, find out more about artificial intelligence.

6. Industries are increasingly
(8A) replacing humans with robots in work that is repetitive or dangerous. However, many argue that this takes jobs away from people who need them. Do you think robots are a good idea? Do some research to support your opinion.

Design Challenge

How can the simple design of most robots help in the design of your remote-control puppet?

Pulleys, Wheel and Axle, and Gears

Rotary motion is one of the most common types of motion found in machines. Many machines generate rotary motion that has to be transmitted from one place to another. This is accomplished by mechanisms that use pulleys, gears, and wheels. As with some levers, there is a mechanical advantage to these mechanisms that is greater than one. But there is a price to be paid—the effort force must move over a greater distance than the load force. Using mechanical advantage and velocity ratio, designers and engineers can choose the most effective mechanism for a particular machine.

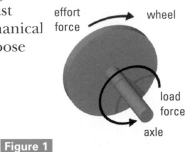

Figure 1
Is the MA of this wheel-and-axle machine greater than 1, equal to 1, or less than 1?

Wheel and Axle

The wheel and axle is the most common wheel mechanism. It consists of a large-diameter disk, (the wheel), which is attached to a small diameter shaft, (the axle). The effort force on the wheel (**Figure 1**) magnifies the load force on the axle. In the screwdriver (**Figure 2**), the handle is larger in diameter than the shaft. This means that a small force on the handle will create a large force on the shaft and thus on the screw. The steering wheel of a car performs the same function of magnifying the driver's force on the steering column. The larger the steering wheel, the more force the driver can send to the wheels.

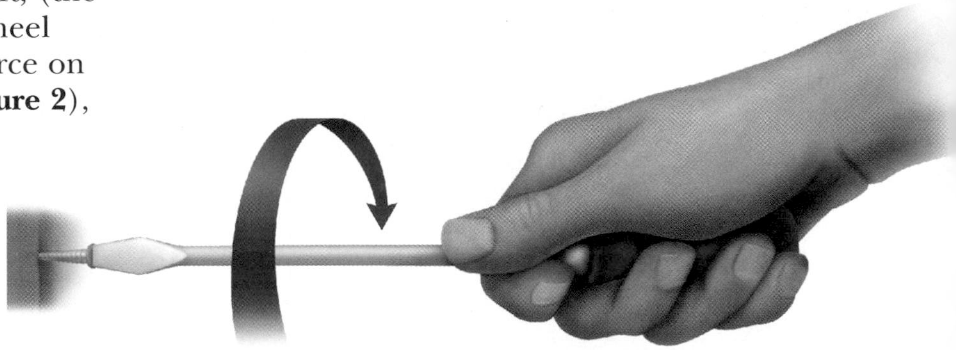

Figure 2
Which part of the screwdriver is the wheel? Which part is the axle?

The wheel and axle can also work the opposite way. With a bicycle, a large effort force is applied to the axle to overcome the smaller load force acting on the rim of the wheel. The advantage is that the rim of the wheel must travel much farther than the axle in the same amount of time, enabling the bicycle to go very fast. Depending on the purpose of the machine, wheel-and-axle mechanisms can be designed to transfer rotary motion to rotary motion, rotary motion to linear motion (**Figure 3**), and linear motion to rotary motion.

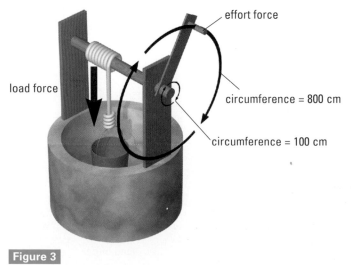

Figure 3
A winch is one type of wheel and axle that is used to move or lift a heavy weight. What is its velocity ratio?

Pulleys

Cranes or the rigging on a sailboat use sets of pulleys joined together by ropes and chains to lift heavy loads or exert large forces. A single pulley is a wheel-and-axle mechanism that is used to change the direction of a force or motion. There are two types of pulley systems: fixed and movable. The simplest system is the single fixed pulley. Its only function is to change the direction of the force. The other systems are designed to multiply the force (**Figure 4**).

The single fixed pulley has a mechanical advantage of only 1, so it is useful only when the object's volume is too large to be picked up by hand or when the space around it is limited. In the single movable pulley, however, half the load is supported by the rope where it is attached to the ceiling, while the other half of the load is supported by the free end of the rope **Figure 4b**. Thus, the effort force required is only one-half the load force. Therefore the mechanical advantage is 2.

A simple method for determining the mechanical advantage of a pulley system without friction is to count the lengths of rope between the pulleys that share the load. For example, in **Figure 4d**, the multiple pulley system shows 3 ropes sharing the load (they pull up). The rope being pulled down does not count since it doesn't support the load. Therefore the mechanical advantage is 3.

With a pulley system that has a MA greater than 1, a smaller effort force allows you to lift a larger load force. However, the effort force will have to move even a greater distance than the load force. This is the penalty you pay for gaining a mechanical advantage. The velocity ratio is:

$$\text{Velocity Ratio (VR)} = \frac{\text{distance moved by effort force}}{\text{distance moved by load force}}$$

The velocity ratio for the multiple fixed pulley in **Figure 4d** is also 3. To raise the weight 2 m, you must pull 6 m of rope through the pulley. In other words, each of the 3 rope lengths sharing the load must be shortened by 2 m to raise the load 2 m.

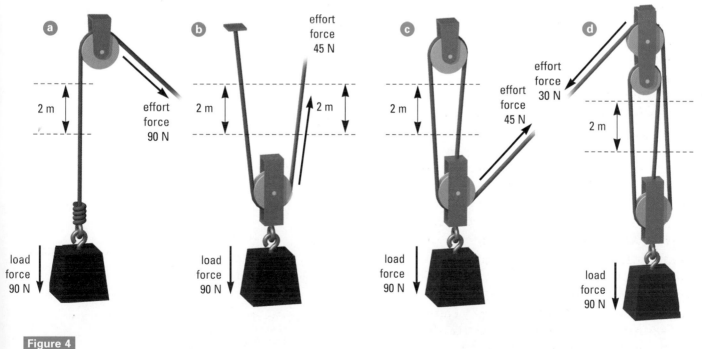

Figure 4

a Single fixed pulley. The force simply changes direction. The effort force is equal to the load force. By pulling in 2 m of rope, the weight will rise 2 m.

b Single movable pulley.

c Double fixed pulley. In this pulley 4 m of rope must be pulled to raise the mass 2 m.

d Multiple fixed pulley. The load force, 90 N, is shared by 3 lengths of rope. The effort force needed is 30 N, and 6 m of rope must be pulled in to raise the weight 2 m.

Gears

Gears are toothed wheels, usually made from metal or plastic, and used to speed up or slow down motion. A **gear train** consists of two wheels (or more) with meshed teeth (**Figure 5**).

Gears work by reducing the required revolving force (**Figure 5a**) or increasing it (**Figure 5b**). The ratio of the circumference of the gears, called the **gear ratio**, is similar to the velocity ratio on a pulley system. Since the teeth on meshing gears are the same distance apart, you can find the gear ratio by simply counting the number of teeth on each gear.

In some cases, like a bicycle (**Figure 6**), the gears turn separately and are joined by a chain. The pedal drives the front gear, and the chain transfers the turning force to the rear gear.

By using a variety of gear ratios on changing terrain, you can increase or decrease the turning force and even out the effort required. This makes you less tired.

Figure 5

The order of the gears in a gear train determines whether motion is speeded up or slowed down.

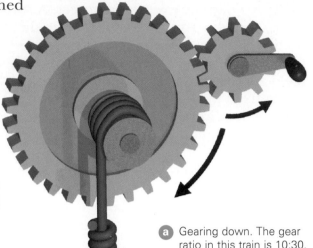

a Gearing down. The gear ratio in this train is 10:30, or 1:3, as you can tell by counting the teeth. A small force on the small gear will eventually raise the weight, but the small gear must be turned 3 times for each turn of the larger gear.

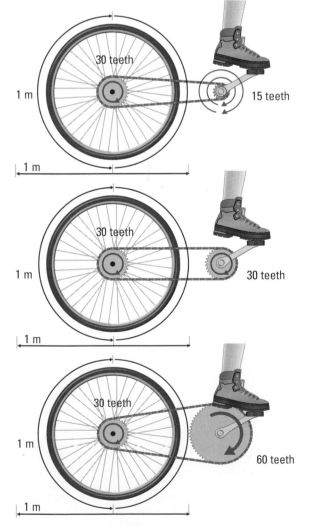

Figure 6

a When going up a steep hill against the force of gravity, it's harder to revolve the gear, so you should switch to a smaller front gear. With a low gear ratio, the gear can be turned with less force than before, but it must revolve farther around to cover the same distance as in (b).

$$\text{gear ratio} = \frac{15 \text{ teeth}}{30 \text{ teeth}}$$
$$= 1{:}2$$

bike covers 1 m with 2 revolutions of the front gear

b When a bike is pedalled on flat ground, and the gears are the same size, both the gears rotate at the same rate.

$$\text{gear ratio} = \frac{30 \text{ teeth}}{30 \text{ teeth}}$$
$$= 1{:}1$$

bike covers 1 m with 1 revolution of the front gear

c When going downhill, gravity helps to pull you downward, and it's easy to revolve the gears, so you should switch to a large front gear. With a high gear ratio, you need to push with more force than in (a), but with just a ½ revolution of the gear you cover the same distance.

$$\text{gear ratio} = \frac{60 \text{ teeth}}{30 \text{ teeth}}$$
$$= 2{:}1$$

bike travels 1 m with ½ revolution of the front gear

(b) Gearing up. The gear ratio in this train is 30:10, or 3:1. Turning the large gear will quickly raise the weight, as the small gear will turn three times faster than the large gear; however, arranging the gears in this way requires more force.

Design Challenge

How does the wheel and axle fit into your design of the windmill-operated water well?

Does the bicycle give you any ideas about how to transfer power from the windmill to the well?

Understanding Concepts

1. How does a pulley system achieve a mechanical advantage?

2. Calculate the mechanical advantage and velocity ratio for the single fixed pulley in **Figure 7** and for the single movable pulley in **Figure 8**.

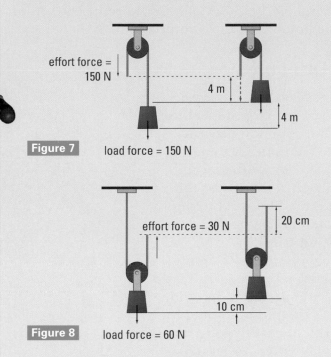

effort force = 150 N

4 m

4 m

Figure 7   load force = 150 N

effort force = 30 N

20 cm

10 cm

Figure 8   load force = 60 N

3. What does a gear ratio describe?

4. Ahman is trying to lift an 8-N load that is attached to a fixed 2-pulley system. His hands move a distance of 1.6 m, while the load moves 0.8 m. What force is required to lift the load?

Making Connections

5. If a wheel and axle has a mechanical advantage of 3, what effort force is required to move a load of 30 N?

6. Natasha has to pull in 25 m of rope to raise a 200-N weight 5 m using a pulley system.

   (a) What is the velocity ratio?

   (b) How much force does Natasha use to lift the weight?

7. Dave drives his jeep off a highway onto a steep, muddy uphill road. Does he need a higher or lower gear ratio?

Exploring

8. **(a)** What type of simple machine is a windmill?

   (b) Find out how a windmill works to grind grain.

   (6C) **(c)** Draw a simple diagram of its operation.

Mechanisms in Giant Machines

Even the largest, most complicated machines are formed from simple machines organized into mechanisms. Each mechanism has a function and, linked together, they all work to reduce strain on parts and lessen the amount of fuel required.

Giant Draglines

Dragline excavators (**Figure 1**) are some of the largest machines made. One common use is in open-pit coal mines, where they are used to remove the layers of soil and rock that cover the coal. They are also used to dig underwater, deepening channels for ships.

A dragline works by simply dropping an empty bucket on the ground from the tip of its crane. A winch is then used to drag the bucket, full of earth, along the ground. The loose, excavated earth that has been pulled in is then piled up so that trucks can remove it at a later time.

(a) Study **Figure 1**. What is the advantage of dragging the dirt instead of lifting it?

(b) What type of lever is the bucket attached to? Where is its fulcrum?

(c) Identify any pulley systems in this machine. What are their functions?

Figure 1

This dragline is one of the largest machines in the world. It operates in a coal mine in Ohio. The bucket on this dragline excavator is larger than a two-storey house and can hold more than a dozen cars.

Figure 2

Power shovels are used to scoop up loose earth or rock. A power shovel is much larger than most machines, and its bucket can hold one car. However, it's small compared to the dragline in Figure 1!

Giant Power Shovels

Power shovels are used to pick up broken-up earth or rock and load it into trucks (**Figure 2**). They may be used to help remove the dirt excavated by a dragline, or they may be used at large construction sites where earth is being removed for a foundation, or in open-pit mines to load mineral-containing rock into trucks.

(d) The bucket of a power shovel is smaller than that on a dragline. Why?

(e) What types of levers can you see in the power shovel? Where are their fulcrums?

(f) What is the function of the pulley system?

(g) Since the load in the bucket requires so much engine power, why don't the engineers include many more pulleys? (Hint: Consider the force acting between each cable and the surface of each pulley).

Understanding Concepts

① Each of these large machines can be thought of as a system. For each machine, identify as many subsystems as you can. Give a function for each subsystem.

Making Connections

② Giant machinery is increasingly being computerized so that the equipment operates smoothly within its designed limits. Explain how this can cut costs.

Exploring

③ Many smaller excavators used to dig foundations for houses have hydraulic systems that perform the digging and lifting motions of the shovel. Why do you think the giant machines are designed with pulleys for these functions instead of hydraulics?

Reflecting

4. Because giant machines such as excavators can work so efficiently, it has become cheaper to mine ore deposits that were not previously considered worthwhile. What environmental concerns must be considered as such machines get bigger and more efficient?

Moving Efficiently

Friction—we couldn't get along without it and yet we try hard to reduce it. **Friction** is the force that resists the movement of objects sliding or rolling over one another. It is created whenever surfaces move across each other. The smoother the surfaces, the less the friction. However, even the smoothest surfaces, such as paper, shiny metal, or plastic, have microscopic bumps on them that cause friction (**Figure 1**). As an object moves across these surfaces, the tiny bumps on the object and sliding surface collide, and force is required to move the bumps past each other.

Figure 1

Paper looks and feels smooth, but through a microscope you can see that even the finest paper is rough enough to cause friction.

Friction Everywhere

Friction is the main cause of inefficiency in machines. As two parts in a mechanism rub together, they lose mechanical energy, which is transformed into thermal energy.

Friction occurs between any solid surfaces that are in contact, but it is also present when an object is moving through a fluid. The bright light of a meteor as it enters Earth's atmosphere is visible evidence of friction between a solid (the meteor) and a fluid (the gas of the atmosphere).

Boats are particularly inefficient because they sit partially submerged in water. Water is denser than air and causes more friction. Because they have to overcome frictional forces as they push through water, boats are slow and require much energy to move. Hovercraft overcome this problem by floating on a cushion of air over the water (**Figure 2**), with very little friction to slow them down.

Figure 2

The hovercraft moves over a low-friction cushion of compressed air by drawing in air from above the craft and forcing it underneath with large fans. This air is trapped beneath the boat by a flexible rubber skirt. Propellers on top move the boat forward, at speeds up to 120 km/h.

Reducing Friction

Friction reduces the efficiency of mechanisms and releases heat that can damage parts, so we often want to minimize its effects. One way is to reduce the surface areas that are in contact. Ball bearings—small steel spheres—achieve this. Both bicycles and skateboards use ball bearings between their wheels and axles (**Figure 3**).

Another way to reduce friction is to use a lubricant. Oil, grease, and graphite are all slippery substances that are used as lubricants. In a car engine, for instance, where pistons move up and down rapidly in their cylinders, the engine surfaces are bathed in a coating of oil. If there's not enough oil, the heat created by the friction of the metal parts rubbing directly against each other can quickly melt some surfaces, destroying the engine.

Positive Effects of Friction

Friction is also extremely useful. When we walk or run, the friction between our shoes and the ground gives us the "grip" to move. The grip on the sole of boots and shoes is important because it provides the security that allows us to travel safely over different types of surfaces. Sometimes friction can be a life saver: it allows a moving object to slow down or stop. Bicycles and cars rely on friction between the brakes and the wheels to slow them down.

Understanding Concepts

1. **(a)** What is friction?

   (b) What is the main reason for reducing friction?

2. How do ball bearings increase the efficiency of many machines?

Making Connections

3. Which parts of a bicycle are designed to increase friction? Decrease friction?

Exploring

4. From what you know about friction, if a car has good brakes, does that make it safe to drive fast on wet or icy roads? Why or why not?

5. Although hovercraft generate little
   (6C) friction when they move, they have a significant drawback: they are difficult to steer in windy conditions. Suggest, in a drawing, a mechanism that would help solve this problem.

axle — wheel — ball bearings — casing that holds the ball bearings

Design Challenge

Do you need to consider reducing friction or overcoming gravity when building your puppet, water well, or can crusher?

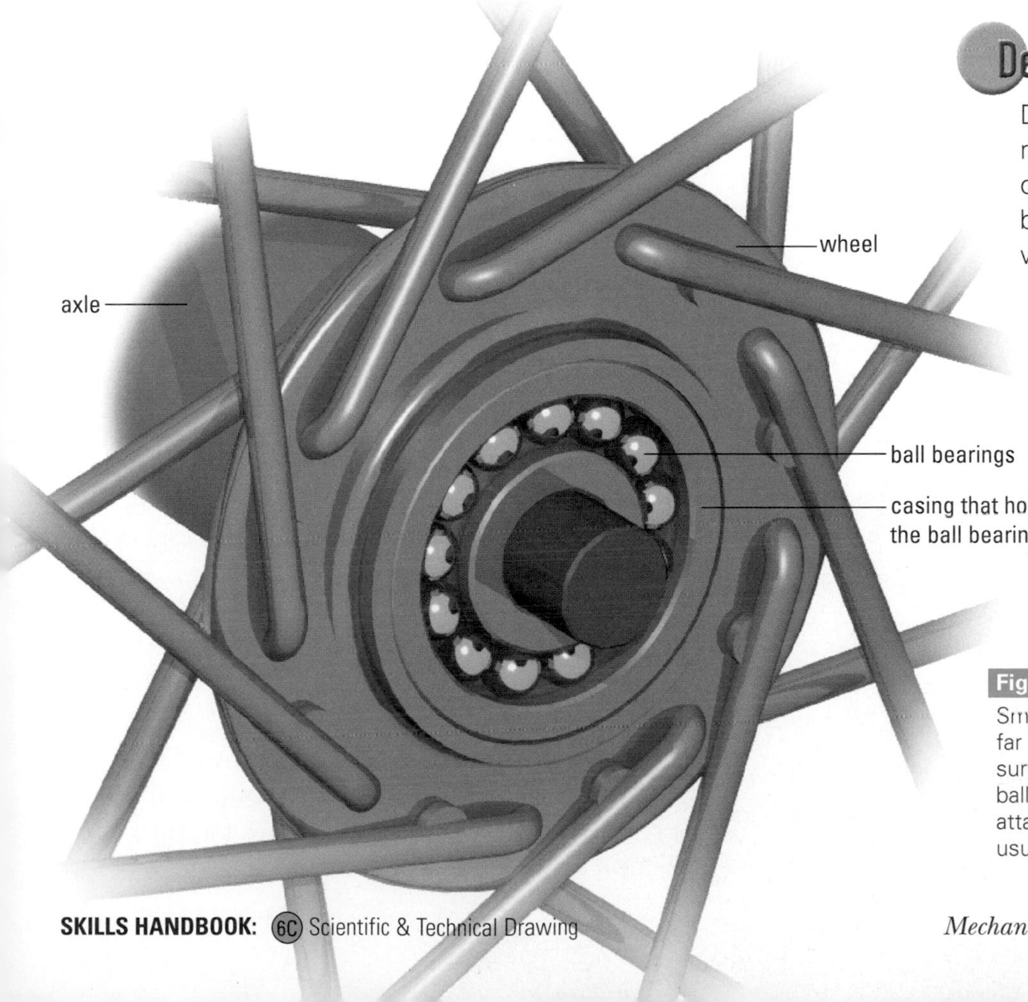

Figure 3

Smooth metal balls called ball bearings create far less friction than two parts with large surface areas rubbing directly together. The ball bearings are contained in a casing attached to the wheel or the axle. They are usually packed in a lubricant, such as grease.

Friction and Mechanical Advantage

When we looked at the mechanical advantage of different mechanisms, we assumed that friction was zero. But in reality, all moving parts in machines experience friction. You've already learned that force must be exerted to overcome the friction between two surfaces before they will slide over each other.

Friction and Levers

With levers, friction is often low because the surfaces rubbing against each other at the fulcrum are small (**Figure 1**).

In **Figure 1**, 5 N of force is needed to overcome the friction at the fulcrum. Therefore, the effort force the girl needs to lift the boy is:

$$\text{effort force} = 250 \text{ N} + 5 \text{ N}$$
$$= 255 \text{ N}$$

The mechanical advantage is

Without Friction

$$MA = \frac{\text{load force}}{\text{effort force}}$$

$$= \frac{500 \text{ N}}{250 \text{ N}}$$

$$= 2$$

With Friction

$$MA = \frac{\text{load force}}{\text{effort force}}$$

$$= \frac{500 \text{ N}}{255 \text{ N}}$$

$$= 1.96$$

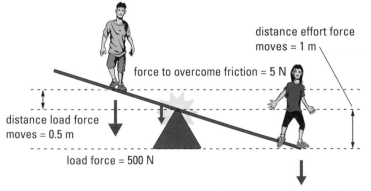

distance effort force moves = 1 m

force to overcome friction = 5 N

distance load force moves = 0.5 m

load force = 500 N

effort force = 250 N +5 N = 255 N

Figure 1

The seesaw's fulcrum consists of greased piping covered by a metal casing.

Friction and Pulleys

Rope that moves over even the smoothest pulleys still generates some friction. This means that extra effort force must be used to overcome the friction between the rope and each pulley. For example, three friends are driving on a small dirt road when a wheel gets caught in the ditch on the side and they can't get it out. The driver gets out her **block and tackle** (rope and pulley system) that she carries for such emergencies and rigs it up as shown in **Figure 2**.

To pull the jeep 3 m, they pull in 12 m of rope. The velocity ratio does not change because of friction:

$$\text{Velocity Ratio} = \frac{\text{distance effort force moves}}{\text{distance load force moves}}$$

$$= \frac{12 \text{ m}}{3 \text{ m}} = 4$$

However, the mechanical advantage is lower.

Without Friction

$$MA = \frac{\text{load force}}{\text{effort force}}$$

$$= \frac{3000 \text{ N}}{750 \text{ N}}$$

$$= 4$$

With Friction

$$MA = \frac{\text{load force}}{\text{effort force}}$$

$$= \frac{3000 \text{ N}}{900 \text{ N}}$$

$$= 3.3$$

The mechanical advantage is lower than it would have been because the group had to exert extra force to overcome the friction of the rope in the pulleys.

Figure 2

The group will pull in 4 times the length of rope needed to get the jeep back on the road. However, friction between the rope and pulleys makes the system less efficient.

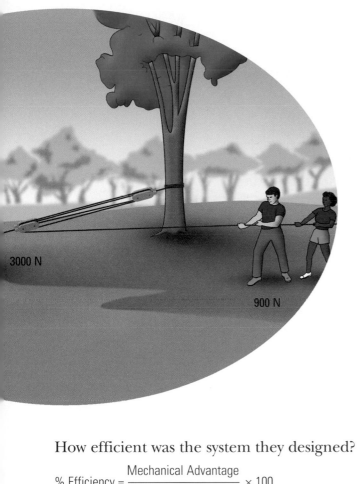

3000 N

900 N

How efficient was the system they designed?

$$\% \text{ Efficiency} = \frac{\text{Mechanical Advantage}}{\text{Velocity Ratio}} \times 100$$

$$= \frac{3.3}{4} = 82.5\%$$

Testing for Friction

Keeping friction to a minimum is an important way of having a machine work efficiently. However, when designing and building a machine or any simple device, it's impossible to predict exactly how much friction there will be between the moving surfaces without experimentation. The only way to find out is to actually measure the effort force needed to overcome the force of friction. If a new machine shows excessive friction, engineers and technicians may try to reduce the loss of efficiency by changing materials, polishing surfaces, or using a more effective lubricant.

Understanding Concepts

1. How does friction affect the e

2. In each of the examples in the mechanical advantage and then with friction.

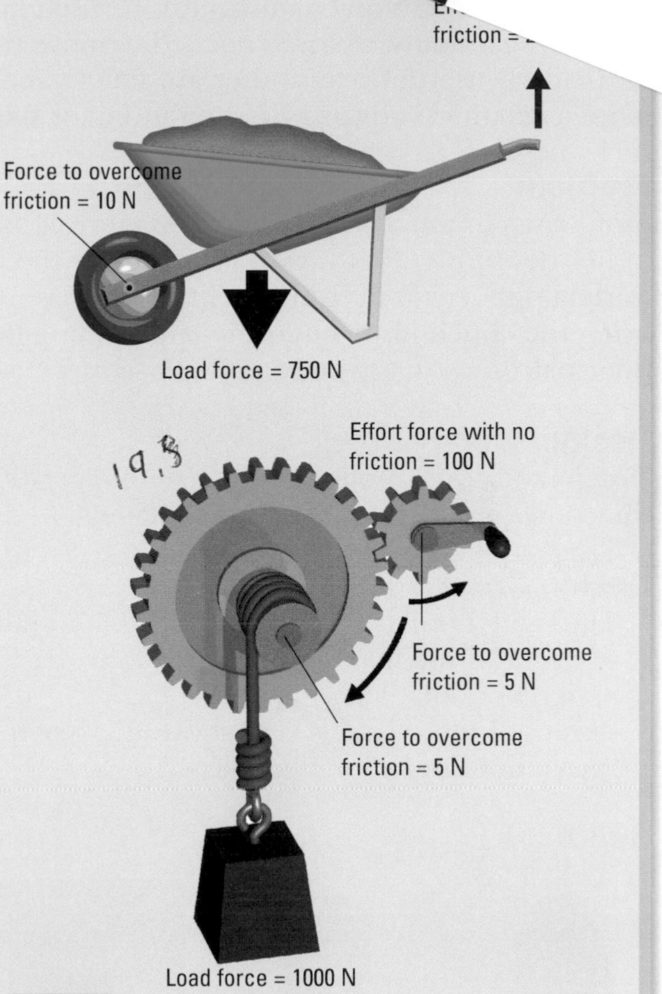

friction =

Force to overcome friction = 10 N

Load force = 750 N

Effort force with no friction = 100 N

19.8

Force to overcome friction = 5 N

Force to overcome friction = 5 N

Load force = 1000 N

Figure 3

3. Study **Figure 2**. How could the three friends improve the efficiency of their system? In the more efficient system, will the friends have to provide more or less effort force?

Design Challenge

The more moving parts a machine has, the more friction you can expect to find in the system. With the can crusher, you are trying to reduce the effort force needed to crush a can. What will you do to reduce the loss of efficiency due to friction?

Mechanical Advantage and Efficiency **167**

Moving the Couch

You have seen that mechanisms can be used in many situations to reduce the amount of force needed to move things. Pulleys are particularly useful because they are simple and they provide such a large mechanical advantage when lifting or moving heavy objects.

Problem

June wants to move a large couch (**Figure 1**) into a second-floor room in her new house, but it won't fit through the front door. She decides to rig a pulley system from the huge oak tree outside the house and bring the couch in through the large sliding doors onto the second-floor balcony. What type of pulley system will work?

Design Brief

Design and test a model pulley system that would allow June to raise the couch onto the second-floor balcony.

Design Criteria

- The model pulley system must be able to raise a 5-N weight a height of 0.5 m with a maximum effort force of 2 N, using only the materials available.
- Because June's rope is very short, the system must work using the least amount of rope necessary.

Materials

- 500 g mass to represent the couch
- 50 g masses, 4
- thin rope or twine
- 5 pulleys
- stand or horizontal rod to support pulley system

Build

1 Use the equation for mechanical advantage to predict the approximate number of pulleys needed to raise the couch.
- Include a rough estimate for overcoming friction.

2 Draw a diagram of the set-up.

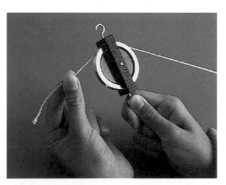

3 With your teacher's approval, build your pulley system.

Test

4 Place the weight on your system to represent the couch.
- Based on your calculations, place the weights on your pulley system that you think will raise the couch.

(a) Did the couch rise?

(b) If it did rise, is your pulley system using the least amount of rope necessary?

5 Redesign and test your pulley system until it meets both of the design criteria.

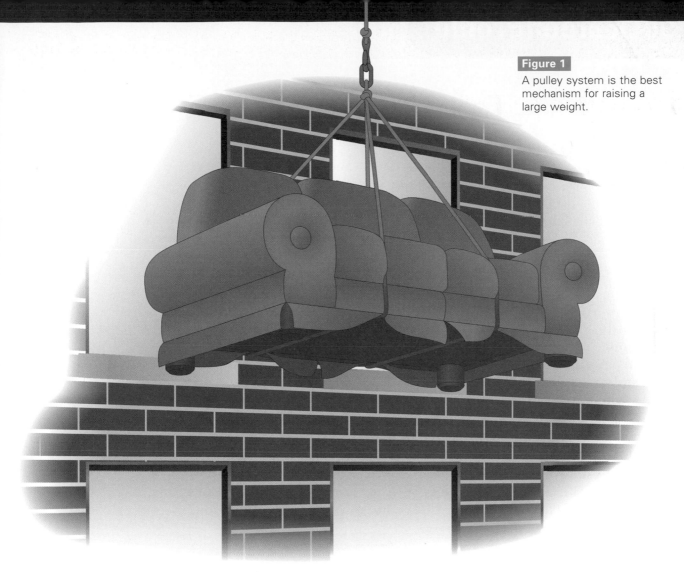

Evaluate

6 Evaluate your results by answering the following questions.

(a) How many pulleys did your model system need to raise the couch?

(b) Did you need to redesign your pulley system before it worked? Explain why.

(c) How much force was needed to overcome friction? How does this compare with your initial prediction?

Design Challenge

In your design of the windmill-operated well or can crusher, you should include friction in your calculations. Where will the friction act?

Making Connections

1. When using a pulley system to lift an object, do you think it is easier to pull downward or upward? Explain.

2. What advice would you give to someone who is going to buy an expensive winch to help raise logs into position while building a small cabin?

Exploring

3. An engineering company that builds heavy equipment for the construction industry is planning to expand its research and design department because of many breakdowns of their equipment. Is this a good investment? Explain.

Testing Force and Endurance

Kim Parker says she wears many hats. A mechanical engineer working at the Bloorview MacMillan Centre's human movement laboratory, Kim is convinced she must be part designer and part engineer. The Bloorview is dedicated to helping children with disabilities and their families adapt to their special needs. She and the others at the lab design and test prosthetic limbs and components to make certain that the equipment the young people use helps them move and play better. To do this, everyone involved must be familiar with more than engineering. "In a lab like this in other countries, you would find engineers, physiotherapists, and kinesiology students working together," Kim says. "But here we have engineers who fulfil all those roles." This suits Kim fine. She enjoys the challenge of satisfying many requirements.

Kim has always had several interests. As a girl growing up in London, Ontario, she loved math and her Barbie dolls. Her father is a math teacher, and she thinks that might be part of the reason she enjoys it so much. Kim attended Queen's University and then the University of Toronto, where she earned her master's degree. For her thesis, she researched modifications of ankle-foot orthoses, which, she says, are "kind of like shoe insoles, only with kids, they wrap all the way up." Not surprisingly, her thesis work brought her to the Bloorview, where she has continued her testing. She enjoys her work and finds it very rewarding.

Doing such varied work in the human movement lab (or gait lab as it is also known) requires many different skills (**Figure 1**). According to Kim, sharpening your analytical abilities and using logic are the stepping stones. Add knowledge of mechanics, basic structure, physics of motion, a little bit about electricity, and a whole lot of math! On top of that, she must be familiar with the human anatomy particular to her area of study—legs—and computers.

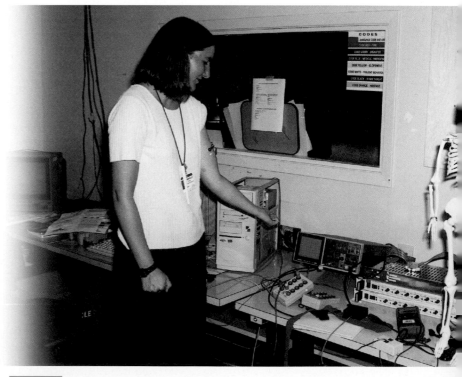

Figure 1

Engineers can use computers equipped with design model software to test a prototype structurally, and apply loads to different areas. In this way, they discover where the model might crack or break. Kim prefers a hands-on method. She starts with a solid structural analysis designed on paper, using her knowledge of the magnitude of force that will be applied. She then estimates where the critical high-stress areas in the design will be. Applying formulas, she can predict whether the design will work or fail if the stresses are beyond the material's capacity. Once this is complete, she builds a physical prototype. Using a jig and a pneumatic cylinder that is electronically controlled by a computer program, she tests the prosthesis or component mechanically. Always mindful of the key movements necessary for walking, she sets up levers to apply force onto the prototype (**Figure 2**). Finally, the prototype is tested on its intended user to measure its ability to help the person walk and to determine whether it is an improvement over the device already in use.

If a design doesn't improve a person's abilities or can't perform as well as the existing prosthesis, it goes back to the drawing board to iron out weaknesses and find new ways to solve its problems. Kim believes that these challenges make her job exciting because she is always experimenting with something different. New and better prostheses and components are being designed all the time. This aspect of engineering allows Kim and her co-workers the opportunity to see their designs make a real impact on peoples' everyday lives.

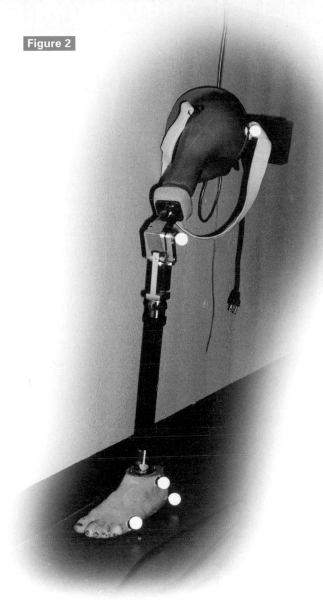

Figure 2

Try This — A Hand Model

A prosthetic hand is designed to perform many functions, including picking up small objects. An important consideration in the design of the hand is the length of the fingers.

Using popsicle sticks, thumbtacks, and elastic bands, set up the two "claws" as shown in **Figure 3**.

Compare the force required to squeeze the arms of the claws together.
Try to pick up a Ping-Pong ball with each claw by squeezing them.

1. How else could you change the force of each claw?

2. How could two claws with the same arm length have different amounts of force?

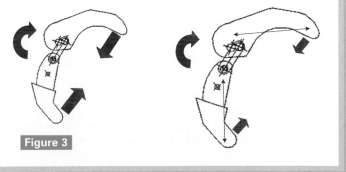

Figure 3

Testing Shoes

Good sports shoes are designed to prevent injuries and are an indispensable part of an athlete's equipment. Runners require special features in their shoes because each running step exerts a large force on the body. When the foot hits the ground, the force travels through the foot, ankle, and through the bones of the leg, including the knee joint. Each foot lands with a force of impact that is several times greater than the force exerted by someone who is walking (**Figure 1**). Shoes for runners need to be designed to absorb a lot of the force of impact.

Not everyone is a runner, but we all put stress on our feet through standing, walking, and climbing stairs. The features of any shoe we wear should provide a cushion from the force of impact and provide "grip" with the surface (**Figure 2**). How can you test and compare the effectiveness of the absorption of impact and grip in two different types of shoes?

Question

2B **1** What question is being answered through this investigation?

Hypothesis

2C **2** Predict what you think the results of the two tests will be. Write a hypothesis explaining your prediction.

Experimental Design

3 Once you have read the two tests you will be conducting, write a detailed procedure considering the following:
- What are your independent and dependent variables for Test 1 and Test 2?
- What variables will you attempt to control in the two tests?
- Begin with an easy test that both shoes will pass. Then, make the test progressively harder until one shoe fails the test.

4 Create a table for recording your data.

5 Submit your written procedure and your table to your teacher for approval.

Materials
- 1 running shoe
- 1 street shoe or boot
- small plastic bags
- eggs
- newspaper
- board, 15 cm × 30 cm
- metre stick

Figure 2

In wet or icy weather, the treads and the type of rubber in the sole can mean the difference between safe and slippery running.

SKILLS HANDBOOK: **2B** Asking a Question **2C** Predicting and Hypothesizing

Procedure

6 Carry out your investigation.

Test 1: Comparing Shock Absorption

- For testing ability to absorb impact, use the egg in your test to represent a person's foot.
- Make sure that no components are loose when you carry out your tests.

Test 2: Comparing Grip

- Grip refers to a shoe's ability to prevent slipping. In your experiment, use the board at different angles to create a slope that will test the shoes' grip.

Analysis

7 Analyze your results by answering the following questions.

(a) Which shoe had the best shock absorption? The best grip?

(b) Do your results support your hypothesis?

(c) Do you think that the egg is a good model for a foot? Why or why not?

(d) Was your surface for measuring grip a good model for a typical running surface? Is this an important factor?

Making Connections

1. Why are the shoes you tested designed differently? Think of the needs of the person who buys the shoe.

Exploring

2. If you could use whatever equipment you wanted to measure the shoes' grip and ability to absorb impact, how would you set up the experiment? What factors would have to be the same for each test to ensure fairness?

3. Use electronic and print resources to research the key features in a good-quality athletic shoe. Draw a diagram of a "perfect" shoe and label the features. For each feature, write a description of its purpose. Summarize how each feature contributes to the product.

Reflecting

4. **(a)** If you could design your own ideal pair of walking shoes or boots, what features would they have?

   (b) What would they be made of, and how would they look?

   (c) Do you think others would buy your shoes if they were available?

Force, Area, and Pressure

Force and Pressure

A thumbtack (**Figure 1**) is a solid object. A force applied to one part of a solid—the head of the thumbtack—is transmitted directly through it to any other solid object it is in contact with—such as a bulletin board. But there's something special about the thumbtack's design that makes it so handy. As shown in **Figure 2**, we see that the force applied to the large surface area (the head of the thumbtack) is transmitted through the tiny pointed end.

The magnitude of the force applied by your thumb hasn't changed, but its distribution has. Instead of the force being spread out over a large area, the force becomes concentrated on the tiny surface area of the sharp point.

The distribution of force over an area is called **pressure**. This can be written as:

$$\text{Pressure} = \frac{\text{Force}}{\text{Area}}$$

The thumbtack works because it has two surface areas: the first one big, and the second one small. When the force is applied to the thumbtack on the large surface the pressure is low. At the point, because the force is distributed over the tiny surface area, the pressure becomes very high. The material of the bulletin board collapses under this pressure.

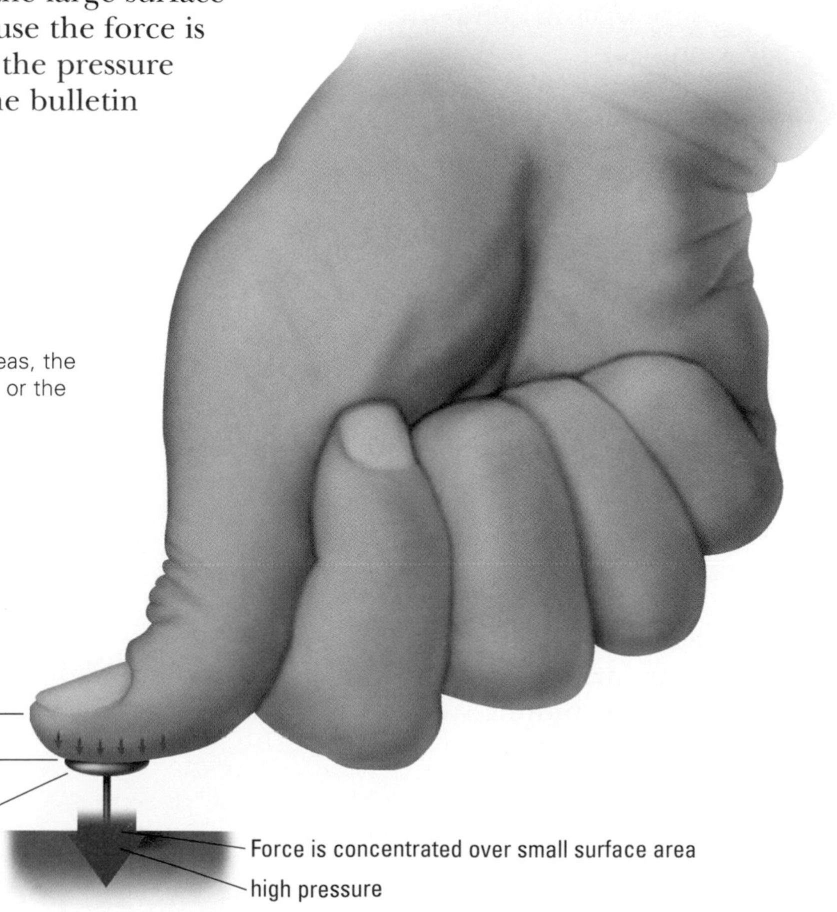

Figure 1

Thumbtacks are useful because they have surfaces that allow us to pierce things easily. How are they designed so that we don't have to use much force to make them work?

Figure 2

If there are 2 surface areas, the distribution of the force, or the pressure, changes.

The thumb exerts force onto the thumbtack

Force is distributed over large surface area

low pressure

Force is concentrated over small surface area

high pressure

Reducing Pressure

Snowshoes are also solids, but they work the opposite way from thumbtacks—they increase surface areas instead of reducing it.

If you walk in deep snow in your boots, the pressure from the boots will compress the snow and you will sink in. However, if you put on a pair of snowshoes, the pressure on the snow is lower and you can walk on the surface and sink only a little (**Figure 3**). The snowshoe reduces the pressure you exert on the snow because the snowshoe has a much larger surface area than the bottom of your boot. Because snowshoes distribute force in this way, they are a more efficient way to get across deep snow than regular boots.

Snowshoes lower the pressure on the snow and prevent the user from sinking in.

Calculating Pressure

As shown below, the equation for pressure is

$$Pressure = \frac{Force}{Area}$$

$$or\ P = \frac{F}{A}$$

Force is in units of newtons (N), and area is in units of square metres (m^2). Therefore, pressure is in units of N/m^2. One N/m^2 is also called 1 pascal (Pa). However, since 1 Pa is a very small amount of pressure, the kilopascal (kPa) is a more common unit: 1000 Pa = 1 kPa.

Suppose a student with a mass of 54 kg is walking on the snow (see **Figure 3**). When the student places all his or her weight on one foot, the pressure on the snow can be calculated as follows:

With Snowshoe

weight of student = 540 N

surface area of snowshoe = 0.20 m^2

$$P = \frac{F}{A}$$

$$= \frac{540\ N}{0.20\ m^2}$$

$$= 2700\ N/m^2 = 2.7\ kPa$$

With Boot

weight of student = 540 N

surface area of boot = 0.05 m^2

$$P = \frac{F}{A}$$

$$= \frac{540\ N}{0.05\ m^2}$$

$$= 10\ 800\ N/m^2 = 10.8\ kPa$$

Design Challenge

How can the concept of transmitting force through a solid and either increasing or decreasing pressure apply to the design of your can crusher?

Understanding Concepts

1. Using your own words, define pressure.

2. Describe the main feature of an object that

    (a) increases pressure;

    (b) decreases pressure.

3. A pile of scrap metal with a weight of 20 000 N is dumped on a platform with an area of 25 m^2. What is the pressure on the platform?

Making Connections

4. Which would hurt more: a large man in running shoes who steps on your toe, or a small woman in high heels? Why?

5. A student going on a winter camping trip with her school will need to carry a heavy backpack. She decides to wear skis for the long trek instead of winter boots. Is this a good idea? Why or why not?

6. A person walking across a frozen lake accidentally breaks through the ice and falls in the water. Using what you know about pressure, explain how a rescue crew can reach the accident site, but not break through themselves.

Pressure on Liquids and Gases

In the previous section you learned that a force can be transmitted through a solid to create pressure. The force, however, is transmitted in only one direction—the direction of the applied force. Liquids and gases behave differently. Unlike the particles in solids, liquid and gas particles are not tightly bound to each other. Without a container to hold the gas or liquid, we cannot apply a force to them because the particles simply flow away (**Figure 1**).

A water bed demonstrates how a liquid in a closed container transmits a force. A force exerted on a liquid is distributed evenly to the entire inside surface area of the container. This principle, called **Pascal's law**, was discovered by Blaise Pascal, a seventeenth-century physicist, after whom the unit of pressure is named. Since Pressure = Force/Area, the pressure created by an external force is distributed over the inside surface area. Both liquids and gases behave in the same way (**Figure 2**).

Forces and Fluids

Have you ever noticed how much air you can pump into a bicycle tire? When you pump more air into a tire, the particles in the air move closer together; the air becomes compressed. Air and other gases can be **compressed** because in a gas there are large empty spaces between the particles that can be filled up (**Figure 3**).

If you ever try to pump more water into a full bottle, you'll soon discover an important difference between gases and liquids. In a liquid, the particles are already very close together, so they cannot be forced closer. Liquids are virtually incompressible.

This difference has an important effect on how gases and liquids in closed containers react to forces (**Figure 4**). If you press down on a liquid in a closed container, the liquid will not "give," because liquids do not compress. The volume of the liquid remains the same. However, if you press down on a gas, the gas will give. It will compress into a smaller volume.

gas: large spaces between particles

liquid: very little space between particles

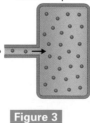

Figure 3

Gases can be compressed: you can add more particles to a gas, or force the gas into a smaller space. Liquids cannot be compressed.

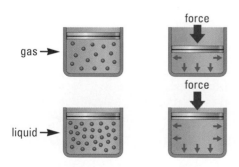

force

force

gas →

liquid →

Figure 4

When you apply a force to a gas, the gas will compress into a smaller volume. The pressure in a compressed gas is higher. Liquids cannot be compressed.

Figure 1

What happens when you press your foot down on an open surface of water?

Pressure and Temperature

Pressure in a container is caused by particles bouncing off the walls of the container. The more collisions there are with the walls, and the faster the particles are moving, the higher the pressure.

When you add thermal energy to a substance (increase its temperature), the particles of the substance move more rapidly. For a fluid in a container, the rapid movement causes an increase in pressure, because the faster-moving particles collide more energetically with the walls of the container. You've probably seen warnings not to heat cans that contain a gas. The reason is that the can might explode because of the rapid increase in internal pressure.

Using the same amount of thermal energy to raise the temperature of a liquid in a container will not result in as big an increase in pressure. That's because there are many more particles in the same volume of liquid: it takes a lot more thermal energy to make all of the particles move more quickly. Also, the particles in a liquid are less free—they are held to each other by attractive forces.

Pressure also increases when you compress a gas (put it in a smaller volume), as you can see in **Figure 5**. In the smaller space, the particles are more crowded together, and bounce off the walls more often. There is another effect of compressing a gas: its temperature increases. If you pump a lot of air into a tire, you'll notice that the valve and the tire get hotter. Some of the energy used to compress the gas is converted into thermal energy. Because liquids will not fit in a smaller space, you cannot increase the temperature of a liquid by exerting a force on its container.

Understanding Concepts

1. Why is a force transmitted differently in a solid than in a fluid?

2. What happens to the temperature when you apply a force to a liquid? a gas?

3. Look at **Figure 4**. Imagine that the pressure is the same in both containers before the force is applied. As the force is applied, the pressure in the gas container will become higher than the pressure in the liquid container. Explain why.

4. Explain, using your own words, what happens to a container full of gas as you heat it.

Making Connections

5. If you blow too much air into a balloon, it will quickly burst. Since gases are compressible, why does this occur?

6. To make a liquid change states to a gas, you add thermal energy. Explain what would happen in a container of liquid as the liquid is heated to its boiling point.

Exploring

7. There are several different designs of hand pumps for bicycle tires.

   (a) What is the purpose of each?

   (b) What are their advantages and disadvantages?

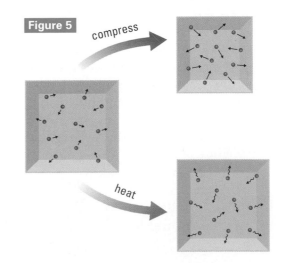

Figure 5

compress

heat

Mechanical Advantage and Efficiency **177**

Squeezing Liquids and Gases

You have already learned that applying a force to a liquid has predictable results. Gases can also be put under pressure, but they are different, because they are compressible. In this investigation you will compare how a liquid and a gas respond to the same amount of force.

Question
Do gases behave the same way as liquids when they are under pressure?

Hypothesis
2C **1** Create a hypothesis for this investigation.

Experimental Design
Using syringes, you will observe the effects of a force on a liquid (water) system, and then again on a gas (air) system.

2 Create a table like **Table 1** to record your data. Use "less than" "greater than" or "equal to" when recording your observations of the force required to raise the 200-g mass.

Materials
- apron
- goggles
- 20-mL plastic syringes, 2
- 50 cm clear plastic 6-mm tubing
- 4 clamps
- 2 support stands
- cardboard squares
- 200-g mass
- 5-mL plastic syringe
- 10-mL plastic syringe

Procedure   Part 1: Force in a Liquid System

3 Connect 2 20-mL syringes with plastic tubing.
- Remove the plunger from each syringe and fill the syringes with water.
- Put one plunger back in. Slowly push the plunger all the way down. Let the water run out of the other syringe.
- Put the plunger back in the second syringe and push it halfway down. The system should have no air in it.

4 Clamp each syringe to a support stand.
- Use cardboard to make two small platforms, large enough to support the 200-g mass. Tape a platform to the end of each plunger.
- Adjust the syringes so one syringe is fully down, and the other is up.

5 Place a 200-g mass on the platform of the plunger that is pushed down.
- Push the other plunger down. Feel how much force is required.
- Move the 200-g mass to the other platform. Push on the empty platform and feel how much force is required to raise the mass.

✎ (a) Record this system as the "standard force" in your table.

Making Connections

1. When a liquid system is being used, similar to that in step 5, why is it important that it doesn't develop a leak?

2. Both liquid and gas systems are used in many types of machinery. When a gas system is used, as in **Figure 1**, what do you think is done with the gas first to make the system work efficiently?

Exploring

3. Design an experiment that investigates how applying the same force to liquid

(2E) containers with different surface areas affects the pressure in the container. With your teacher's approval, carry it out.

Figure 1
Truckers rely on closed air systems to operate their brakes.

Table 1

Fluid	Size of pushed syringe	Size of syringe supporting 200-g mass	Force required
water	20 mL	20 mL	standard
water	20 mL	20 mL	equal to standard
water	10 mL	20 mL	?
water	20 mL	10 mL	?

Part 2: Force in an Air System

6 Disconnect the system and repeat steps 3, 4, and 5 using several different combinations of syringes.

✎ (a) In your table, record the amount of force you use for each combination of syringes.

7 Investigate the same combinations of syringes using only air.
- When connecting syringes filled with air, make sure the *smaller* plunger is extended outward and the *larger* plunger is pushed down as far as it will go *before* you connect the tubing.
- Clamp the syringes as in steps 4 and 5.

✎ (a) Record the amount of force for each combination of syringes.

Analysis

8 Analyze your results by answering the following.

(a) What arrangement of syringes allowed you to raise the 200-g mass using the least force?

(b) Suppose you needed to raise a 200-g mass using even less force. How could you modify your system?

(c) Compare the plungers for the 5-mL, 10-mL, and 20-mL syringes. Using the relationship $P = F/A$, explain qualitatively your results for both water and air systems.

(d) Did this investigation support your hypothesis?

(e) Write a summary comparing a liquid system with an air system.

 Designing an Inquiry Investigation

Mechanical Advantage and Efficiency **179**

Pressure in Fluid Systems

When landing a big jet, the pilot lowers the plane's main wing flaps (**Figure 1**). The flaps must fight against the force caused by the air rushing by at 300 km/h or more, yet they lower smoothly and reliably. The system that operates the flaps uses liquids under pressure. An enclosed liquid that is used to transmit force is called a **hydraulic system**. Most hydraulic systems use an oil rather than water. Water is corrosive and is a poor lubricant.

You know how much force it takes to stop a bicycle in an emergency. Now imagine how much it takes to stop a fully loaded tractor-trailer travelling at 100 km/h. And yet that truck can be brought to a halt with a fairly light touch on a brake pedal. How does such a small force have such a great effect? Trucks use an enclosed gas system, a **pneumatic system**.

The advantage of hydraulic and pneumatic systems is that a small force can be used to lift or push very heavy things, over long or short distances, and with very little friction.

The Hydraulic Press

You learned that a force exerted on a liquid in a closed container is transmitted equally in all directions to the inside surfaces of the container.

The hydraulic press shown in **Figure 2** illustrates an application of Pascal's law. It contains two **pistons**, metal cylinders that slide up and down inside a tube. As you can see, a small force can be magnified many times in a hydraulic system. The amount of force magnification is equal to how many times the area of the larger piston is greater than the area of the smaller piston.

Calculating the Mechanical Advantage of a Hydraulic System

We can calculate the mechanical advantage of the system in **Figure 2**. The effort force of 100 N is applied to the small piston. The resulting load force on the large piston is 2500 N.

$$\text{Mechanical Advantage} = \frac{\text{load force}}{\text{effort force}} = \frac{2500 \text{ N}}{100 \text{ N}} = 25$$

This system can lift objects that are 25 times heavier than the input or effort force.

Figure 1
Many of the mechanical systems in an airplane use hydraulics to transmit forces, including the systems that raise and lower the landing gear and raise and lower the flaps on the wings.

Small Piston
Area (A) = 1 m²
F = 100 N
$P = \frac{F}{A}$
$= \frac{100 \text{ N}}{1 \text{ m}^2}$
$= \frac{100 \text{ N}}{\text{m}^2}$
$= 100$ Pa

Large Piston
area (A) = 25 m²
P = 100 Pa
= 100 N/m²
$P = \frac{F}{A}$

This formula can be rearranged:
F = A x P
$F = 25 \text{m}^2 \times \frac{100 \text{ N}}{\text{m}^2}$
F = 2500 N

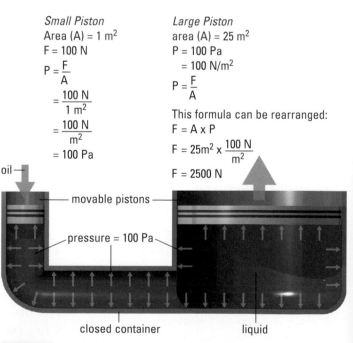

Figure 2
A force of 100 N is applied to the small piston in a hydraulic press. Note that the pressure is the same throughout the system (100 Pa), including at both pistons. However, the larger piston has a much larger area, so the force acting on the larger piston is much greater.

Cars and Hydraulics

By using different ratios of piston surface areas, hydraulic systems can create whatever multiplication of force is needed. A hydraulic car lift operates like the system in **Figure 2**, but with a much greater ratio of large to small pistons. A car's brake system also uses hydraulics (**Figure 3**).

Pneumatic Systems

Because pneumatic systems require pressurized gas to transmit force, they are connected to an electronically operated compressor, which greatly compresses the gas. The pressure of the compressed gas on the container's inside walls is very high, and a pneumatic system can generate a very large force. Large trucks, for example, use pneumatic brakes to apply a larger braking force than a hydraulic system could. Pneumatic systems have other advantages. Air is always available and in an inexhaustible supply, is less of a fire hazard, and is more environmentally friendly than hydraulic fluids. However, pneumatic systems require lots of room for the compressor, pressure boosters, and other components, and their complexity makes them more expensive. So, when there is minimum space and extra-large forces aren't needed, hydraulic systems are preferred.

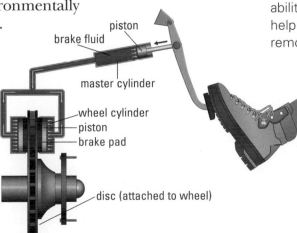

brake fluid
piston
master cylinder
wheel cylinder
piston
brake pad
disc (attached to wheel)

Understanding Concepts

1. **(a)** What is a hydraulic system?
   (b) Why is it useful?
2. What is a pneumatic system?
3. What is the major advantage of pneumatic systems over hydraulic systems? A major disadvantage?

Making Connections

4. A force of 750 N is applied to a small piston of a hydraulic system. If the large piston has 10 times the surface area of the small piston, how much weight can the large piston raise?
5. A mechanic wants to raise the weight of 10 000 N on a hydraulic system that has a ratio of piston areas of 20:1. What minimum force will she need to do it?
6. Since liquids are virtually incompressible, how far down does a small piston have to be pushed to raise the large piston 1 m, when the ratio of their surface areas is 1:5?

Exploring

7. Much of modern machinery relies on hydraulics. Research the use of hydraulics in construction, farming, or mining equipment. Be prepared to share your findings with the class, using diagrams.

Design Challenge

How can the pushing or lifting ability of hydraulic systems help in planning your hydraulic, remote-controlled puppet?

Figure 3

The foot exerts a small force which pushes a piston, transferring the force through the brake fluid in the master cylinder. This force places the brake fluid under pressure. The pressure is transferred to brake cylinders attached to each wheel. In the cylinders, pistons then push the brake pads against the brake disc with a much larger force.

Mechanical Advantage and Efficiency **181**

A Hydraulic Solution for a Pain in the Neck

Almost all of us, young and old alike, are spending more and more time sitting in front of computers. But how we sit and look at the monitor is important (**Figure 1**), since poor posture often results in neck or back pain, or headaches. For the best posture, the monitor should be at the same height as your face. It should also be straight in front of you so that you're not twisting any part of your body.

Problem

In an elementary school, where many children of different heights use the computers, how can the heavy computer monitors be easily lifted to the proper height by a child who sits down to use it?

Design Brief

Design and build a model hydraulic system that can reliably lift a model monitor, using only the materials available.

Materials

- 50-mL syringes, 2
- 25-mL syringe
- 10-mL syringe
- 2 support stands
- 2 burette clamps
- narrow rubber tubing
- 1-kg mass

Figure 1

Design Criteria

- The hydraulic model must smoothly lift a weight of 10 N.
- The force used to lift the weight must be as small as possible.
- A technical drawing must show how the monitor is attached to the hydraulic system.
- A set of instructions must accompany the model, explaining why the device is there, when to use it, how to use it, and any safety precautions.

Build

1 Draw a complete diagram of the hydraulic system and computer system.

2 Build the system.

(a) How can you ensure that the monitor will rise smoothly?

Test

3 Put the 1-kg mass on your device and test it.

(a) Did the weight move up easily?

(b) How do you know that your design is using the smallest possible force, given the materials available?

4 If your system does not meet the criteria, analyze the system, redesign it, and test it again.

5 After writing your own instructions, including safety precautions, have a classmate use your system.

(a) Were any of your instructions unclear? Did you leave out anything? Modify your instructions as needed.

Evaluate

6 Evaluate your results by answering the following questions.

(a) Explain, using what you know about hydraulics and forces, why you chose the syringes that you did.

(b) Give two advantages of using a hydraulic system over another system in this situation.

(c) What part would you change to make this hydraulic system remote-controlled? Explain.

(d) Why is a clearly worded set of instructions important?

Making Connections

1. Referring back to your technical drawing, indicate where you could install a lever as a link with the hydraulic system to make it even easier to use. Explain your reasoning.

Exploring

2. Most products come with instruction manuals so that people can learn how to use them properly and safely. Instructions should be clear, thorough, and easy to follow.

   (a) Find a manual for a product in your home.

   (b) Are the instructions understandable and user-friendly? Give examples.

   (c) Suggest some improvements for the instructions.

Design Challenge

How could this hydraulic system be used or modified for the design of the remote-control puppet?

What have you learned about instructions that will help you in putting together your own set of instructions for your Challenges?

A Student-Friendly Classroom

Your classroom and your living room at home look very different, from the floors to the furniture (**Figure 1**). Why are they so different? What factors do designers need to consider?

The most important reason for designing something is to solve a problem and satisfy a need. A successfully designed machine or product must function properly. But we have feelings and emotions. We do some things easily, others only with difficulty. We are influenced by the media and our surroundings. All of these factors must be considered in design.

Esthetics and Ergonomics

Esthetics relates to the qualities that make a design attractive. We appreciate these qualities through our five senses. Aesthetic factors such as texture, colour, and pattern are considered when designing products.

Ergonomics is the study of how to design objects so that people can use them safely, efficiently, and easily. For example, an ergonomically designed desk chair may provide back support for long periods of sitting. Designing products ergonomically means considering people's needs carefully, and analyzing how they will most likely use a product. Other ergonomic factors may include materials, durability, and health benefits.

Good designers consider many factors to try to meet the needs and expectations of consumers. Cost, of course, must also be considered. In this case study, you will design an ideal classroom based on ergonomics and esthetics.

Classroom Chairs

The most important design requirement for chairs is stability (see **Figure 2**). A chair must be symmetrical to balance properly. Classroom chairs have to be comfortable for students of many sizes, but they must also fit under desks. They must be strong to withstand years of use, but light enough for students to move easily. Finally, the cost of manufacturing the chairs should not be high.

(a) Examine your chair. Is it well-designed? Why or why not?

(b) How could your chair be improved? Consider specific factors, such as its shape, its materials, how it moves, its appearance, or any other features.

Figure 1
Are classrooms a comfortable place for students?

Figure 2
How well could you work sitting in such a chair?

Classroom Desks

Like classroom chairs, desks must be symmetrical for stability and balance. Desks should include space for storing schoolwork, and also comfortably accommodate students of different heights (**Figure 3**). Finally, the cost of making the desk must be reasonable.

(c) Look at your desk. Do you think it's well-designed? Why or why not?

(d) What improvements can you suggest for your desk? Consider factors such as work area, materials, height of the desk, storage space, or any other features. Ensure that each idea has ergonomic and esthetic benefits.

Figure 3

Desk size is limited by classroom size, but designers must ensure students have enough room to work.

The Ergonomic Classroom

A classroom should be spacious enough that students don't feel crowded and can enter and leave safely, especially in emergencies. The room must be well lit, with an efficient light source. Natural lighting from large windows is also beneficial and pleasant, and windows should be openable in warm weather. In addition to a blackboard at the front, bulletin boards or shelves on other walls can be useful.

(e) Examine your classroom. Do you think it is well-designed? Why or why not?

(f) What improvements would you make? Consider size, shape, colour, arrangement of furniture and work areas, and additional resources. Remember that cost is also a factor.

(g) Draw a floor plan for your redesigned classroom.

Design Challenge

What ergonomic factors should you consider in the design and operation of your remote-control puppet or can crusher?

Understanding Concepts

1. What does ergonomics refer to?

2. Why is ergonomic design important in the classroom?

Making Connections

3. What are the important ergonomic features of a baby crib?

4. Ergonomics are important when designing safety devices. When airbags were first introduced in vehicles, they were designed for an average-sized man. However, they proved to be dangerous for shorter women and children. Describe a testing process that would avoid such problems.

Exploring

5. Tools and simple, everyday items, from lawnmowers to light switches, are also designed ergonomically, both for safety and ease of use. At home, analyze an item for its ergonomic features.

   (a) Do you think these features are effective?

   (b) If not, how do you think they could be improved?

Designing for People with Special Needs

Products that are designed ergonomically for some people may not be well suited for others with different needs. Left-handed people find that scissors designed for the right hand don't work very well. Many people with special needs have difficulty using mechanisms not designed with their needs in mind. Modern technology combined with ergonomic design has created or modified many devices to help such people in their everyday lives (**Figure 1**).

Modified Car Controls

Recall how hydraulics work in a car's braking system: a little force exerted by the foot on the brake pedal causes a large force to be exerted on the brake. This system can be modified for people who are paraplegic (paralyzed in the lower part of the body) or who cannot use their legs very well. In modified cars, a lever system is attached to the accelerator and brake pedals so that they can be conveniently and easily operated by hand. In this system, a combination of levers and hydraulics works well.

Designing Cars for Older People

What are the ergonomic needs of older people with stiff joints or worsening eyesight for seeing up-close? To understand how these problems can cause difficulties, ergonomic car designers wear special suits that restrict their movement at all of their joints (**Figure 2**). Back and neck braces further restrict their movement, and special goggles impair their vision. Applying what they have learned wearing this restrictive gear, the engineers have developed new car designs that include larger car doors, higher roofs, raised seats, and simpler, larger controls. These new designs are one way to help accommodate the changing needs of aging consumers and to continue to have a successful product.

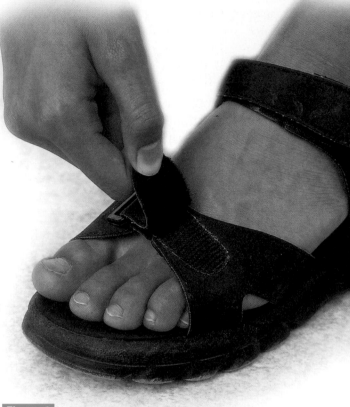

Figure 1
Not all designs involve complicated technology. Simple ideas, such as using Velcro instead of shoelaces, can be very useful for people with arthritis in their finger joints.

Figure 2
By wearing restrictive clothing, a design engineer can feel what it's like for a person with stiff joints to get in and out of a car and operate its controls.

A Modified Sailboat

Sailboats have also been modified so that people who are paralyzed in their arms and legs (quadriplegics) can enjoy the excitement of sailing. A pneumatic system operated by a sailor's breath, called "sip and puff," allows the sailor to adjust both the sails and the steering of a sailboat (**Figure 3**). When the sailor blows into a straw and tube system, the force of his or her breath activates winches that unwind rope to let the sails out. Sucking causes a drop in pneumatic pressure, which reverses the winches and pulls the sails in. The quadriplegic sailor can also steer. By first biting the straw and then either blowing or sucking, the steering system is activated and he or she can turn the boat left or right.

Levers Are Easier

Levers provide another simple way of modifying items so that people can use them more easily. Doorknobs and taps on sinks are often modified with levers (**Figure 4**), since people with arthritic hands usually find knobs and taps difficult to turn.

Figure 3
This sailboat is designed so that it can be sailed using a pneumatic system that is activated by the breath of the sailor.

Figure 4
Levers need only a simple, easy motion to operate.

Design Challenge

How could you improve your Challenge design to better accommodate people with special needs?

Understanding Concepts

1. What is the main idea behind redesigning ordinary objects for people with special needs?

2. Why are levers often included in the design of objects for people who can't use their hands easily?

Making Connections

3. How might your ideal classroom from the previous section be improved to better serve people with special needs?

4. Many people use inventions designed to help with very common physical impairments, such as aids for hearing and sight. How are these products designed to make them more acceptable to people who use them?

Exploring

5. Many buildings are not well adapted or designed to provide easy access for physically challenged people.

   (a) Research ways buildings can be improved to suit their needs.

   (b) Design ways to make your school more user-friendly. Include technical drawings of any mechanical systems that are used. (8B)

Mountain Bike or Road Bike?

Cycling is becoming more and more popular. From leisurely riding on city bike paths to steep, boulder-filled descents down mountainsides, there is something for everyone. Such different riding conditions require different bike designs. Good ergonomic design involves careful consideration of how a product will be used. A bike that has been ergonomically designed for riding on flat pavement has very different features from those of a bike that is meant to be ridden offroad. Comparing the features of a typical mountain bike and road bike (**Figure 1**) can be helpful for the consumer trying to make an informed purchase.

Rugged vs. Light

One important difference between a mountain bike and a road bike is the design of their frames. Because a mountain bike is designed for rough riding on uneven dirt paths that may have obstacles such as rocks or logs, it is essential that the frame is durable and rugged. Durability means having a thick, heavy frame. Mountain bikes usually weigh several kilograms more than road bikes do. Because a road bike is designed for pavement, it is lighter and can go much faster. However, hitting even a small rock on a road bike can result in a dented wheel.

(a) Some bike frames are made of very lightweight, super-strong, expensive materials. Why aren't all bikes built this way?

Stable vs. Fast

Much-needed stability on a mountain bike means having lots of friction between the tires and the ground. When riding over round, wet boulders in a stream, or through mud, wide tires with a thick tread give lots of grip. In contrast, a road bike has thinner tires with less tread, reducing friction. Less friction means greater efficiency—less effort and more speed.

The handlebars, too, are designed differently. The straight, wider handlebars on a mountain bike give the rider more leverage to make quick turns around obstacles using little force. The narrower, down-curved handlebars of a road bike allow the rider to lean down and reduce wind resistance, which means less effort is needed to pedal.

(b) How are the tires and handlebars on a mountain bike better designed for going up and down steep hills?

Not All Hills Are Alike

Another difference is in the range of gear ratios available. Lower gear ratios help riders to keep moving when the terrain becomes difficult, as they can turn the pedals with less force and still make headway. The very lowest gears on a mountain bike allow the rider to pedal up steep or difficult terrain that would be impossible to climb on a road bike. Although road bikes often have as many as 18 gears, compared to 21 on mountain bikes, their range isn't as great, which restricts these bikes to steep but smooth, paved hills. Both bikes have comparable higher gears.

(c) If 21 gears are better than 18, why don't bike designers put that many gears on all bikes?

Speed Shift

How fast can you shift gears? On a mountain bike, very quickly. Just rotate the handlebars—front gears on the left, back gears on the right. If a cyclist comes around a bend and suddenly encounters a steep uphill climb, the gears on a mountain bike are placed ergonomically for quick shifting. On a road bike, changing gears takes a bit longer. It requires not only changing hand position to the levers located lower on the frame, but also riding momentarily with only one hand. This is fine on smooth, roads where you can see where you're going, but it's slow and awkward on trails.

(d) Some road bikes have gear shifts on straight handlebars, thicker tires, or other design features more like those of mountain bikes. Why would some consumers want such a mixture?

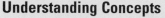

Understanding Concepts

1. Describe three features of road bikes that increase efficiency on paved roads.

2. Describe two features of mountain bikes that increase efficiency while going up steep dirt trails.

Making Connections

3. (a) Which bike has the best features for city cycling?

   (b) Can you think of a combination of features that would be safer and more efficient?

Exploring

4. Mountain bikes have more (8A) powerful brakes than road bikes because the former are heavier and riders often need to stop suddenly while going down steep slopes. Research how these special brakes work and create a report.

5. There are at least three different types of simple machines on a bicycle, in a variety of locations, and with different functions. How many can you find?

Reflecting

6. Bicycle helmets are required in some provinces in Canada but not in others. Some people think that this requirement will discourage people from riding. Should helmets be required? Why or why not?

Figure 1

Mountain bikes are designed with special features for riding on rough terrain. Road bikes have features specifically designed for efficient riding on pavement.

The Life of a Product

We live in a highly technological society. Our way of life, our standard of living, and the wealth of our country depend on the efficient manufacture and use of many different products. Although we usually think of efficiency in terms of how much effort is required to move something, efficiency also relates to efficient use of resources. North Americans are much less efficient users of resources than people in many other parts of the world. We are among the largest users of the Earth's resources and also create more garbage than almost everyone else. It's a vicious cycle. Because we throw away so much, we also use up more resources.

When creating a product, designers must consider not only a need or purpose to be satisfied but also the effect on people and the environment of the manufacturing process and the disposal of the product. How much pollution occurs while products are being made? How are products disposed of? Could alternative, longer-lasting products help us produce less pollution and garbage? Could some products be done away with entirely?

How can we become more efficient?

Metal: Stoves to Trucks

Iron is used more than any other metal in the world. This isn't surprising, when you consider that steel is made mostly of iron, with some carbon added. Steel is used in many places—reinforcing concrete in high-rises and bridges, and in vehicles, appliances, and computer parts. Scrap steel has become an important source of metal.

Recycling metal (**Figure 1**) slows the depletion of iron deposits and uses less energy than manufacturing new steel from raw materials. It also reduces the air and water pollution that results from the steel production process.

Figure 1

Once the metal scrap is sorted and graded, hydraulic shears and shredders are used to break it up. The metal is then squeezed into bales for steel makers, who rework it into coils or sheets for manufacturers.

Paper: Paper Towels to Drink Boxes

The use of chlorine in the manufacturing of paper products produces a serious amount of pollution. Chlorine bleaches the wood pulp so that items such as toilet paper and paper towels will be white (**Figure 2**). The use of chlorine creates highly toxic chemicals called organochlorines (carbon-containing molecules plus chlorine), which end up in the air and water systems. These poisons affect fish and wildlife at very low concentrations. Their effect on humans is not yet fully known.

Non-recyclable paper products such as diapers are also a problem, since they end up in landfill sites. To reduce this problem, reusable cloth or plastic products can replace disposable diapers, paper towels, or drink boxes.

Throwaway Plastics: Food Containers to Cameras

Plastic has drastically changed how we live in the past 60 years. It is used everywhere, from grocery bags to throwaway cameras. Plastic is handy because it is strong and durable. However, these same features cause problems when items are no longer needed.

Recycling plastic is only part of the answer. Recycling is expensive, and there are many types of plastic that must be separated before they are melted for reuse. Plastic is made from non-renewable oil resources, but some plastic products are used for only a few minutes (**Figure 3**).

Figure 2
Should consumers demand non-bleached alternatives for products such as paper towels and coffee filters?

Figure 3
Plastic packaging made from oil, a non-renewable resource, is a huge source of garbage. Buying loose fruit and vegetables can reduce inefficient use of materials.

Design Challenge

Consider the different types of materials you are using in your Design Challenge. Can they be recycled when they are no longer needed?

Understanding Concepts

1. How does the amount of garbage indicate inefficiency in the use of resources?

2. Name two benefits of recycling products made of steel.

3. What pollutant results from using chlorine to bleach paper products?

Making Connections

4. Make a list of plastic products at home that are used for a few hours at most.

   (a) Are all of these products necessary?

   (b) Suggest some longer-lasting or less wasteful alternatives.

Exploring

5. People continually buy faster and more sophisticated computers as they become available. But what happens to the old ones? Using the Internet and other sources, research recycling programs for old but usable computers.

Reflecting

6. Many products are wrapped in plastic. Suggest some reasons why. Are there alternatives?

7. Some manufacturers choose cheaper materials over the more expensive environmentally friendly ones. Do you think this reflects consumer preferences?

A World Without Cars?

Many people use cars to go to work, do their shopping, and travel on vacation. You may have gotten a ride to school. But use of these machines can conflict with other needs. (See **Figure 1**.) Are there more efficient products? What design factors should be considered when planning transportation systems?

Convenience vs. Danger

Cars are convenient, and allow people to travel comfortably in all kinds of weather. In rural areas with no public transportation, they may be the only way to get around quickly.

One drawback is that driving a car can be hazardous to your health. In Canada, approximately 5000 people are killed and approximately 200 000 are injured each year in car accidents.

In cities, pollution from car exhaust can affect people with respiratory diseases such as asthma. Also, the exhaust contributes to the pollution of the atmosphere, adding to global warming and acid precipitation.

Jobs vs. Materials

Making cars and trucks is one of the major industries in Canada. Factories employ thousands of people, from engineers to business people to assembly-line workers, while others are employed in selling and servicing cars and refining and selling gasoline.

However, the manufacturing of cars uses vast amounts of materials, including steel, aluminum, rubber, plastic, and glass. Many of these end up in car dumps. Used tires get piled into hills that occasionally catch fire, releasing poisonous fumes into the air.

Gasoline is a nonrenewable resource that comes from the world's oil deposits. Once we run out, we can't get any more.

Alternatives

Do we really need cars and trucks in cities? Can more efficient public transportation ease the congestion on city streets and reduce the need for cars?

Would more people walk or cycle on downtown streets if they were closed to vehicle traffic?

Figure 1
Cars can cause many problems, from traffic tie-ups to pollution.

Role Play — Downtown: A Car-Free Zone? (8D)

The municipal council of a large city is considering banning cars and trucks, except for emergency vehicles, from the one-square-kilometre downtown area. Traffic is congested during rush hour, and in summer, pollution can reach dangerous levels. However, many commuters feel that they need their cars to get to work, and some downtown store owners worry about losing business if people can't get to their stores by car.

The people listed below are part of a committee making recommendations to the city council regarding the proposed ban. Choose a role, write a report for the council, and be prepared to defend it in a municipal meeting.

The Roles

- A downtown resident whose respiratory disease is worsened by air pollution
- A suburban commuter without easy access to public transportation
- A downtown store owner who worries that the ban will discourage business
- A representative of a citizens' association that supports greater access to streets by pedestrians and cyclists
- An urban planner who wants to improve public transportation in the suburbs and create an attractive pedestrian environment downtown
- A traffic engineer who believes that the ban would cause even worse traffic tie-ups in other areas

How Would You Act?

- Choose a role, write a report, and prepare to defend your views.
- Which other players have similar opinions? Who will be harder to convince? Do you think their points are valid?
- To help support your position, look in newspapers, on the Internet, and at the library for information about cities that have had similar problems, as well as their solutions to those problems.

Design Challenge

SKILLS MENU
- Identify a Problem
- Planning
- Building
- Testing
- Recording
- Evaluating
- Communicating

Design and Build a Mechanical Model or Device

Making a machine begins with an idea. Then technical drawings are created to show how the machine will work. Included with these drawings are calculations that estimate forces needed to push, pull, or lift. From these calculations, materials can be chosen and a final design created. Appropriate instructions are written describing how to operate the machine efficiently and safely.

1 A Can Crusher

Figure 1
More people would recycle if there was space for their cans.

Problem situation

Public recycling bins for cans fill up quickly because the cans are not crushed. The containers must be emptied often, and people simply throw their cans in the garbage when the recycling bins are full.

Design brief

- Design and build a wall-mounted can crusher that can be operated simply and safely.

Design criteria

- The force needed must be small enough that a child could operate the crusher.
- Technical drawings must show what the mechanical advantage of the crusher is, and how it will be achieved.
- The crusher must be able to crush many cans one at a time without requiring repair.
- It must be accompanied by simple instructions, including any safety precautions.

2 A Windmill-Operated Water Well

Figure 2
Can wind power drive farm machinery?

Problem situation

Many people who rely on a deep well for their water live in rural areas. It takes power to raise water from a well, and the wind is a cheap source of power.

Design brief

- Design and build a model windmill that will raise water to the surface of a well.

Design criteria

- An electrically operated fan at high speed, directed at the windmill, must be able to raise a weight of 0.5 N a height of 20 cm.
- The windmill must raise and lower the weight 10 times.
- It must be as efficient as possible.
- There must be an accompanying set of technical drawings and instructions, including safety precautions.

Figure 3
Puppets can provide hours of fun for small children.

3   A Remote-Control Puppet

Problem situation

Young children want puppets that they can operate remotely so that they can set up a puppet show. However, they need a system that is easy to operate and rugged enough that it will endure rough use.

Design brief

- Design and build a mechanically operated puppet that is controlled hydraulically or pneumatically.

Design criteria

- The puppet must be operable from 2 m away.
- It must be easy to operate, with as little force as possible.
- It must withstand small children playing with the puppet and pulling at the different parts.
- Technical drawings and instructions must be included, along with any safety precautions.

Assessment

Your model or device will be assessed according to how well you:

Process
- understand the problem
- develop a safe plan
- choose and safely use appropriate materials, tools, and equipment
- test and record results
- evaluate your model, including suggestions for improvement

Communicate
- prepare a presentation
- use correct terms
- write clear descriptions of the steps you took in building and testing your model
- explain clearly how your model solves the problem
- make an accurate technical drawing for your model

Produce
- meet the design criteria with your model
- use your chosen materials effectively
- construct your model
- solve the identified problem

When preparing to build or test a design, have your plan approved by your teacher before you begin.

Mechanical Advantage and Efficiency **195**

Unit 3 Summary

In this unit, you have learned that machines benefit us by making many tasks easier to perform. You have also learned to measure their efficiency and assess their environmental impact.

Reflecting

- Reflect on the ideas and questions presented in the Unit Overview and in the Getting Started. How can you connect what you have done and learned in this unit with those ideas and questions? (To review, check the sections indicated in this Summary.)
- Revise your answers to the Reflecting questions in ❶,❷,❸ and the questions you created in the Getting Started. How has your thinking changed?
- What new questions do you have? How will you answer them?

Understanding Concepts

- determine the mechanical advantage of various mechanical systems 3.2, 3.3, 3.8
- explain velocity ratio 3.2
- describe how pulleys, levers, and gears provide mechanical efficiency 3.2, 3.3, 3.5
- investigate and measure the force of friction 3.7, 3.8, 3.11
- describe the relationship between force, area, and pressure 3.12
- explain Pascal's law 3.13
- compare the effects of pressure on solids, liquids, and gases 3.12, 3.13, 3.14, 3.15
- explain how pressure is affected by temperature on liquids and gases 3.13

- explain how hydraulic and pneumatic devices help us 3.4, 3.6, 3.15, 3.16
- explain how a knowledge of levers aids in building artificial limbs 3.4, 3.10, 3.18

Applying Skills

- investigate how a linkage system can raise a weight 3.2, 3.3, 3.6, 3.9
- design, plan, and carry out the construction of a robotic arm 3.4
- describe how friction affects a machine's efficiency and suggest ways to reduce it 3.7, 3.8, 3.19

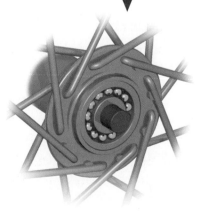

- design a mechanical system that is operated by hydraulic or pneumatic power 3.15, 3.16
- understand and use the following terms:

block and tackle
compressed
effort force
ergonomics
esthetics
friction
gear ratio
gear train
hydraulic system
linkage
load force

machine
mechanical advantage
mechanism
Pascal's law
pistons
pneumatic system
pressure
self-correcting
velocity ratio

- explain why gas  under pressure in a container can be dangerous 3.13, 3.14
- explore the impact on the environment that results from the manufacture, use, and disposal of products 3.20, 3.21
- investigate the relationship between esthetics and ergonomics 3.17

Making Connections

- explain how the subsystems of a bicylce enable it to function 3.5, 3.19
- identify the kinds of information that help consumers make informed decisions when buying a product 3.11, 3.18, 3.19

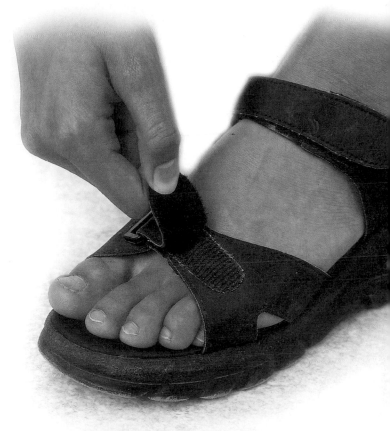

- assess the impact on the environment of the use and disposal of various products 3.20, 3.21

- explain the use of ergonomics in designing functional products 3.17
- identify a career that uses modern technology to reproduce human movements 3.4, 3.10

Unit 3 Review

Understanding Concepts

1. List 3 ways in which machines can make things easier for us.

2. When a human operates a machine, he or she can adjust the amount of force depending upon the task. What features must a machine have in order to meet the requirements of a specific task when there is no human controlling it?

3. Classify each of the following as a Class 1, Class 2, or Class 3 lever.

   (a) broom
   (b) bottle opener
   (c) seesaw
   (d) fly swatter
   (e) nutcracker

   For each one, draw a rough sketch in your notebook and label the load force, effort force, and fulcrum.

4. How is a pulley a Class 1 lever? Explain.

5. What are some of the benefits of friction? Describe a situation where friction is necessary.

6. Explain how we can reduce friction. Why is it important to be able to control friction?

7. Compare the different types of pulleys. What are the different features of a single fixed pulley, a single movable pulley, and a multiple pulley system?

8. Describe the difference between mechanical advantage and velocity ratio. What does each type of calculation represent?

9. Write the equation for calculating pressure. How does increasing the surface area that an object covers change the pressure?

10. Explain the different effects that applying pressure can have on a liquid or a gas. Use the terms compression, particles, and temperature in your explanation.

11. Why do aerosol cans contain warnings not be left near a stove?

12. Outline the advantages of using either a hydraulic or a pneumatic system. When is one system preferable to the other?

13. Compare the different effects on the pressure applied to car brakes using either a gas or a liquid.

14. List some of the benefits of using recycled products. Give at least three specific examples and show how they help the environment.

15. What factors would help you determine how an office chair or desk should be designed?

16. List 3 plastic products or containers you use. Are there ways which you could avoid using them? What would be the benefit of using an alternate material or product?

Applying Skills

17. What would be the mechanical advantage of a lever that can lift 80 N with an effort of only 20 N?

18. In order to lift a load a distance of 6 m by a pulley, it is necessary to move the effort load by 3 m. What would be the velocity ratio?

19. In the gear mechanism in **Figure 1**, calculate the gear ratio if A is the gear being driven. How many rotations would be required for one complete rotation of B? Repeat your answer if B is the gear being driven.

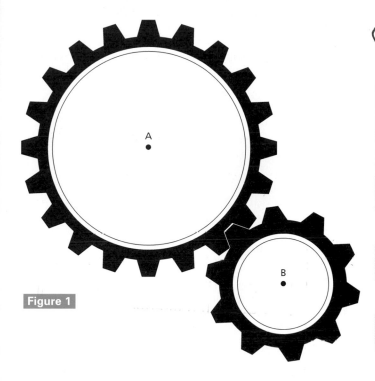

A

B

Figure 1

20. A single movable pulley is being used to lift a 135 N object by using 75 N of effort. There is also an allowance of 5 N for friction in the pulley. Will it work? Why or why not? Would it work with a single fixed pulley?

21. Describe how an elevator uses a pulley system. Draw a diagram, labelling the load force, effort force, and fulcrum.

22. You use a single movable pulley to lift an object weighing 1000 N. You apply an effort of exactly 500 N. Will the object lift?

23. A wheel and axle system has a mechanical advantage of 4. The effort used is 12 N. Without accounting for friction, what is the maximum load force that can be moved?

24. How much pressure would b surface with an area of 2 m² in an weighing 500 N were sitting on it?

25. A surface, measuring 0.2 m by 0.5 m, can withstand 2.5 kPa of pressure. What is the heaviest weight, in newtons, that can be placed upon the surface?

26. Match the following terms in **Table 1** with the correct descriptions:

Table 1

Term	Description
1. Compression	A The amount of space an object fills
2. Mechanical Advantage	B An object that is moved by a machine
3. Volume	C Speed at which an object moves in a given direction
4. Mechanism	D Squeezing together gas particles to fill a smaller volume
5. Hydraulics	E The number of times a machine increases or decreases an effort force
6. Velocity	F Forces are transferred in fluids in all directions
7. Load force	G A system of moving parts that changes an input motion to an output motion
8. Pascal's law	H A pressure system using liquid

27. Design an experiment comparing the efficiency of a hydraulic and a pneumatic system.

28. Mountain bikes and road bikes are designed differently. Complete **Table 2** indicating the differences and the reasons for them.

Table 2

Bicycle Part	Mountain Bike	Road Bike	Why?
Handlebars	Straight	Curved	Leverage on Road
?	?	?	?

29. How does a blender combine simple machines, such as a wheel, axle, and lever, to form a mechanism that makes work easier?

A machine that requires more effort to lift an object than the load itself is useless." Explain why you think this statement is true or false.

31. How have robots, using a combination of simple machines, become useful in industry?

32. Use print media or the Internet to research prostheses. How have levers and other important machines become important for their design?

33. A new car factory is being built. The owners must decide whether to use people or robots at different points on the assembly line. Give some advantages and disadvantages of each to help them make a decision.

34. While building a high-rise apartment building, workers often perform much of the construction on the ground that will eventually end up near the top of the building (**Figure 2**). How do pulleys allow workers to do this?

Figure 2

35. In the mid-1990s, Toronto began building a new subway tunnel. A giant machine was used to bore the tunnel. Which mechanisms do you think would be part of this machine?

36. While driving at night, a motorist notices smoke coming from the engine of his car. The light indicating low oil is on inside the car. Explain what could be causing the smoke.

37. During rainstorms, drivers on wet roads are told to use extra caution (**Figure 3**). Describe, scientifically, why this warning is necessary.

Figure 3

38. A commonly used magician's trick is to lie down on a bed of many nails. It looks quite dangerous, but the magician never gets poked. Apply what you know about pressure, force, and area to explain why this is so. What would happen if the magician lay down on only a few nails?

39. A nail is hammered into a wall, then a picture is hung on the nail. Describe the transfers of pressure involved in this process. Why is it sometimes necessary to use two nails?

40. You have been commissioned to design the layout for a new classroom.

   (a) Your task includes ergonomic designs for the chairs and desks, along with explanations for why they look the way they do.

   (b) Design special features that would make the room and equipment suitable for someone in a wheelchair.

41. An automobile manufacturer is designing seats for a new car model (**Figure 4**).

   (a) What are some of the design and ergonomic considerations that must be considered?

   (b) Identify some of the concerns that a consumer will have when examining the seat. How will she decide if the car seat is acceptable?

Figure 5

Figure 4

42. Playground equipment is designed with ergonomic considerations in mind (See **Figure 5**). For example, the type of slide may vary depending upon the age of the children using the slide. Design one for children 8–10 years old and one for children 5–7 years old. Consider the materials, shape, and height of the slide, as well as any other considerations you think are appropriate. Draw the two slides next to each other.

43. Your drink at lunch today could come in a plastic, paper, or metal container. What would be the advantages or disadvantages of each type?

Water Systems

Water a...

As our kno...
our ability t...
our awaren...
sustaining l...

You will b...

- describe
  have faci...

- evaluate
  effects o...
  of natur...

- compare
  saltwater

- investigat...
  affect the
  water env...

- pose ques...
  relating t...

Unit 4 Overview

Getting Started: How Does Water Shape Our World?

4.1   Water in Our World

4.2   Inquiry Investigation: Comparing Salt Water and Fresh Water

4.3   The Water Cycle

4.4   Case Study: The Power of Water

4.5   The Water Table

4.6   The Human Side of Water Systems

4.7   Water Treatment and Disposal

4.8   Career Profile: Floods: Water Untamed

4.9   Geological Features at Sea and on Land

4.10 Glaciers: Rivers of Ice

4.11 Inquiry Investigation: Rising and Falling

4.12 Currents

4.13 Case Study: Water, Weather, and Climate

4.14 Waves

4.15 Inquiry Investigation: Investigating Tides

4.16 Exploring the Deep

4.17 Oil: Wealth from the Ocean Floor

4.18 Diversity

4.19 Inquiry Investigation: Productivity of Organisms

4.20 Inquiry Investigation: The Brine Shrimp Experiment

4.21 Explore an Issue: People, Resources, and Water Systems

Design Challenge: Design and Build a Device to Live Safely with Water

Unit 4 Summary

Unit 4 Review

Getting Started

How Does Water Shape Our World?

1 Your school is an example of a **system**, a combination of interacting parts that form a unified whole. Teachers, superintendents, and custodians depend on each other and work together to help students learn. In a boiler system, water and steam travel through pipes to heat a building. Systems also exist in the natural world. In what ways does water in all its forms make up a system? How might the parts of a water system interact?

> **Reflecting**
>
> Think about the questions in 1,2,3. What other questions do you have about water systems? As you progress through this unit, reflect on your answers and revise them based on what you have learned.

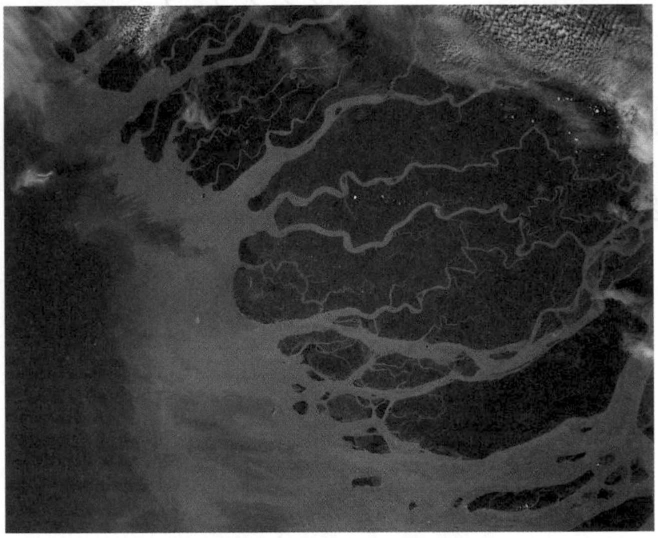

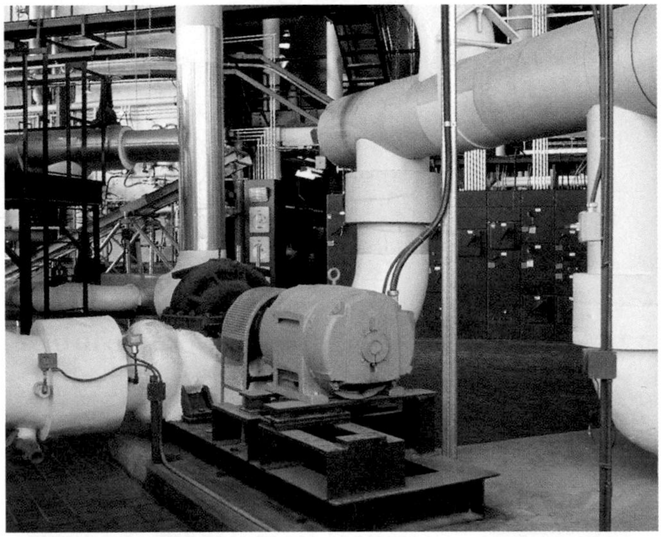

2 As water flows, it carves and shapes the land over which it travels. Water cascading over Niagara Falls has moved the edge of the falls upstream by about 11 km in the last 12 000 years. Water also has an impact on an area's climate. How does water help shape our physical landscape? How does it affect our climate and weather?

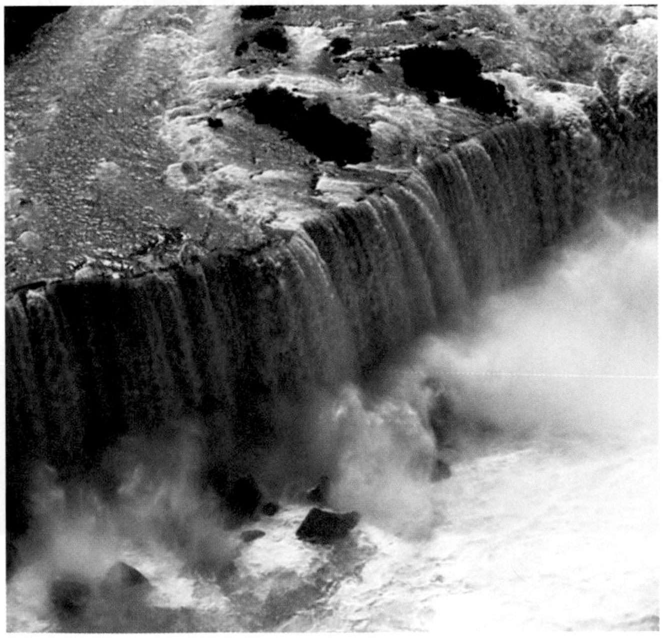

3 Water, in all its forms, is essential for life on Earth. Some organisms can live their entire life in a single drop of water, while others require vast oceans to survive. How are water systems and ecosystems linked? How do humans use or abuse water systems? Why is it important for humans to consider the environment when taking advantage of the riches water has to offer? ▼

Try This — Water: What's the Difference? ⑥A

In this activity, you will compare water that you collect from various sources around your community.

- Begin by brainstorming as many different sources of water as possible. Be creative. Decide what type of container should be used.

✋ If collecting water from rivers, ponds, etc., go with an adult. After handling water samples, wash your hands before putting them near your mouth or face.

- Collect your water samples, with your teacher's approval. For each water sample, label the container with the date, time, and specific location of collection.

- Put on an apron. Observe and compare the samples' similarities and differences. Let the containers stand.

1. Does anything float? Sink?

- Describe the colour, odour, and clarity (clearness) of each sample before and after shaking.
- Compare water samples under a ⑤A microscope.

2. What differences do you observe?

- Leave each container in a sunny location.

3. Do any changes take place?

in Our World

Imagine that you're on a space mission, orbiting Earth. As you travel above Africa and Eurasia, you might think there is considerable land below you. However, as your space ship passes over the Pacific Ocean, you begin to realize that most of Earth's surface is composed of water, as shown in **Figure 1**.

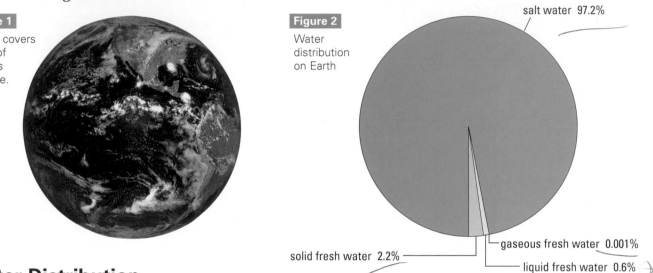

Figure 1

Water covers 71% of Earth's surface.

Figure 2

Water distribution on Earth

salt water 97.2%

solid fresh water 2.2%

gaseous fresh water 0.001%

liquid fresh water 0.6%

Water Distribution

Most of the world's liquid water is in the oceans as salt water. Of all the water in the world, less than 1% is in the form of fresh, liquid water. (See **Figure 2**.) **Fresh water** is water, whether liquid, solid, or gaseous, that contains a low concentration of dissolved salts. But don't let the name fool you! The word "fresh" does not necessarily mean drinkable or "potable." Most liquid fresh water contains dissolved chemicals and living organisms that might make you sick if you drank it. Even water from clear mountain streams may need to be treated before you can consume it.

Salt Water

Oceans contain most of the world's salt water. The **salinity** (average concentration of salt) of ocean water is about 3.5%. Salt water may also be found in swamps, marshes, lakes, and estuaries. Salt swamps and salt marshes occur where ocean waters come onto shore lands and fill low-lying areas or depressions. Salt swamps have numerous trees while salt marshes are dominated by grasses.

Estuaries, where rivers flow into the ocean, are affected by tidal action. High tides extend upstream, pushing the ocean's salt water inland to mix with the fresh river water. This mixed water is less salty than the water in the ocean and is called brackish water. Some inland salt lakes, such as the Dead Sea between Jordan and Israel, are actually more salty than the ocean.

a Although Canadians can face regional water shortages, we are fortunate to live in a land where fresh water abounds.

b Many people live in places with little fresh water available.

Figure 3

Fresh Water

If you travelled across Canada, you would cross numerous rivers and pass by glaciers, lakes, marshes, bogs, and swamps. (See **Figure 3**.) Most contain fresh water and play vital roles in the water system. These wetlands (swamps, marshes, and bogs) filter and clean fresh water and help to moderate water levels in times of flood or drought. Like their saltwater counterparts, freshwater swamps are dominated by trees, marshes by grasses, and bogs by mosses. Wetlands are home to a tremendous variety of plants and animals.

The Three States of Water

On Earth, water is one of the few substances that exist naturally in all three physical states: solid, liquid, and gas. Water also changes easily from one state to another. Not all water is in liquid form. In fact, just over 2% of the world's water is solid, in the form of snow, glaciers, and polar icecaps. The melted water from glaciers, called "meltwater," as it runs into rivers, is an important source of fresh water for many people.

Water is also present in the atmosphere in the form of fog and clouds, and in its gaseous state as water vapour. You, like many other animals, exhale water vapour with every breath. Plants add vast amounts of water to the atmosphere. Almost all the liquid water absorbed by the roots of a plant passes out through its leaves as water vapour in a process known as transpiration.

The roots of some plants gather moisture directly from airborne water. This is also true of the head-stander beetle, an insect that lives in the Namib Desert. As fog rolls in off the Atlantic Ocean, the insect elevates its back end, exposing small hairs on which the moisture condenses (becomes liquid again). The insect then drinks this water.

Understanding Concepts

1. List two examples for each of the following forms of water:
   (a) solid water
   (b) airborne water
   (c) salt water
   (d) fresh water
2. Why must water be treated before drinking?
3. Create a T-chart like that shown in **Table 1**. Use it to compare the characteristics of fresh and salt water. Include differences as well as similarities. Leave space so you can continue to add to it throughout the unit.

Table 1

Salt Water	Fresh Water
found in oceans, some salt lakes and marshes	found in rivers and streams

Making Connections

4. With so much water in the world, explain why some places suffer water shortages. Make a list of ways that a water shortage would affect your life.

Exploring

5. Wetlands are often drained or filled in to construct roads or buildings or increase farmland. As a member of an environmental group, research how a proposal to build a farm in a local wetland area might affect other parts of the water system. Be prepared to present your findings.

Reflecting

6. Why is it important to find new sources of fresh water and to conserve the sources now available?

Comparing Salt Water and Fresh Water

Just how different are salt water and fresh water?
You can examine their physical characteristics,
such as density and buoyancy. Density is the
mass of a substance for one unit of its volume.
For example, 1 cm³ of distilled water has a mass
of 1 g, so the density of distilled water is written
as 1 g/cm³. Buoyancy is the upward push on an
object by a fluid.

Question
How is salt water different from fresh water?

Hypothesis
Salt water has a greater force
of buoyancy, a greater density,
and more residue left after
evaporation than fresh water
does.

Never drink or even
taste anything from
a science class.

Materials
- apron
- safety goggles
- salt water (3.5% saline solution)
- fresh water
- distilled water
- microscope slides
- eyedropper
- desk lamp
- microscope
- 100-mL graduated cylinder
- triple-beam balance or scale
- beakers
- drinking straw
- food colouring
- 30-cm wooden dowel

Experimental Design
You will compare the
properties of salt water
and fresh water listed in
the hypothesis.

1 Copy **Table 1** into your
notebook.

Procedure
2 Obtain samples of fresh
water and salt water from
your teacher.
- Examine the appearance
and odour of both water
samples.

✎ (a) Record these observations
in your table.

3 Measure 3 drops of
fresh water on a clean
microscope slide. Rinse
the eyedropper in distilled
water. Measure 3 drops of
salt water on another
slide.
- Place the slides under a
desk lamp to evaporate
the water.
- Using a microscope,
5A examine any residue
on the slides.

✎ (a) Record your
observations.

4 Measure the mass of an
empty graduated cylinder.

✎ (a) Record the mass.

- Pour 100 mL of fresh
water in the cylinder and
measure the mass of both.

✎ (b) Record the mass of the
cylinder and water.

✎ (c) Calculate and record
the mass of the water.

- Rinse the cylinder with
distilled water. Repeat
step 4 using salt water.

Table 1	Comparing Salt Water and Fresh Water		
		Fresh Water	Salt Water
A.	Appearance (include colour)	?	?
B.	Odour	?	?
C.	Residue after evaporation	?	?
D.	Density		
	mass of empty graduated cylinder		
	mass of graduated cylinder and 100 mL of water	?	?
	mass of 100 mL of water		
	density of water sample (per 100 mL)		
	density (per 1 mL)		
E.	Buoyancy		
	depth to which dowel sank		
	float test: fresh water over salt water	?	?
	float test: salt water over fresh water		

Design Challenge

How could you use your knowledge of what happens when salt water evaporates to help you with the safe drinking water challenge?

Making Connections

1. Fresh water from rivers mixes with salt water when the river reaches the sea. Write a paragraph predicting whether the fresh water mixes completely with, floats above, or sinks below the ocean water. Support your prediction using evidence from this investigation.

Exploring

2. How would increasing the amount of salt in salt water (2E) affect buoyancy? Design an investigation to answer this question.

Reflecting

3. When conducting today's (9D) investigation, did your group share the recording and physical work equally? How might you work differently in upcoming investigations?

5 Place a wooden dowel in a graduated cylinder containing 100 mL of fresh water.
- Use the markings on the graduated cylinder to measure the depth at which the bottom of the dowel floats.

🖉 (a) Record the depth in your table.

- Repeat for salt water.

6 Add 1 drop of food colouring to 50 mL of fresh water.
- Half fill a beaker with uncoloured salt water.
- Use a straw to transfer the coloured water to the surface of the salt water. Repeat several times.

🖉 (a) Record your observations.

- Repeat the above process, this time transferring coloured salt water onto uncoloured fresh water.

Analysis

7 Analyze your results by answering the following questions.

(a) How does salt water residue differ from fresh water residue? What appears to make up most of the residues?

(b) Explain any difference in the density of the samples.

(c) How have you demonstrated that salt water exerts a greater force of buoyancy than fresh water? Explain using your results.

(d) How do the densities of salt water and fresh water help explain the difference in their buoyancy?

The Water Cycle

Sometimes quickly, sometimes slowly, water is always on the move, forever changing state and location. This movement is not restricted to Earth's surface, for water sinks deep below ground level and rises high into the atmosphere. It is this movement of water, known as the **water cycle** and illustrated in **Figure 1**, that is responsible for much of our weather, that keeps rivers and lakes full, and that allows water to purify itself and sustain many forms of life.

c Eventually, so much water gathers in the clouds that the air currents can no longer keep it aloft. It falls to Earth as **precipitation**: rain, hail, sleet, or snow.

b As the air rises, it cools, and cannot hold as much water vapour. The cooled water vapour in the air becomes liquid again, a process called **condensation**. Tiny drops collect around dust particles, forming clouds or fog.

a Heat energy from the sun causes water on Earth's surface to change to water vapour, a process called **evaporation**. Salts, pollutants, and impurities are left behind as the pure water rises into the air as water vapour. Water also evaporates from the soil, animals, and plants. Water evaporating from plants is called transpiration.

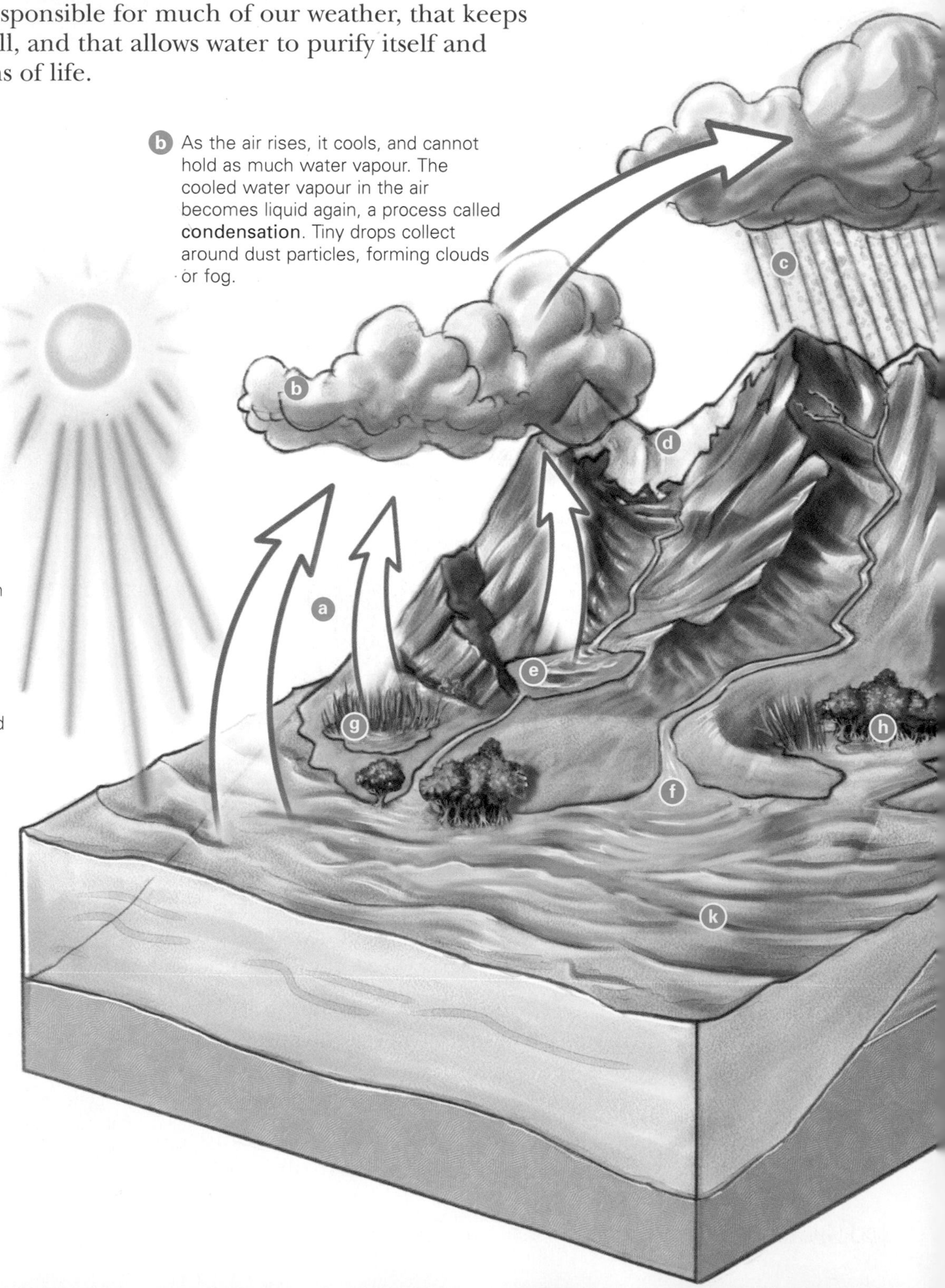

Figure 1

The water cycle

(d) Snow falling in the mountains or polar regions may remain frozen for years. Gradually, layers accumulate and their pressure turns the bottom layers of snow to ice, forming a glacier. Some snow and ice at the surface can also change directly back into water vapour. This is called sublimation.

(e) Water flowing along the surface of the ground is called **runoff**. This water gathers in rivers, lakes, and oceans. Lakes or ponds form wherever a **basin** (a natural depression) allows water to gather.

(f) Estuaries are areas where fresh water from rivers and salt water from the oceans mix to form moderately salty or brackish water.

(g) Marshes are low-lying, treeless areas of soft, wet ground that is usually covered by water for at least part of the year. Marshes may contain either fresh or salt water and are characterized by the grasses, cattails, and other plants that grow there.

(h) Swamps, like marshes, are areas of low-lying, wet land that at times is covered by water. Swamps also can be fresh or salt water but, unlike marshes, contain many trees and shrubs.

(i) You sometimes find deserts on one side of mountains. Air loses much of its moisture as it blows over the mountains, therefore little precipitation falls on the far (leeward) side.

(j) **Ground water** is water that has soaked into the earth, where it passes through gravel, sand, soil, and porous rock on its way back to rivers, lakes, and oceans.

(k) Water that returns to the ocean is not the same pure water that evaporated. Even precipitation that falls directly into the oceans may contain trace amounts of acid or other chemicals from reactions that take place in the atmosphere. Because of water's ability to dissolve many substances in both liquid and vapour form, pollutants, chemicals, and dissolved minerals and salts can be carried by ground and surface water into lakes and oceans.

Understanding Concepts

1. What is the water cycle?
2. Name and describe any four changes of state that occur in the water cycle.

Making Connections

3. How has the water cycle helped determine population patterns in North America? Can you give examples of where people have ignored the water cycle's effects in determining where to live?

Exploring

4. Unfortunately, pollutants can enter the water cycle at any stage.
(4A) Using the Internet, newspapers, and other resources, research one type of pollution. Describe and illustrate how it can enter the water cycle. Propose some ways to remedy the problem.

5. Imagine that you are a droplet of water on the calm surface of a lake. It is a warm summer's day. You feel the sun beating down on you, warming you, giving you energy. You begin to move, faster, then faster still. The warmer it gets, the more energy you have. You move more freely. Suddenly, you break free from the water's hold. Now you are floating ....
(8C)   Create a presentation of the water cycle in an interesting way for young children—through a story (as in the example above), visually, dramatically, or musically.

Reflecting

6. What does the word "cycle" mean? Apply this meaning to the water cycle.

Design Challenge

How might you use your knowledge of the water cycle and the changes of state that take place to help you design a water purifier?

The Water Table

The next time it rains, watch the raindrops hitting a window. Some of them run down the glass while others seem to stay stuck to the window. Two forces appear to act on the water: the force of gravity pulling it downward and a force of attraction to the glass. Water shows a "stickiness," an attraction to many materials, because of its structure.

Water is composed of hydrogen and oxygen. The chemical formula for water is H_2O, since there are two hydrogen atoms for every oxygen atom. One part of the molecule has a slightly positive charge and the opposite side has a slightly negative charge. These charges cause water molecules to act like tiny magnets, with the positive and negative charges attracting one another, as well as other types of molecules, like those in the window. This also affects how water behaves underground. (See **Figure 1**.)

a Rain strikes the ground. The attraction of water molecules to soil particles causes the water to spread outward, moistening the ground where it hits.

b Gravity causes the water to sink into the ground, dissolving salts and minerals as it moves through the spaces between the soil particles. This process is called **percolation**.

c The water eventually reaches an **aquitard**, an impervious layer of clay, silt, or rock that will not allow the water to pass through it fast enough to be used as a water supply.

d As more rain falls, water completely fills the spaces above the impervious layer, causing the soil to become saturated with water. This is called the **saturated zone**.

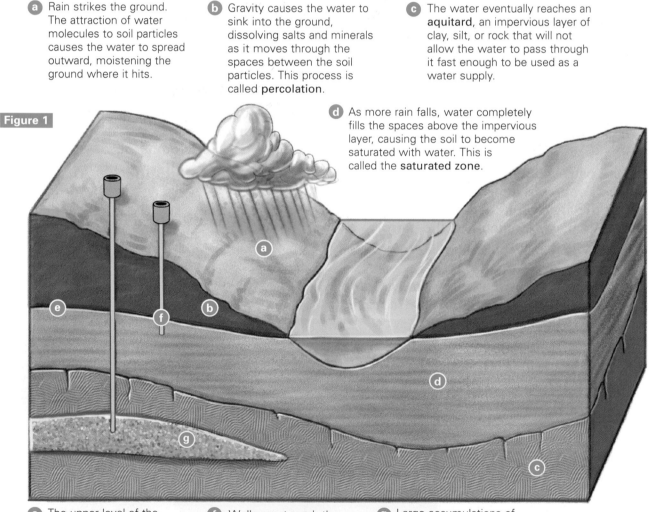

Figure 1

e The upper level of the saturated zone is called the **water table**.

f Wells must reach the saturated zone to be good sources of water for human use.

g Large accumulations of underground water in soil or rock are called **aquifers**. Aquifers are excellent sources of water, but some can be depleted just like oil deposits.

The depth of the water table is directly affected by what is happening locally in the water cycle. As rain falls, the water table starts to rise. During times of little rainfall, water evaporates from the ground's surface much faster than it is replaced. As water evaporates, **capillary action** draws more water up from below ground due to the attraction between the soil particles and the water. Considerable water is also lost through evaporation from ponds, rivers, and lakes. Water from the saturated zone moves to replace some of this lost water, and the water table drops. When a well "runs dry," the water table has sunk lower than the depth of the well.

Humans can affect water table levels. Some wells, for example, supply entire towns with water. If too much water is pumped from a well, the water table in the ground around the well can drop. Surrounding farms, with shallower wells, may completely lose their water supply.

Design Challenge

How might you use your knowledge of water molecules' attraction in the design of an oil spill eliminator?

Understanding Concepts

1. Explain how the water cycle affects water table levels.

2. Explain why, as rain begins to fall, the water doesn't flow down to the saturated zone immediately.

3. Describe how the following affect the movement of water underground:

   (a) aquitard

   (b) capillary action

   (c) percolation

Making Connections

4. During a dry season, a couple had 6000 L of water pumped into their dry well. By that evening, only 4000 L remained. They didn't have a swimming pool, they hadn't yet taken any baths, and they didn't have livestock. Explain how 2000 L of water could disappear in less than a day.

Exploring

5. Research one of the following using print (4A) and electronic resources. Prepare a report (8A) for your classmates:

   (a) a comparison between dug wells and drilled wells;

   (b) how a well pump works; or

   (c) the use of dugouts and sloughs for watering farm animals.

Try This Capillary Action in Soil (6)

You can build a model to demonstrate capillary action.

- Put on an apron. Roll a sheet of clear plastic into a tube and tape the seam.
- Place the tube upright in an aluminum pie pan and fill the tube with sand.
- Pour water into the pan and let it stand for several minutes. (See **Figure 2**.)

Figure 2

- Observe how high the water travels up the tube.
  - Try using different tube diameters to see if the distance changes. Measure the diameters and the distances.
  - Use a chart to record your results.

1. Does changing the type of soil or type of liquid affect your results?

The Human Side of Water Systems

How often do you see signs like those shown in **Figure 1**? As populations increase and we use our water systems for more purposes, such as recreation and the dumping of wastes, such signs may become more common. What causes the conditions that force such closures? How can water be safe one day and unsafe the next?

Figure 1

Water becomes unfit for human use for many reasons, some natural, some the result of human activity.

Microorganisms in the Water

Water in the natural environment contains many microorganisms. When you swim, you may swallow small amounts. Usually your digestive system disposes of the small quantities of the microorganisms easily, but if their concentration is too high, health problems may result.

A common organism associated with beach closures is coliform bacteria. Coliforms normally live in the intestines of animals, including humans, and are present in most water in nature. If raw or improperly treated sewage is discharged into the water (**Figure 2**), coliform numbers can increase rapidly. This is especially true during summer, when warmer temperatures provide ideal growing conditions. Nausea, vomiting, and diarrhea are common symptoms of ingesting water with a high coliform count.

Microscopic parasites also live in water. One common parasite causes the condition known as "swimmer's itch" when it attaches itself to your skin. Fortunately, a good shower will remove this organism, as it normally lives in ducks and cannot survive on humans.

Humans and Waterways

Canada faces a dilemma. As more people enjoy the beauty of our waterways, more people demand that these areas be protected. At the same time, as use of waterways increases, so too does the stress upon them. Boating practices such as using electric rather than gas-powered motors and camping practices such as using biodegradable products will help to conserve our shorelines.

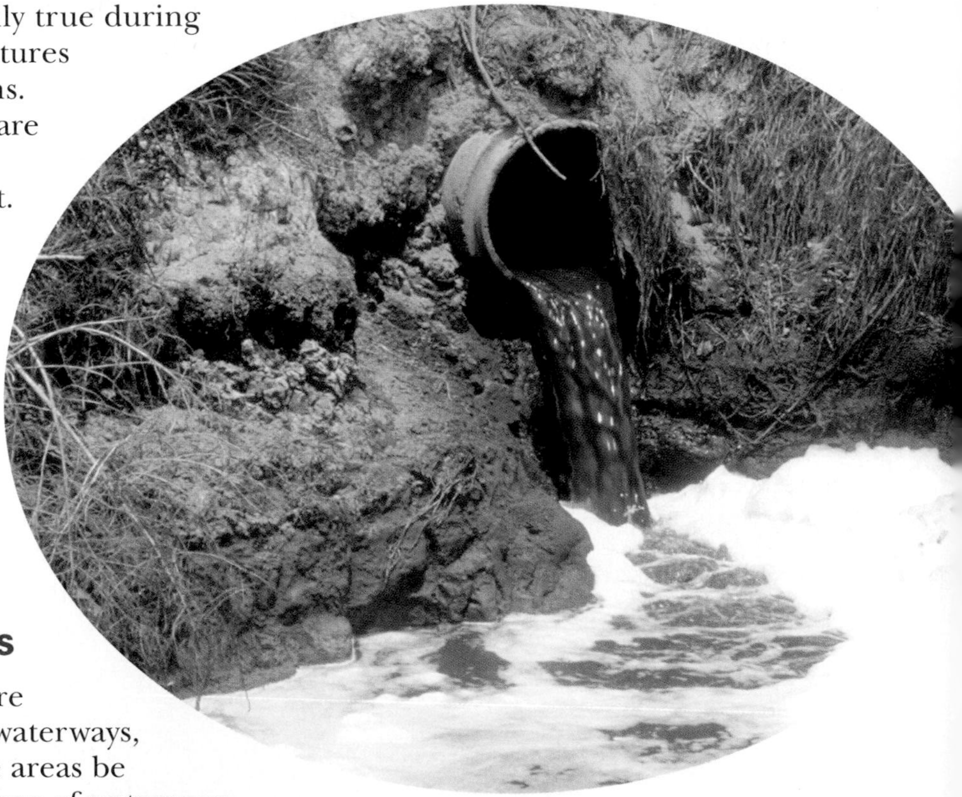

Figure 2

Sewage can increase the coliform count, and wastes can pollute the water with toxic chemicals.

While beautiful, acid lakes are commonly called "dead lakes" due to the lack of phytoplankton (small plantlike organisms) in the upper waters.

Understanding Concepts

1. What health risks are associated with the presence of coliform bacteria?

2. Why are populations of many lake bacteria higher in the summer?

Exploring

3. Make a poster informing the public why it is important to reduce boat and jet ski speeds along sensitive shorelines.

4. What stresses are being placed on the waterways (4A) in your area? Research what people are doing to help alleviate the problems. Summarize your findings in a paragraph.

Reflecting

5. What actions can you take to live safely with water and to keep water systems healthy?

Acid Precipitation

Water systems can also become polluted when toxins are discharged into the air. **Acid precipitation** occurs when water vapour reacts with airborne pollutants, particularly sulphur dioxide and nitric oxide. The resulting sulphuric acid and nitric acid dissolve in the atmospheric moisture and fall back to Earth as acid rain or acid snow. Acid precipitation harms plant growth (**Figure 3**) and even dissolves rocks and building materials.

Economic losses due to acid rain include reduced agriculture and timber production, fish kills, livestock damage, and less attractive recreation facilities. The governments of some countries, such as Canada, limit the types and amount of pollution that industries can emit. Some industries voluntarily control their emission levels. Reduction of air pollution is the only sure way to reduce acid precipitation.

Try This   Water Wise/Water Waste—A Survey   (4B)

Each Canadian uses about 300 L of water daily.

- Using a table like the one below, identify activities in your home and school that use water wisely and those that are wasteful.

Table 1   Description of Water Use

Water Wise?	Water Waste?	Suggestions
?	?	?
?	?	?

- Make suggestions to help improve people's wise use of water.
- Using the results of your survey, write a Charter of Water Rights and Responsibilities. Do research to check the information in your charter.

Include:
- five water rights you think every Canadian is entitled to; and
- five responsibilities every Canadian should fulfill regarding water use.

(8) Be prepared to share your charter with the class.

Floods: Water Untamed

How communities plan against, prepare for, and deal with floods often depends on their location. Manitoba responded to a devastating 1950 flood by constructing a 47-km floodway around Winnipeg—a precaution that saved the city during the 1997 Red River Valley flood. (See **Figure 1**.) Municipalities in Ontario responded to floods and other environmental issues by establishing Conservation Authorities.

Water Management

Hazel Breton is the Water Resources Engineer for the Credit Valley Conservation Authority in Mississauga, Ontario. Interested in reducing flood damage, she helps monitor the quantity and quality of water in local systems. She also examines the way land is used in these areas. Any major change in land use can have an effect on ground water and the water cycle. In many places, what was once agricultural land has been turned into parking lots, roads, and subdivisions—most of it paved. Water that used to soak into the ground and return to the water table now runs directly into the river system. Hazel says, "In spite of these land-use changes, however, we strive to ensure that flood levels do not increase beyond historical levels."

The effects of floods that occur in areas of open, flat land can be dramatic (**Figure 2**), because once water flows over the banks of the river, there is very little to stop it. Since most of the Credit River is located in a valley, the damaging effects of floods can be reduced by preventing people from building on **flood plains**, those relatively flat areas next to a river that experience regular flooding. Hazel uses computer models to help determine these areas. She simulates what flood levels would be like if a major storm, like a hurricane, hit the Credit Valley. She then warns people against building in these areas. "That way," she explains, "when rivers overflow, there is less danger to people and property."

Some older communities were built close to flood plains before the Conservation Authority began regulating land use. It is important for people in these areas to receive early information about when floods might occur. "We use computer simulations to predict the approximate timing and extent of flooding," says Hazel.

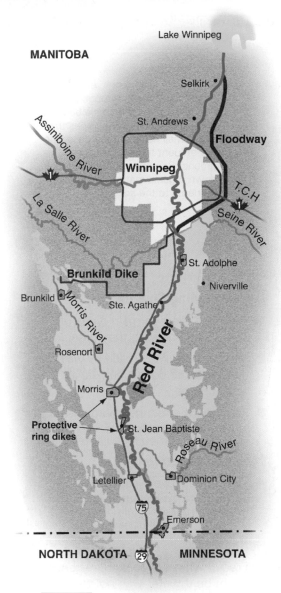

Figure 1

During the 1997 Manitoba flood, a large ditch, known as a floodway, diverted much of the water around the city of Winnipeg. Flooded areas are shown in light blue.

A River's Response to Rain ⑥

You can simulate what happens when rain strikes a river bed at different rates. You should wear an apron and gloves during this activity and wash your hands afterwards.

- Take 2 aluminum pie pans. Bend the aluminum at one end of each pan to make a spout. Fill the pans with garden soil and press firmly.

1. Can you guess what might happen if the soil were not pressed down?

- Scoop a "river bed" down the centre of each pan and gently slope the soil on either side towards it. Try to make the rivers identical.

- Tilt the pans so the spout is on the low end and place beakers to catch any water that may pour out.
- Using a watering can, pour 250 mL of water over each pan, but pour it slowly over one, and very quickly over the other.
- Measure the amount of water that pours off the pans.

2. How do the quantities compare?

3. Is there a difference in the quality of the water?

4. Would different soil types give different results?

5. What do your results suggest to you ⑦ₑ about the force of water during a major storm?

Working Together

Monitoring the local water system is not a one-person job, and Hazel is quick to give credit to others. "As Project Manager, I work with a team of specialists and depend on their skill and expertise in helping to protect our environment. That is why it is so important for students to learn how to work, share information, and solve problems together."

Whenever a major change in land use is planned, Hazel and her team determine how it will affect the local water systems. Yet it is not just water that Hazel is concerned about, but also plants and animals. "People must understand that all aspects of the environment are connected," she cautions. "Failure to recognize these connections can ruin both water and habitat unless we are very careful."

Figure 2

In the spring of 1997, much farmland in Manitoba's Red River Valley lay under water.

Geological Features at Sea and on Land

Nearly one hundred years ago, Alfred Wegener, a German scientist, thought that the map of the world looked like a giant jigsaw puzzle. This thinking has led to the theory of "plate tectonics," the present model of the movement of Earth's crust. Geologists have found evidence that Earth's crust is divided into huge sections, called plates, that move slowly as they float on the hot mantle beneath. As plates collide with, slide beside, slip under, or separate from one another, they shape Earth's crust, both on land and at the bottom of the oceans.

Continental Shelves

Extending outward from the continents, the ocean floor slopes downward gently. Called the **continental shelf** (**Figure 1**), it abounds in sea life. Some of these shelves are as narrow as a kilometre, while others, like the Grand Banks off Newfoundland, extend several hundred kilometres.

Underwater Mountains

You might be surprised to know that the longest mountain range in the world lies under water! The Mid-Ocean Ridge extends 60 000 km through all four oceans. Different sections of the Mid-Ocean Ridge, such as the Mid-Atlantic Ridge, have more specific names depending on their location. **Figure 2** illustrates the development of underwater mountains by volcanic activity.

Figure 1

At the edge of a continental shelf is a steep underwater cliff called a continental slope, which drops to the ocean floor.

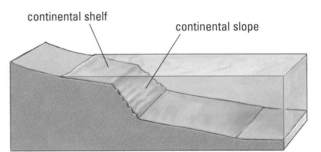

continental shelf

continental slope

c Eventually, enough layers of rock may build up on a seamount that it rises above the surface of the ocean, forming a volcanic island (such as Hawaii).

volcano

volcanic island

Figure 2

a Volcanoes are mountains formed when hot lava erupts through Earth's crust, cools, and solidifies into rock as it flows down the surface of the volcanic cone.

b An underwater volcano is called a **seamount**.

seamount

Canyons and Trenches

Canyons are deep, steep-sided valleys. Most are formed by rivers that cut their way through the surrounding rock. As these rivers run into the ocean, they may continue to erode the sea bed, carving valleys and canyons into the continental shelf. Geologists think that many sea canyons were caused by rivers flowing over the coast before sea levels rose.

Trenches (**Figure 3**), which run parallel to the coast, may be as much as 200 km wide and 2400 km long. The Challenger Deep, in the Pacific Ocean's Mariana Trench, is the world's deepest point, extending 11 km below the surface of the ocean.

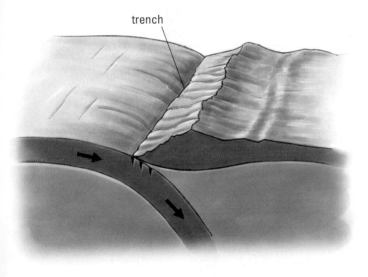

trench

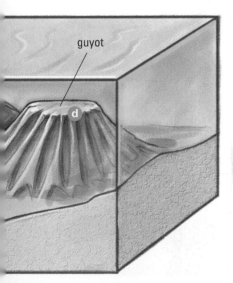

guyot

d **Guyots** were volcanic islands. Over time, their tops eroded enough that the ocean covered them again.

Lakes

Water lying in low spots or basins (depressions in Earth's surface) form lakes. Lakes are similar to oceans or even mud puddles—all are bodies of water trapped in basins. (See **Figure 4**.) These basins are formed in several ways. For example, craters often form at the tops of volcanoes as they cool. Water from precipitation gathers in the crater, making a volcanic lake.

During the last Ice Age, glaciers formed many of the lakes in the Northern Hemisphere. As they moved over the land, they carved basins and deposited natural dams of earth, rock, and gravel. When the climate changed and the ice melted and receded, meltwater was trapped in the basins behind the dams.

Figure 4

a If a river is blocked, water may build up, forming a lake. These blockages, or dams, may be natural or built by humans.

b Natural dams are caused by landslides, lava flows, river deposits, ice, and even beavers.

Water enters lakes through precipitation, ground water, and inlets. A river enters a lake at an inlet, and another river flows out at an outlet. Some lakes are landlocked, with no apparent inlets or outlets. Depending on their location and the type of land mass around them, these lakes may be even saltier than the ocean. Why is this? Ground water dissolves salts and minerals from the soil and rock, then carries these materials into the lake. A landlocked lake, like the ocean, loses only pure water through evaporation, leaving the dissolved minerals behind. Over time, these salts accumulate and the lake becomes salty.

Rivers

Most rivers begin in highlands from springs (water welling up from underground) or as streams of glacier meltwater. Pulled by gravity, the water makes its way downhill. **Tributaries** (smaller rivers and streams) join the river, adding water. As it moves, the river erodes its bottom and banks. Eroded material is carried downstream. As the water's movement slows, this sediment is deposited, possibly changing the river's course as bends, or meanders, develop. (See **Figure 5**.)

Figure 5

a Rivers take many forms as they age. Young, fast-flowing rivers tend to carve out steep banks.

b Older rivers often have noticeable flood plains— gently sloping land on both sides of the rivers.

Try This Making Watersheds and Divides

- Lay a plastic garbage bag in a plastic dishpan so that it lies flat on the bottom and extends up the sides.
- Fold the bag over the edges of the dishpan and tape it, allowing spaces for air to seep in and out between the dishpan and the bag.
- Cut 5 pieces of string 40 cm long. Using duct tape, tape one end of each piece of string to the bag at different places where it rests on the dishpan. Loop the string once around the tape before taping it to prevent the string from slipping.
- Wearing an apron, mix a batch of Glacial Goo using 700 mL cornstarch, 300 mL water, a mixing bowl, and a spoon or stirring rod.
- Mix the water and cornstarch together slowly, stirring until completely mixed.
- Hold the loose end of the strings while you pour the Goo into the dishpan.
- Now, slowly pull up the strings until the plastic bag "land" rises above the "sea level" of the Goo. Observe how the Goo flows.

1. What land forms did you make?

2. Did you create separate watersheds in your basin?

3. Did you create a Great Divide? How do you know?

4. What is the effect of raising and lowering individual strings?

Watersheds and the Continental Divide

Imagine a large, flat land. The land is covered by a calm, shallow sea. Over millions of years, the land buckles and heaves as the plates of Earth's crust move. Large areas rise up, forming mountains and highlands. Pulled by gravity, the water moves with the changing land. As the ground rises, the waters are divided, some flowing down one side of the up-thrust land, some flowing down the other. The flowing water carves valleys and canyons in the new landscape, forming pathways for future waters to travel.

A **watershed** is an area, surrounded by high land, in which all water runs to a common destination. (See **Figure 6**.) A large river, such as the Fraser River in British Columbia, is fed by rivers from several watersheds on its way to the Pacific Ocean. Small watersheds lie within larger ones, which lie within even larger ones. As **Figure 7** shows, all Canadian waters eventually flow into one of three oceans: the Atlantic, the Pacific, or the Arctic.

Figure 6

These two watersheds are separated by areas of higher elevation, which direct the flow of water.

Figure 7

The major watersheds of Canada

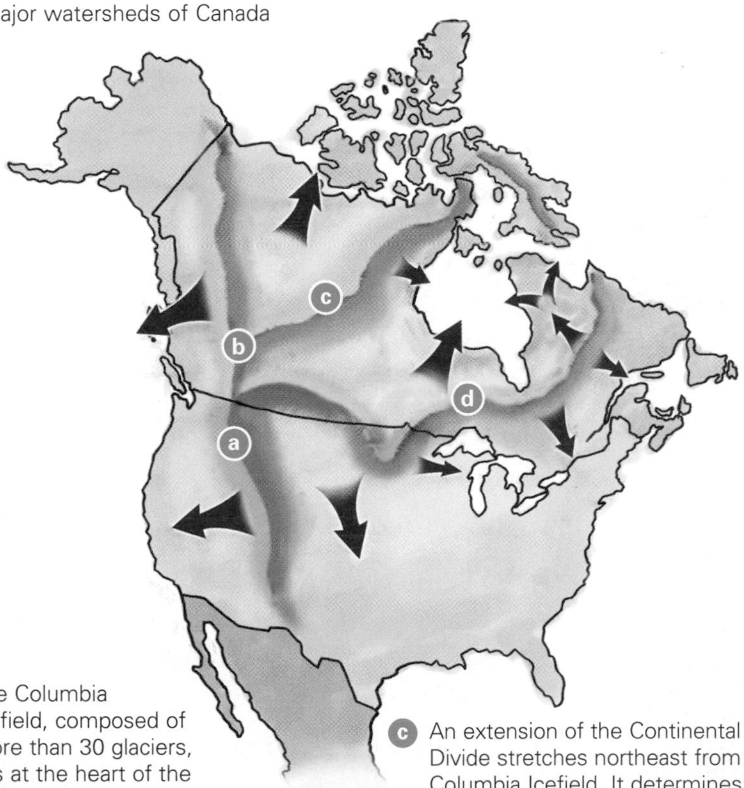

b The Columbia Icefield, composed of more than 30 glaciers, lies at the heart of the Continental Divide. The meltwaters from this ice field drain into all three oceans.

a **The Continental Divide** (also called the Great Divide) separates waters flowing into the Pacific Ocean from those flowing north and east.

c An extension of the Continental Divide stretches northeast from the Columbia Icefield. It determines which east-flowing rivers flow into the Arctic Ocean and which into the Atlantic Ocean or Hudson Bay.

d Another extension separates waters flowing into Hudson Bay from those that flow into the Missouri–Mississippi system or the Great Lakes–St. Lawrence River basin.

Understanding Concepts

1. Compare the formation of seamounts and volcanoes.

2. Draw a cross section of the ocean floor illustrating and labelling 6 major features. Write a description of each feature.

3. Explain the relationship between river valleys and sea canyons.

Making Connections

4. Should water resources be managed by individual communities, or on a watershed basis, where all communities within a watershed make decisions as a group about how water is used? Explain.

Exploring

5. Imagine you dropped a stick into a river or lake near where you live. Using an atlas and a map of your province, trace the stick's course to the ocean and list the bodies of water through which it would travel.

6. Some legends tell of the appearance or disappearance of islands. Explain how such a legend might be true. Write your own legend.

Reflecting

7. What would happen to our water supply if land use was not regulated?

Glaciers: Rivers of Ice

Glaciers, masses of ice and snow built up over thousands of years, occur in the high altitudes of mountains (alpine glaciers), as shown in **Figure 1**, and on the lands near Earth's poles (continental glaciers). The lower layers of glaciers are turned into clear ice because of the weight of the snow above. This great weight also causes alpine glaciers to ooze slowly down the mountains.

A continental glacier covers the entire continent of Antarctica. Another covers most of the island of Greenland, an area of 1.8 million square kilometres. At its thickest point, Greenland's continental glacier extends 2700 m from top to bottom. (See **Figure 2**.) Continental glaciers are usually thickest at the centre and slowly flow out in all directions from there.

Cold air flows off continental glaciers, cooling the surrounding area and helping to form strong winds known as the polar easterlies. Because these winds are so cold, they provide little precipitation. Antarctica, for example, is a true desert with the harshest conditions on Earth: average temperatures around −50°C and an annual precipitation of less than 3 cm.

The large sheet of ice on the Arctic Ocean, called the polar icecap, is not a glacier because it lies over water, not land. Although conditions at the North Pole are less severe than those in Antarctica, this icecap produces similar weather effects to those caused by continental glaciers. **Figure 3** illustrates arctic pack ice, floating ice that has been driven together to form a single mass.

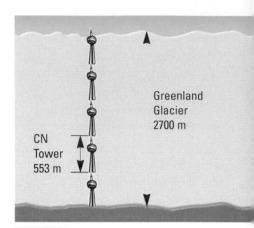

Figure 2

Greenland's continental glacier is almost equal in height to five CN Towers.

Greenland Glacier 2700 m

CN Tower 553 m

Figure 1

Supervised hikes attract many tourists to Rocky Mountain glaciers.

Figure 3

Spring conditions cause the ice to break up into large ice floes.

Glaciers store huge amounts of fresh water as snow and ice. Some of this water, especially at the melting edges of the glacier, rejoins the water cycle fairly quickly as a valuable source of liquid water. When the glacier finally oozes its way to the ocean, icebergs break off into the water. Icebergs can threaten shipping lanes and offshore oil rigs. The most famous shipping disaster occurred in 1912 when the *Titanic* struck an iceberg and sank. However, icebergs may have benefits. Since they consist of fresh water, people may start towing icebergs to places where drinking water is needed.

Glaciers of Old

The largest glaciers of today are small compared with the glaciers of the last major Ice Age. Beginning about 2 million years ago, ice sheets spread over most of North America (**Figure 4**) and Eurasia. When the ice began to melt at the end of the last Ice Age, sea levels rose. Land that was pressed down by the immense weight of the ice continues to move upwards, or rebound. The remains of the last Ice Age include the Greenland and Antarctic ice sheets. Today people are concerned about global warming and fear that coastal lands will be covered with water if polar ice melts quickly.

a 18 000 years ago

b 8000 years ago

Figure 4

Since 18 000 years ago, the ice covering North America has gradually melted.

Understanding Concepts

1. Describe three effects glaciers have on the environment.

Exploring

2. Design a simulation of how a glacier turns snow into ice.

3. Research print and electronic
(4A) resources to explore one of the
(8C) following topics. Be prepared to present your findings in an interesting way. End your presentation with three new questions you thought of during your research.

   (a) During the last Ice Age, the ice receded due to changing climate. How might global warming affect glaciers and the world in the future?

   (b) Explain why fossils of marine animals are found in places where no oceans exist. (See **Figure 5**.) Provide specific references to glaciation.

Northwest Territories

Fort McMurray

British Columbia   Alberta

Figure 5

Why were fossils of this prehistoric marine reptile found hundreds of kilometres from any ocean?

   (c) Draw at least 2 maps like those in **Figure 4**, showing the position of ice today and at one or more other time periods.

Reflecting

4. Describe, using specific examples, how this section on glaciers is related to the water cycle.

4.11 Inquiry Investigation

SKILLS MENU
○ Questioning   ● Conducting   ● Analyzing
○ Hypothesizing   ● Recording   ● Communicating
○ Planning

Rising and Falling

Imagine you are sitting at the edge of a lake on a windless summer day. All seems so peaceful and still, especially the water. Yet, you think back to what you learned about water constantly moving. Does the water move below the surface? If so, what causes it to move?

Question

How does a difference in water temperature affect the movement of water in lakes and oceans?

Hypothesis

Differences in water temperature will affect how quickly and the way water mixes below the surface.

Experimental Design

You will be observing the movement of coloured water from a melting ice cube in water of different temperatures.

1 After reading the Procedure, design an observation
6D chart for recording your observations.

Materials

- apron
- safety goggles
- 2 Pyrex beakers, each 600 mL
- ice-cold water and water at room temperature
- coloured ice cubes (2 different colours)
- tongs or plastic fork
- hot plate
- retort stand
- ring clamp
- watch with second hand

Procedure

 When using a hot plate, keep hands and clothing away from the surface.

2 Measure 400 mL of ice water into a 600-mL beaker. Let the water stop moving.

- Using tongs, gently place a coloured ice cube in the water at one side of the beaker.

✎ (a) Make a series of quick sketches to show what happens when the ice cube is placed in the water and at 1-min intervals.

3 Repeat step 2, using 400 mL of water at room temperature.

✎ (a) Sketch your observations. Did the coloured water mix more quickly this time?

4 Your teacher will demonstrate what happens when a coloured ice cube is placed in hot water.

✎ (a) Sketch what you observe immediately and at 1-min intervals.

(b) Note the time it takes for mixing to occur. Did the coloured water mix more quickly this time?

Making Connections

1. Use evidence from the experiment to predict the movement of ocean water near the equator and near the poles. (See **Figure 1**.)

2. In **Figure 2**, Earth's mantle is close to the surface, making the lake warmer near point A. Describe the movement of water at the points A, B, C, and D.

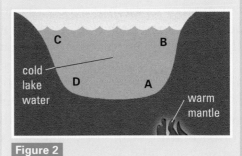

Figure 2

Cross section of lake

Exploring

3. Design an experiment to test whether changing the salt content of water affects the movement of the water (the water current). With the approval of your teacher, conduct the experiment, observing safety precautions.

Reflecting

4. Can you think of ways to improve the experimental design of today's investigation? How would you modify your observation chart?

Figure 1

The temperatures of the ocean waters around the world differ greatly.

5 Set up the materials as shown in the photograph above. Make sure the retort stand is secure and only a small portion of the Pyrex beaker rests over the hot plate.
- Pour 400 mL of ice-cold water into the beaker. Wait for the water to stop moving.
- Turn the hot plate on to medium high, then wait 1 min.

6 Gently place a coloured ice cube in the beaker against the side farthest from the hot plate.
- Place an ice cube of a different colour in the beaker at the side over the hot plate.

(a) Using a labelled diagram to help, describe your observations.

Analysis

7 Analyze your results by answering the following questions.

(a) Which appears to be more dense, warmer water or cooler water? Why?

(b) How did the different temperatures of the beaker water affect the speed at which water mixed?

(c) Write a report for your investigation.

Currents

Why is the surface water of a lake much warmer than its deep water? You saw in the last investigation that cooler water is more dense than warmer water, and therefore sinks. As it does, it pushes the warmer water upward. This creates a type of **current** or movement in the water. Currents caused by temperature differences are called **convection currents**.

Convection currents help redistribute nutrients and oxygen in lakes that are ice-covered in the winter. Plants get many of their nutrients from decaying plant and animal matter, some of which sinks to the bottom of the lakes. Oxygen enters the upper water layer mainly when aquatic plants produce oxygen during the day, and by waves, which mix air with the water. **Overturns** occur in the spring and fall, when convection currents mix the surface and bottom waters, and nutrients and dissolved oxygen are redistributed throughout the lake.

Ocean Currents

Convection currents exist in the oceans on a global scale. Cold water at the poles sinks and tends to flow toward the equator. Because it is warmer, equatorial water is pushed upward and warmed even more. It flows along the surface of the oceans to replace the water moving away from the poles. These surface currents are helped along by winds. As the water moves farther from the equator, it becomes cooler and begins to sink, thus completing the cycle.

The frigid waters around continental glaciers also contribute to deep ocean currents. As sea water freezes to form ice, salt remains in the water. This increased salt content makes the frigid water even more dense. It sinks, spilling into the deep ocean basins. Helped by Earth's rotation, this water moves toward the equator. Cold water currents, forced upward by continents and underwater landforms, carry nutrients that benefit living things.

 Gyres in a Pan ⑥

You can simulate the effects of a spinning globe on ocean currents using a round, clear pan, some coloured ice cubes, water, and a lazy Susan. Set up the materials as shown in **Figure 1**.

Figure 1

Materials you can use to simulate the effects of a spinning globe on ocean currents

- Wearing an apron, fill the pan about half full with very cold tap water.
- Place several coloured ice cubes at one side of the pan.
- Wait approximately 1 min for the colour to begin spreading.
- Now turn the lazy Susan very slowly in one direction. Try not to create waves in the water.
- Record how turning the pan affects the pattern left by the coloured water.

However, in real life, as in school, things are rarely as simple as they seem. Earth is not merely a stationary ball floating in space. It spins on its axis and revolves around the sun at the same time. Its waters are pulled by the gravitational force of both the Sun and the Moon. Strong winds blow across its surface, and massive landforms mark the ocean floor. In addition, the continents force the waters to flow around them. All of these forces affect the flow of ocean waters. It is helpful to picture currents as huge rivers flowing through the waters of the ocean, mixing only a little with water at their edges.

Ocean currents do form consistent, circular patterns called **gyres**. (See **Figure 2**.) Each gyre is made up of several specific currents. **Figure 3** illustrates some of the currents that make up the North Atlantic Gyre. As the Labrador Current meets the Grand Banks off the coast of Newfoundland, the current's cold, nutrient-rich waters are forced upward. This increases the productivity of plants and animals, resulting in one of the world's great fishing areas.

Figure 2

The five main gyres of the world: **a** the North Atlantic Gyre; **b** the South Atlantic Gyre; **c** the South Indian Gyre; **d** the North Pacific Gyre; and **e** the South Pacific Gyre

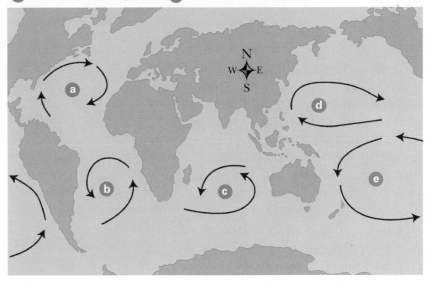

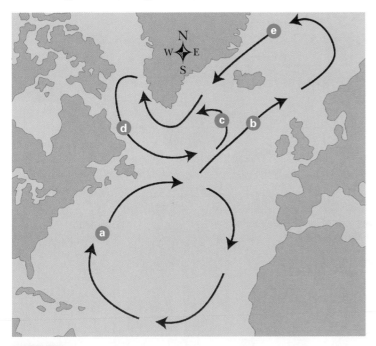

Figure 3

Some of the major currents in the North Atlantic Ocean: **a** the Gulf Stream; **b** the North Atlantic Current; **c** the Irminger Current; **d** the Labrador Current; and **e** the Greenland Current

4A Research Skills

Understanding Concepts

1. Explain the significance of convection currents to the survival of many aquatic organisms.

2. Describe the similarities and differences between gyres and currents.

3. Why do gyres flow in giant circular patterns instead of straight lines?

Exploring

4. Using resources such as **4A** encyclopedias or CD-ROMs, research what is meant by the Coriolis effect. How does this apply to the movement of gyres? Sketch how this effect would change **Figure 2** if Earth spun on its axis in the opposite direction.

5. Where are some of the other important fishing areas in the oceans? What causes these areas to generate such large numbers of fish?

Reflecting

6. Where have you noticed the effects of convection currents in your own life?

Water, Weather, and Climate

Have you ever made a pizza, let it cool slightly and then taken a big bite—only to have something on the pizza burn your mouth? How could some parts of the pizza be hotter than others when they were all heated at the same temperature for the same amount of time?

Materials with a low heat capacity require only a little heat before their temperature starts to rise, while others require much more. These latter materials then take much longer to cool down because they have more heat energy to give off. Water, like tomato sauce, is one of these materials. Large bodies of water, such as oceans, warm up and cool down much more slowly than the surrounding land and can affect the weather and climate of that area. You may recall that weather refers to daily conditions of such things as temperature, precipitation, and humidity, while climate refers to average weather conditions over many years.

(a) How might a lake or ocean affect the weather of the surrounding area during the summer? During the winter?

We often use graphs to compare weather and climate patterns of different locations more easily. As **Figures 1** and **2** show, line graphs are usually used to graph temperatures, bar graphs to graph precipitation.

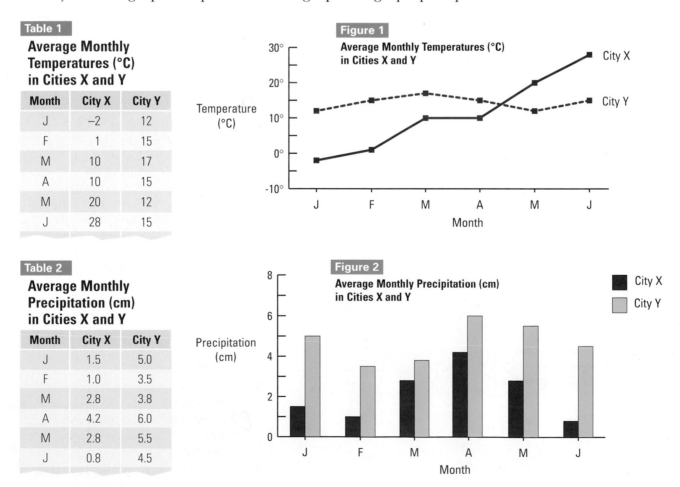

Table 1

Average Monthly Temperatures (°C) in Cities X and Y

Month	City X	City Y
J	−2	12
F	1	15
M	10	17
A	10	15
M	20	12
J	28	15

Figure 1
Average Monthly Temperatures (°C) in Cities X and Y

Table 2

Average Monthly Precipitation (cm) in Cities X and Y

Month	City X	City Y
J	1.5	5.0
F	1.0	3.5
M	2.8	3.8
A	4.2	6.0
M	2.8	5.5
J	0.8	4.5

Figure 2
Average Monthly Precipitation (cm) in Cities X and Y

(b) Use **Figures 1** and **2** and **Tables 1** and **2** to 7C help you construct comparison graphs for the data in **Tables 3** and **4**.

(c) Cities A and B lie at about the same latitude and both are close to water. Which city do you think has the larger body of water next to it? Why?

(d) How does a large body of water affect the weather and climate of an area?

Currents and Climate

Ocean currents have a major effect on world climates. Currents moving away from warm equatorial waters have a warming effect on the air above them and the lands they pass near. On the other hand, currents flowing from the cold waters near the poles have a cooling effect.

Winds of Change

When you studied the water cycle, you saw how condensation causes clouds to form as warm, moist air rises and cools. Currents have the same effect on ocean winds. Winds passing over warm currents absorb a great deal of evaporated water. When these warm, moist winds blow across a cold current, the air cools and dense fog forms. The air loses much of its moisture. If these winds then blow over land, they warm up once again, providing little or no rain for the land. This interaction between winds and ocean currents is seen along the west coasts of Africa, Australia, and Southern California and has created some of the driest areas on Earth.

(e) Look at **Figure 3** showing the Alaska Current. How do you think this current affects the climate of western British Columbia and southern Alaska? Why?

Table 3		
Average Monthly Temperatures (°C) in Cities A and B		
Month	City A	City B
J	−7	−6
F	−6	−6
M	−1	−2
A	6	4
M	12	9
J	17	15
J	21	18
A	20	18
S	15	14
O	9	9
N	3	3
D	−3	−3

Table 4		
Average Monthly Precipitation (cm) in Cities A and B		
Month	City A	City B
J	4.6	14.7
F	4.6	11.9
M	5.7	12.3
A	6.4	12.4
M	6.6	11.1
J	6.9	9.8
J	7.7	9.7
A	8.4	11.0
S	7.4	9.5
O	6.3	12.9
N	7.0	15.4
D	6.6	16.7

Understanding Concepts

1. Which heats up more quickly, water or land? Why?

2. Describe the effect that the Labrador Current (section 4.12) has on Newfoundland.

3. Describe the difference between weather and climate.

Making Connections

4. Every few years, a situation known as El Niño occurs when great amounts of warm ocean water gather along the west coast of North, Central, and South America. This happens when winds that usually keep the warm water out in the Pacific Ocean diminish. From your knowledge of winds and currents, how does El Niño affect the climate of North America? Predict possible economic and environmental costs of any change in climate.

Reflecting

5. If an ocean current flowing along a coastal area suddenly changed from warm to cold, describe what you think would happen to the climate along the coast.

Figure 3

Some of the major currents in the North Pacific Ocean:
ⓐ the Kuroshio Current;
ⓑ the Aleutian Current;
and ⓒ the Alaska Current

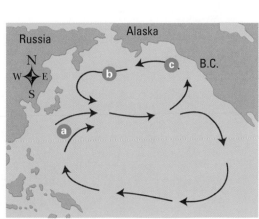

Waves

On July 17, 1998, a wall of water up to 15 m high slammed into the beaches of Papua New Guinea. It tore through several villages, flattening many of them, and within seconds left 6000 people homeless. Many lives were lost when the wave first hit; others perished as the water rushed back into the ocean carrying bodies with it. In all, more than 2200 villagers died, including at least 230 children. Days later, a village spokesperson being interviewed on television captured the sadness of the situation with a simple statement, *"There are no more children."*

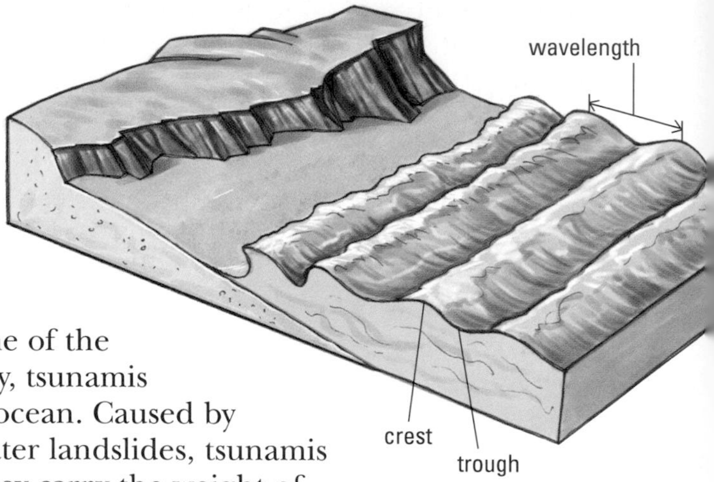

Tsunamis (formerly called tidal waves) are some of the largest, most devastating waves known. Surprisingly, tsunamis are barely noticeable where they first form in the ocean. Caused by earthquakes, volcanic eruptions, or giant underwater landslides, tsunamis may be less than 50 cm high on the surface, yet they carry the weight of the ocean's depth with them, and can travel at speeds of up to 800 km/h. When that force is squeezed into shallow waters, the energy contained in the wave becomes focused, and the wave grows rapidly. Fortunately, advancements in satellite technology are improving our ability to predict these waves and evacuate in advance.

Figure 1

The distance between one wave crest and the next is called the wavelength.

wavelength

crest

trough

Waves and Wind

Less dramatic than tsunamis, but much more common, are waves caused by wind. Waves on lakes and oceans may begin when wind pushes down unevenly on their surfaces. As the wind continues to blow across the water surface, the waves swell larger. The top of a wave is called the crest, the bottom is the trough, and the distance between crests is the **wavelength**. (See **Figure 1**.)

When waves make their way across water, it is energy that is moving, not water. If you were floating in the water, you would not be swept across the surface at the same speed as the waves. Instead, you would be moved up and down in a circular pattern, as shown in **Figure 2**.

Figure 2

Cross section of waves hitting beach

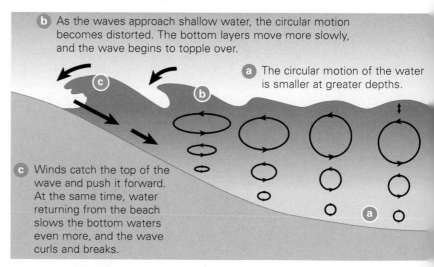

b As the waves approach shallow water, the circular motion becomes distorted. The bottom layers move more slowly, and the wave begins to topple over.

a The circular motion of the water is smaller at greater depths.

c Winds catch the top of the wave and push it forward. At the same time, water returning from the beach slows the bottom waters even more, and the wave curls and breaks.

Wave Power

Wind-blown waves can also reach tremendous heights. Tropical storms and hurricanes produce especially large waves due to their high wind speeds. Fortunately, these waves, unlike most tsunamis, come with considerable warning, giving people time to take precautions.

Waves can have both positive and negative effects on coastal areas. Tourists are drawn to places famous for surfing, and to areas where erosion by waves has carved out spectacular scenery. But similar wave action has caused cliffs to collapse, sometimes resulting in property damage. Waves are also responsible for longshore drift, the movement of beach material along a shoreline. People spend considerable time and money building structures (**Figure 3**) and replanting shorelines to reduce the effects of wave action.

Figure 3

The concrete extension shown here helps prevent beach sand from moving along the shore. This robs the beach of new sand. Millions of dollars are spent annually on pumping sand on shore to repair beaches. Working with the natural flow of beach sand and landscape design can prevent wave damage.

> ### Try This   Making Waves
>
> - Put on an apron. Using wet sand, make a sloped beach across one side of a shallow dishpan. Pack the sand down tightly to a depth of about 5 cm at its deepest side.
> - Slowly add water to a depth of 2–3 cm.
> - Using a ruler, make a series of waves to strike your beach head on.
>
> 1. How do they affect your beach?
>
> - Make waves that strike the beach on an angle.
>
> 2. What effect does this have?
>
> 3. How does changing the angle of the waves affect your sand beach?

Understanding Concepts

1. Would it take a long or short time for a note in a bottle to travel to land if thrown from a ship at sea? Explain.

2. Why are the rocks and stones found on pebble beaches usually rounded and smooth?

3. What observations did you make during the Try This activity that would help explain longshore drift?

Making Connections

4. List factors that need to be considered before deciding to develop a beachfront resort.

Exploring

5. Research "natural harbours" using print and (4A) electronic resources. How do they help protect against the negative effects of waves?

Reflecting

6. If you floated on a wave in the ocean, you would merely bob up and down. How then are surfers carried along by the waves they ride?

Design Challenge

After doing the Try This activity, what changes (if any) will you make to your plan for the Design Challenge on erosion control? Why?

Investigating Tides

Imagine you are walking along an ocean beach. You see marks left by the water and a line of debris washed ashore. As you continue to explore, you notice that the water level seems to change during the day. You are witnessing the effect of tides. **Tides** are high and low water levels caused by the gravitational pull of the moon and the sun and the spinning of Earth. The difference between the water levels at high tide and low tide is called the **tidal range**. (See **Figure 1**.) The line of debris shows the high water mark, that is, the water level at high tide.

Question
What geological factors affect tidal ranges?

Hypothesis
The slope of a coastline affects the tidal range.

Experimental Design
You will examine the effect that changing the slope of a coastline has on the tidal range, using models that you will construct.

Materials
Your teacher may provide you with some or all of the materials below.

- apron
- plastic dishpan
- pails or other containers
- 1- or 2-L containers
- ruler
- rocks, gravel, or pebbles
- thin sheets of wood, plastic, acetate, or Plexiglas
- water
- block to rest edge of the dishpan on
- waterproof tape or duct tape

Always obtain teacher approval to use any materials other than those provided.

Procedure

1 Measure the amount of water you use to create a low water level ("low tide") in your empty dishpan. Place a block under one edge to create the high tide.

✎ (a) Record the tidal range.

- You will use this as a control to compare the effects of changes you make to the dishpan.

2 Select some of the materials from those listed. Plan 3 or 4 different coastlines to construct, using the same materials each time. Remember to vary the slope of the coastlines as you plan.

3 Once your plans have been approved by your teacher, begin building and testing your models.

4 Using the same amount of water as in step 1, measure the low tide, high tide, and tidal range for each model that you build.

✎ (a) Record your results.

Figure 1

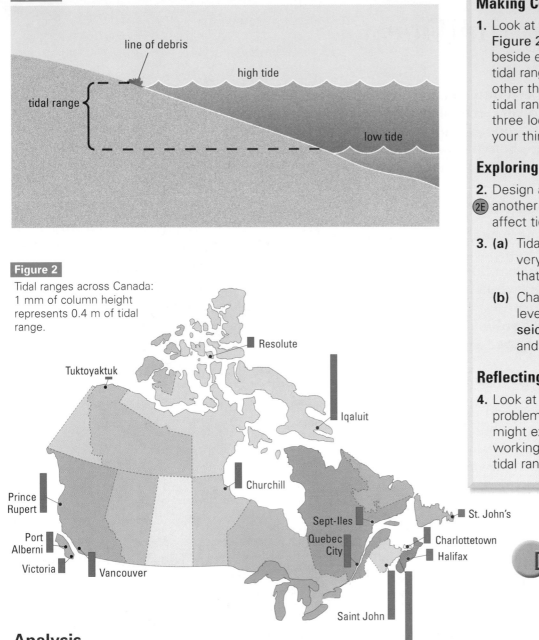

line of debris

high tide

tidal range

low tide

Figure 2

Tidal ranges across Canada: 1 mm of column height represents 0.4 m of tidal range.

Resolute

Tuktoyaktuk

Iqaluit

Churchill

Prince Rupert

Sept-Iles

St. John's

Port Alberni

Quebec City

Charlottetown

Halifax

Victoria

Vancouver

Saint John

Bay of Fundy

Making Connections

1. Look at the map of Canada in **Figure 2**. The water column beside each location shows the tidal range there. What factors, other than slope, might affect tidal ranges? Use at least three locations as evidence for your thinking.

Exploring

2. Design an experiment to test ②E another factor that might affect tidal ranges.

3. (a) Tidal ranges in lakes are very small. Why might that be?

   (b) Changes in lake water levels are often due to **seiches**. What is a seiche and how is it caused?

Reflecting

4. Look at **Figures 2** and **3**. What problems do you think people might experience living and working in areas with large tidal ranges?

Analysis

5 Analyze your results by answering the following questions.

(a) How did changing the slope of the coastline affect the tidal range in your simulation?

(b) Does the height of the coastline also affect the tidal range?

Figure 3

The Bay of Fundy in Nova Scotia experiences some of the highest and lowest tides in the world. At some places in the bay, tidal ranges average about 14.5 m, and ranges of 16.5 m have been recorded.

Design Challenge

What did you learn about the sequence of planning, constructing, and testing in this investigation that might help with your Design Challenge?

Exploring the Deep

Humans have always been intrigued by the sea with its hidden caverns and darkest depths. Today's technology allows us to explore and research the ocean in ways early explorers could hardly have imagined. (See **Figure 1**.) Underwater photography, for example, once requiring sophisticated equipment, is now possible for casual explorers.

Plumbing the Depths

Since the late 1700s, more and more sophisticated means of underwater transportation have been developed. Today's nuclear-powered submarines can stay submersed for weeks and are used mostly for defence purposes. The technologies developed for building submarines have led to deep-sea submersibles. (See **Figure 2**.)

From the Surface

Oceans can also be explored using surface vessels. Perhaps the most famous ocean research vessel, the *Calypso*, was captained by Jacques Cousteau. During his 50 years of ocean research, Cousteau helped perfect the aqualung, an early type of scuba gear. Through his television specials, Cousteau brought to public awareness the wonders, complexity, and fragile nature of the oceans.

Technology such as remote video (**Figure 3**), sonar (**Figure 4**), and core sampling allows researchers to explore the ocean's bottom while never venturing below the surface. Lowered from a ship, core samplers allow oceanographers to gather undisturbed layers of bottom sediment. With such samples, they study bottom deposits, nutrient concentrations, and the presence of organisms.

Figure 1

Scuba (Self-Contained Underwater Breathing Apparatus) gear was invented in the 1940s. Also used for recreation, scuba equipment is essential in the study of underwater ecosystems and for underwater work such as oil rig maintenance. Scuba divers are limited to short time periods and relatively shallow depths. Unlike wetsuits, dry suits keep water away from a scuba diver's body, allowing exploration in extremely cold waters.

Figure 2

The French submersible *Nautile* was used by explorers to photograph and retrieve items from the *Titanic*. To survive the incredible pressure of the deep ocean (the *Titanic* lies at 3780 m below sea level), the *Nautile*'s hull is made from titanium metal, with thick curved Plexiglas for the portholes. Launched from a ship, researchers in the *Nautile* can remain submerged for eight hours. The *Nautile* is equipped with sonar, floodlights, a video camera, and an arm for retrieving objects on the sea bed.

Figure 3

This remote video camera can be steered into places too small, too deep, or too dangerous for human exploration. Less expensive to run, the deep-sea video camera can also be used for "scouting" trips before launching a submersible.

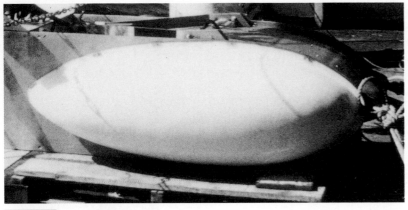

Figure 4
In World War I, echo sounding was used for simple depth measurements. Single sound pulses were sent down from a ship. The time taken for the echo to return indicated how deep the sea bed was at that point. By WW II, sonar (SOund NAvigation and Ranging) equipment was used to locate ships and submarines. Cartographers now use sonar for mapping the sea floor. The Deep Tow Seismic System shown here was developed by a Toronto firm and is used by scientists to map sediments on the continental shelf.

Oceans from Above

Aerial photography can give scientists and geologists additional information when studying such things as shoreline movement and the source and extent of chemical and thermal pollution (the addition of excess heat to a water body). **Figure 5** illustrates the power of satellite imaging. With their instruments and computers, meteorologists (scientists who investigate weather) gather information about the force, path, and potential destructiveness of hurricanes and tropical storms.

Figure 5
Satellite imaging is allowing oceanographers to look at oceans in ways never before possible. Using special imaging programs, they can see patterns of depth, thermal activity, phytoplankton production (shown here), and global pollution.

Understanding Concepts

1. What devices on the *Nautile* can aid ocean research? How might these devices have been used in exploring the *Titanic*?

2. Choose a device described in this lesson (or, with your teacher's approval, a related one) and design a poster describing the device in detail and explaining its role in ocean exploration and research. Alternatively, write a story that involves the technology and capabilities of at least one device.

Making Connections

3. Explain why we have not been able to study the ocean depths closely until just recently.

4. Evaluate the effectiveness of visual images and TV specials in increasing public awareness and concern about ocean resources.

5. In some harbours, battleships are being sunk for recreational diving expeditions. Discuss the positive and negative effects of this practice.

Exploring

6. Discuss the social and environmental issues involved in 4B salvaging shipwrecks. Interview a recreational scuba diver on the dos and don'ts of diving to wrecks.

7. What are some of the problems that must be resolved when living and working underwater for long periods of time?

Reflecting

8. Name one question or concern you have regarding the oceans. What type of technology could help discover an answer or solution?

Oil: Wealth from the Ocean Floor

Oil is the liquefied remains of plants and animals that lived millions of years ago. After these organisms died, they were covered by layers of mud and silt. As more layers were added, time and pressure gradually turned the remains into fossil fuel. During this process, gas escaping from the fuel may have collected above the liquid oil. Most oil deposits are trapped under layers of rock, many beneath the ocean floor.

Figure 1

In 1859, oil flowed from the world's first successful oil well at Oil Springs, near Petrolia, Ontario.

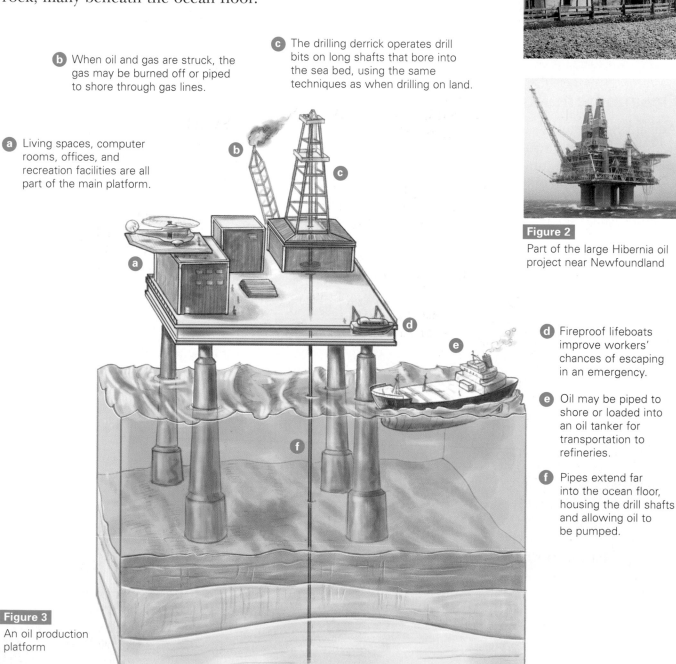

b When oil and gas are struck, the gas may be burned off or piped to shore through gas lines.

c The drilling derrick operates drill bits on long shafts that bore into the sea bed, using the same techniques as when drilling on land.

a Living spaces, computer rooms, offices, and recreation facilities are all part of the main platform.

Figure 2

Part of the large Hibernia oil project near Newfoundland

d Fireproof lifeboats improve workers' chances of escaping in an emergency.

e Oil may be piped to shore or loaded into an oil tanker for transportation to refineries.

f Pipes extend far into the ocean floor, housing the drill shafts and allowing oil to be pumped.

Figure 3

An oil production platform

Drilling for Oil

Since the success at Oil Springs (**Figure 1**), countless wells around the world have tried to satisfy our ever-increasing demand for oil. With many oil reserves on land already tapped, we now look offshore to the ocean to meet our oil needs. Geologists use sophisticated equipment to locate deposits by sending shock waves through the ocean, deep into the rock below.

After a potential deposit is located, workers do a "wildcat" or test drill to see if a full drilling operation is worthwhile. If an undersea deposit looks promising, a production platform like the ones in **Figures 2** and **3** is constructed. Some platforms, such as those in the Gulf of Mexico, are stationary, fixed permanently to the ocean floor. Others are mobile so they can move out of the way of approaching icebergs.

Following a spill (**Figure 4**) during extraction or transportation, some oil settles on the bottom, some evaporates, and some is dispersed by the sea. A large portion, though, washes onto the nearby coast. Clean-up can last for months as waves continue to deposit oil clumps on the shore.

Oily feathers can cause birds to drown or freeze as feathers lose their insulating ability. (See **Figure 5**.) As birds try to preen themselves, they ingest or inhale the oil. Plankton, oysters, fish, lobsters, and various sea mammals are also at risk.

Figure 4

Because oil companies want to maintain safe wells, the amount of oil spilled into the oceans is decreasing. However, accidents still happen.

Figure 5

Since most offshore rigs are on continental shelves close to shore, spills can have devastating effects on plant, animal, and microscopic life.

Understanding Concepts

1. Create a flow chart to show the steps from locating oil below the ocean floor to extracting it.

Making Connections

2. Copy and complete **Table 1**. Identify the activities associated with oil exploration and drilling and list the possible benefits and costs of each activity.

Exploring

3. Research and describe specific (4A) effects oil spills have had on marine organisms.

Reflecting

4. What commercial products are made from oil? Which ones would you and your family be willing to do without, in the event of an oil shortage?

Design Challenge

Review what happens to oil when it spills into sea water. Think of how you might alter your oil spill eliminator to keep the oil contained.

Table 1	Oil from the Ocean Floor—Benefits and Costs	
Activity	**Benefits**	**Costs**
• burning waste gases on rig	• easy • less expensive than piping to shore • quick	• air pollution • danger of uncontrolled fire

Diversity

As you look into a freshwater pond, past the cattails and arrowheads growing at the side, you spot small stickleback fish darting back and forth. Water striders scoot about on the surface and dragonflies zip above the water in their search for mosquitos. On the far side, a turtle lazes on a rock while ducks paddle past. Redwing blackbirds nest in the reeds, and below them diving beetles, boatmen, and water scorpions hunt for food.

Figure 1

Diversity in fresh water

a Freshwater swamps lie in lowlands where the ground's surface is covered in water for at least part of the year. Swamps have many trees, which in parts of Canada include red and silver maple, black ash, white cedar, and willow. Daphnia, closteria, and rotifers are among the many microscopic organisms found in freshwater swamps.

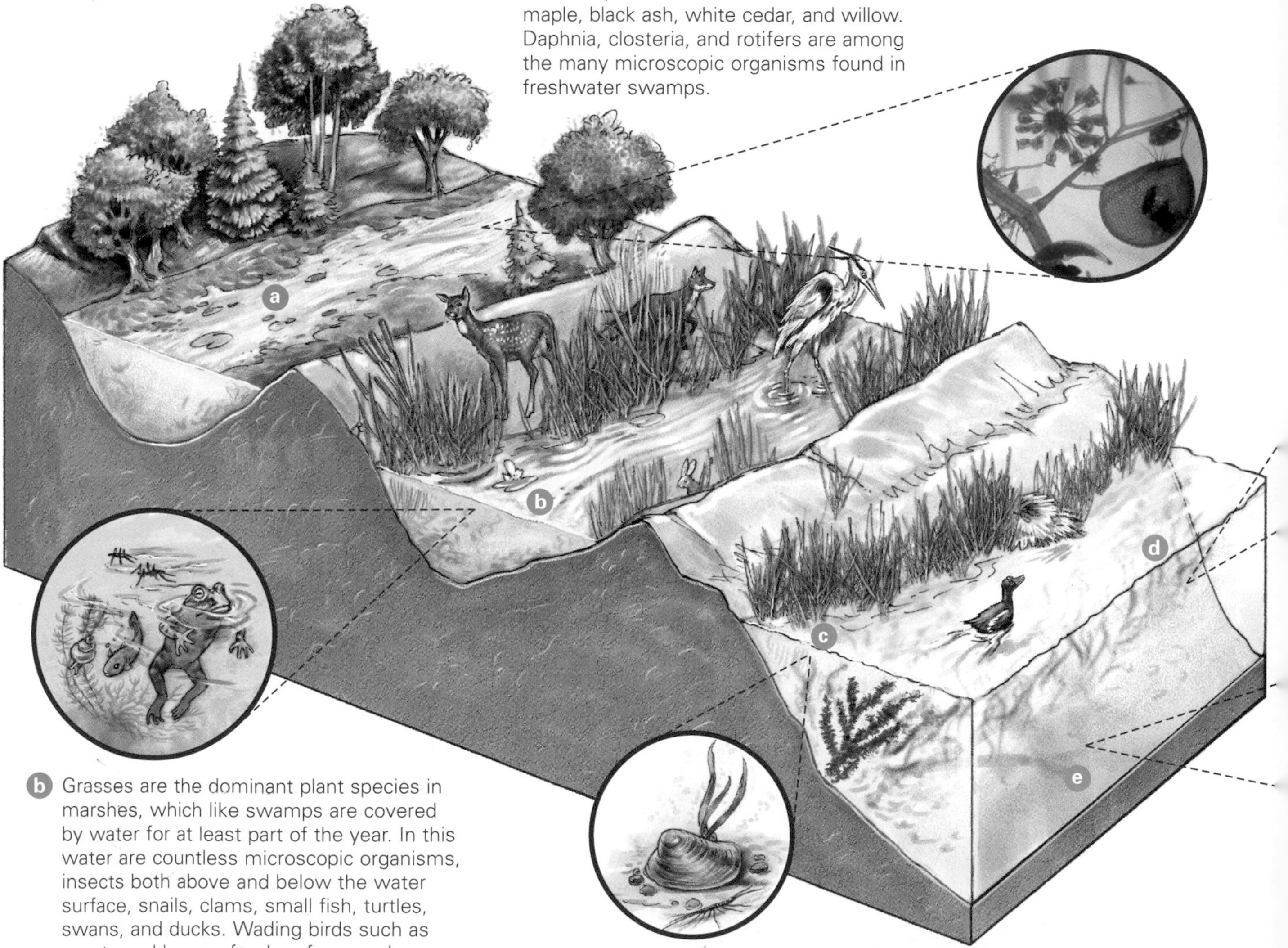

b Grasses are the dominant plant species in marshes, which like swamps are covered by water for at least part of the year. In this water are countless microscopic organisms, insects both above and below the water surface, snails, clams, small fish, turtles, swans, and ducks. Wading birds such as egrets and herons feed on frogs and small fish. Occasional inhabitants of the marsh include fox, raccoon, weasel, deer, and rabbit.

c At the edge of a freshwater lake, you could find reeds, cattails, and water lilies. Algae could grow on the rocky bottom. Suspended in the water are many microscopic diatoms. Frogs, snails, mussels, and crayfish live in the shallows, as do insects such as dragonfly larvae, water striders, and water scorpions. Fish include minnows, sunfish, and pumpkinseeds. Ducks and coots could nest along the shores, and beavers could build lodges.

Later, you stop by a fast-moving stream. Most of the rocky bottom is clear except for a scattering of algae-covered stones. After searching for a while you find two crayfish and some caddis-fly larvae in their stone-encrusted shelters. You glimpse the quick darting of a brook trout. Both ecosystems are healthy. The pond simply has greater diversity. **Diversity** is a measure of the number of different types of organisms in an area.

d Phytoplankton and algae dominate the open water as deep as the sunlight penetrates. Zooplankton (single-celled creatures and tiny animals) feed on these organisms. In warm-water lakes, sunfish, pike, and smallmouth bass are typical species of fish, with trout and whitefish in colder, deeper lakes.

Figures 1 and **4** (pages 246–7) show the types of organisms that can be found in the areas described, plus some of the factors governing their distribution. These diagrams are not to scale. No diagram could possibly capture the truly awesome complexity or diversity that exists across Canada and around the world.

You know that food chains like the one in **Figure 2** tell partial stories of which organisms eat which other organisms. Food webs are made up of several interconnected food chains. (See **Figure 3**.) Food webs are useful because they tell a more complete story of the feeding patterns within an ecosystem than food chains do.

Figure 2

This food chain is read as "algae are eaten by tadpoles, which are eaten by sunfish, which are eaten by smallmouth bass, which are eaten by humans."

algae → tadpole → sunfish → smallmouth bass → human

Figure 3

A partial food web in a marsh ecosystem

e Bottom feeders in the lake might include sturgeon, catfish, and bullheads, depending on the depth and temperature.

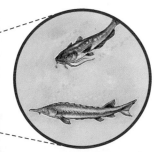

Adapted for Survival

Plants and animals have adapted to life under specific conditions, and typically can tolerate only minor changes in environmental conditions before their health and reproductive abilities suffer. Most freshwater organisms would die quickly if placed in salt water, and the same is true for marine organisms placed in fresh water.

Even within freshwater and saltwater systems, plants and animals are found only in very specific places. For example, trout, which require the high levels of oxygen found in cold waters, would die in warm, oxygen-low waters occupied by many catfish. In oceans, only very specialized organisms can tolerate the changing conditions of light, moisture, and temperature experienced along the shores between high and low tides. Fewer still can survive under the conditions of total darkness and extreme pressure found on the ocean floor.

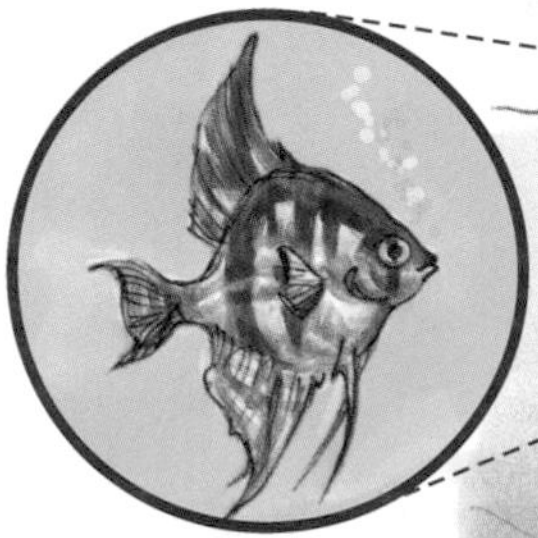

i The coral reef is another specialized ocean ecosystem that is extremely diverse. Made from the skeletons of countless corals, it provides shelter to incredible numbers of sea creatures. Common species include many types of coral, sea anemones, sea slugs, clown fish, and angel fish. One of the best-known coral reefs is the Great Barrier Reef off the northeast coast of Australia.

h Vents are hot springs in the ocean floor. At these sites, found in the Pacific and Mid-Atlantic Ridges, superheated water spews out of the ocean floor, carrying large quantities of dissolved minerals. The mineral deposits form smokestack-like structures called chimneys. In this unique ecosystem, specialized bacteria actually obtain their energy from the minerals; they are considered as producers. These bacteria are food for giant tube worms, eyeless shrimp, and hairy snails.

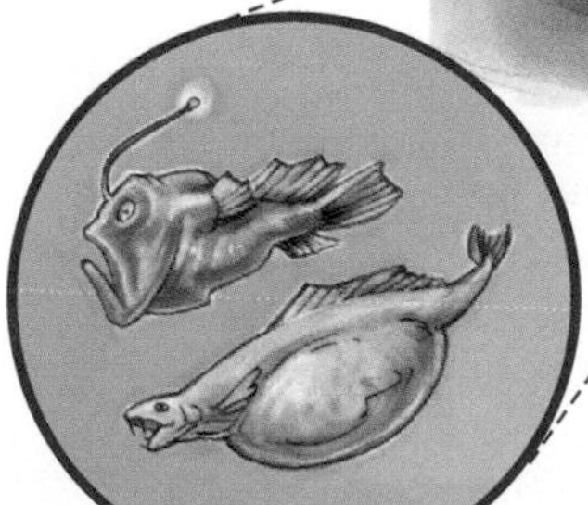

g The deep, dark abyss of the ocean shows the least diversity but is home to some of the strangest-looking fish known. Many have huge mouths and expandable stomachs so that when they find food, they can consume as much as possible. They also have light-emitting organs used for communication or attracting prey. Fish species include the anglerfish, the whipper fish, and the gulper eel. Brittle stars and sea cucumbers may be found on the sea floor. Because of the lack of light, no producers are found in this region.

a In saltwater swamps, mangrove trees rise above the water on their stiltlike roots. Crabs, conchs, shellfish, and a wide variety of bird species are found here. Many fish and other marine animals breed among the mangrove roots.

b In saltwater marshes, the grasses and other plants found must be adapted to extremely harsh conditions because water levels and salt concentrations change frequently. Similar to freshwater marshes, saltwater marshes are home to small fish, crabs, snails, and other mollusks. Song birds and wading birds such as egrets and herons are found among the grasses, along with ducks, frogs, and turtles. Rabbits, foxes, and snakes use the marsh for food and shelter.

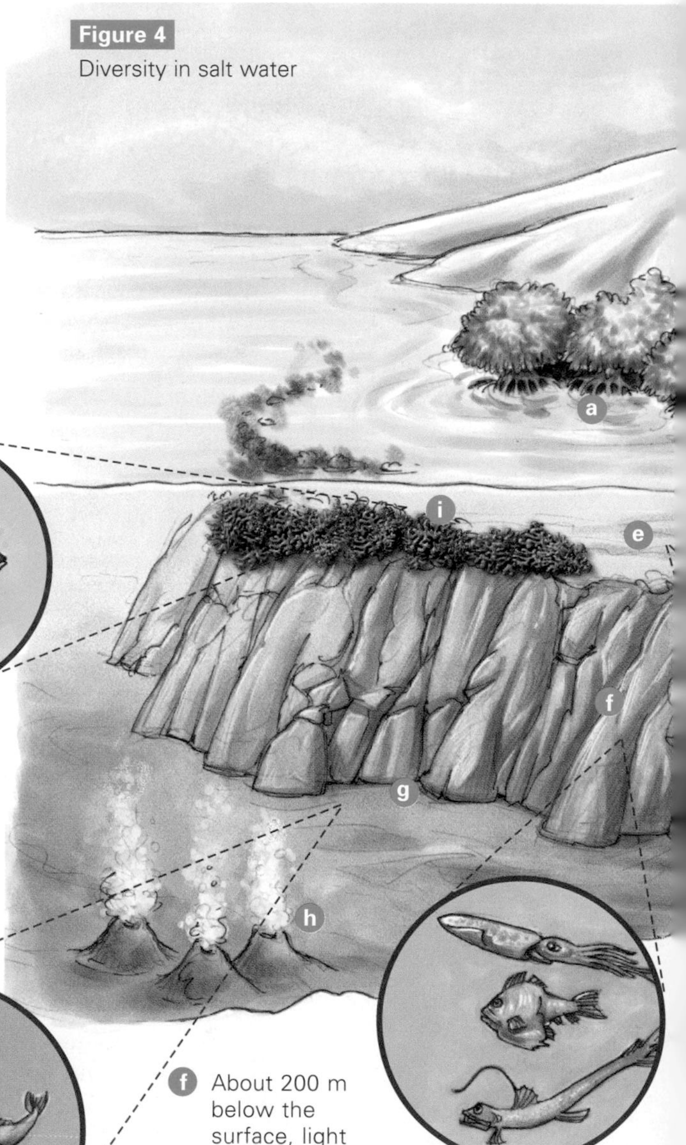

Figure 4

Diversity in salt water

f About 200 m below the surface, light does not penetrate. Few producers exist. Fish species here include hatchet, lancet, and viper fish. Squid also live in this zone. Many animals travel to the upper waters at night to feed, and the scavengers and decomposers feed on the dead plants and animals that rain down from the waters above.

c Much of the shallow ocean floor on the continental shelf, covered in sand and mud, supports little plant growth. Bottom-dwelling animals include flounder, weaver fish, the manta and eagle rays, clams, crabs, and many burrowing worms.

d Rocky seabeds, also found on the continental shelf, allow seaweed, like kelp, to anchor and grow. This again increases diversity by providing food and shelter. Lobster, starfish, clams, mussels, and sea anemones are a few of the species found here. Sea otters can be seen feeding on the clams.

e The upper layers of the ocean, where light penetrates, are the most productive. Plantlike phytoplankton and algae photosynthesize (use light to make food), grow, and reproduce. These are consumed by zooplankton, such as opossum shrimp, crab larvae, and water fleas. Zooplankton are eaten by schools of small fish such as herring, which are then eaten by larger fish, seals, seagulls, dolphins, and whales.

Benefits of Diversity

Usually, the more diverse an ecosystem is, the more easily it can withstand change. If one organism, say a type of fish, disappeared, other fish species would continue to consume insects and provide food for larger fish. Ecosystems with little diversity are usually extremely fragile. If an organism disappeared from or entered into this type of ecosystem, it could cause very rapid, dramatic change.

Understanding Concepts

1. What is meant by diversity?

2. Why must all food webs contain producers?

3. Choose one area of a freshwater system and a similar area of a saltwater system. Compare the types of organisms that have adapted to live there.

4. Why does diversity tend to decrease the deeper you go in an ocean or lake?

5. If all food webs must include producers, how do organisms in the deepest parts of lakes or oceans survive where no producers exist?

Exploring

6. Select one organism from a saltwater ecosystem and build a food web that includes that organism. Do the same for an organism from a freshwater
4A ecosystem. Use encyclopedias, on-line search engines, or other resources to do some research on these organisms to get sufficient information. Once the food webs are complete, share them with other students. Compare the freshwater food webs with the saltwater ones. What do you notice?

Reflecting

7. Based on what you have learned, what effect do you think a sudden change in environmental conditions would have on the diversity of an ecosystem?

Productivity of Organisms

Productivity is a measure of how well organisms reproduce. Productivity can be affected by an organism's age, health, and environmental conditions. Humans affect the productivity of organisms by dumping foreign material into their water systems. Think of what leaves your home in a single day: hand soap, dish detergent, food particles, and human waste. For many years phosphates were used in detergents. Perhaps you've used fertilizers or pesticides on your lawn. Could they change the productivity of aquatic organisms? (See **Figures 1** and **2**.)

Question
How do fertilizers and phosphates affect the productivity of algae?

Hypothesis

1 Develop a hypothesis about how fertilizers and phosphates
(2C) affect algae growth. State your reasons.

Experimental Design
In this investigation, you will examine the effects of fertilizers and phosphates on one type of aquatic organism.

2 Design a data table to record the amounts of materials
(6D) used and your observations for each test tube.

Materials
- apron
- safety goggles
- 10 large test tubes
- labels
- test-tube stand
- graduated cylinder
- water
- eye dropper
- liquid plant fertilizer solution
- phosphate solution
- algae suspension

 Wear safety goggles and an apron during this investigation. Fertilizer and phosphate solutions are toxic and irritants. Handle with care.

Procedure

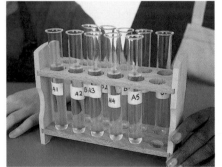

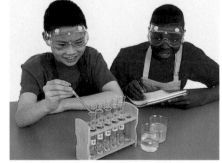

3 Mark the first 5 test tubes A1, A2, A3, A4, A5 and the second set B1, B2, B3, B4, B5.
- Add the same amount of water to each of the 10 test tubes.

✎ (a) Record whatever you add to each test tube.

4 Add increasing amounts of the plant fertilizer solution to the set of test tubes marked "A." For example, put 0 drops in A1, 2 drops in A2, 4 drops in A3, and so on.

5 Add increasing amounts of phosphate solution to the set of test tubes marked "B."

6 Add equal amounts of algae suspension to each of the 10 test tubes.

✎ (a) Record your observations for each test tube.

SKILLS HANDBOOK: (2C) Predicting and Hypothesizing (2E) Designing an Inquiry Investigation

Figure 1
Fertilizers and chemicals can leach into the water system and affect organisms there.

Figure 2
The water below the surface cover in this pond also appears green because algae in the pond have reproduced at an incredible rate. Such a population explosion is called an algae bloom. Algae blooms can seriously deplete the oxygen levels in ponds, especially when algae dies and decays, which can seriously harm fish and other water organisms.

Making Connections

1. In 1972 the Canadian government regulated the amounts of phosphates in soaps and detergents. Why?

2. Agriculture workers, golf course maintenance workers, and home owners use many pesticides and herbicides—poisons designed to kill certain insects and plants. Often these poisons affect other organisms. How might these chemicals enter local water systems? Describe their effects on the organisms living there. How could any negative effects be minimized?

Exploring

3. Design an experiment to
   (2E) compare the effects on algae productivity of "phosphate reduced" detergents with detergents that make no such claim.

Analysis

7 Place the 10 test tubes where they will all receive the same amount of heat and sunlight.
- Mark the tubes with your name, class, and start date.

(a) Examine the test tubes each day and record your observations for two weeks.

8 Analyze your results by answering the following questions.

(a) Which amount of fertilizer solution appeared to have the greatest effect on algae productivity? Which amount of phosphate solution? State your evidence.

(b) If test tube A1 contains no fertilizer, it is a control. Did you have a control for the "B" test tubes? Why or why not?

(c) Write a paragraph explaining any similarities between the effects of fertilizer and the effects of phosphates on the algae.

4.20 Inquiry Investigation

SKILLS MENU
- Questioning
- Hypothesizing
- Planning
- Conducting
- Recording
- Analyzing
- Communicating

The Brine Shrimp Experiment

Saltwater monkeys? Growing in an aquarium? Have you ever seen an advertisement for such creatures? In 1960, a toy inventor and lover of science named Harold von Braunhut brought fame to a species of tiny creatures commonly known until then as brine shrimp. Obviously not "monkeys," brine shrimp are a species of small, marine animal. (See **Figure 1**.) As a food source for small fish, they play an important part in many food chains. Since they are found in a variety of salt water locations, they often face different levels of salinity (concentrations of salt).

Even in the ocean, salinity levels fluctuate. This happens in estuaries, where fresh river water mixes with salty sea water. (See **Figure 2**.) It also happens in warm and cold latitudes, where evaporation or freezing can draw off fresh water, leaving saltier solutions behind. Is it possible that these varying salt concentrations can affect animal productivity?

In this investigation, you will examine whether different salinity levels have an effect on the hatch rate of brine shrimp cysts ("eggs"). To keep within the shrimp's range of tolerance for salinity (the upper and lower limits between which an organism functions best), vary the salt concentrations in small steps from that suggested on the instructions that come with the cysts. Levels should always be between 5 g and 30 g of salt per 1 L of water.

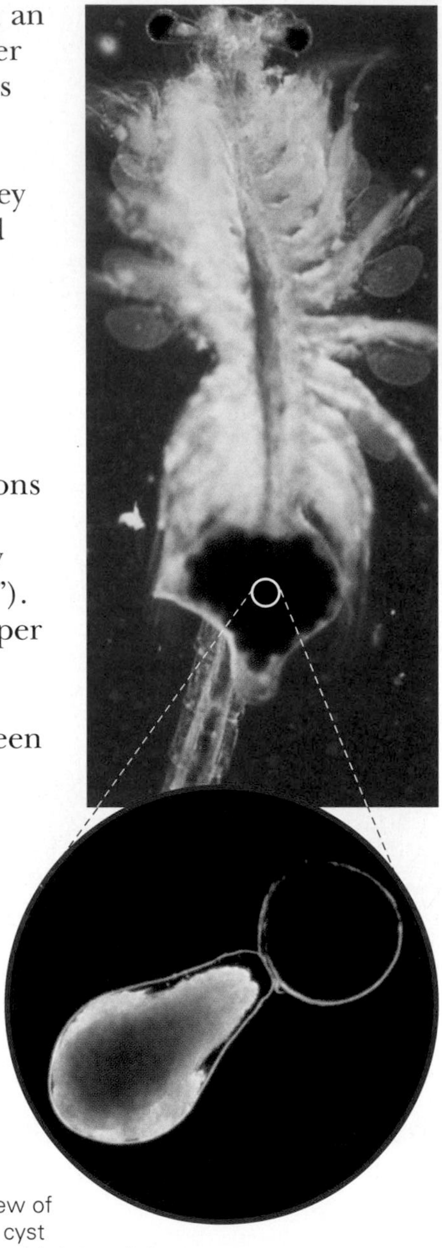

Figure 1
Magnified view of brine shrimp cyst ("egg") with adult brine shrimp

Question

1 After reading the above paragraphs, write a question that
(2B) you will try to answer. State the question in a testable form.

Hypothesis

2 Predict what you think you will observe. Write a hypothesis
(2C) explaining your prediction. State your reasons.

Experimental Design

3 Design an experiment to test your
(2E) hypothesis. Read the instructions that come with the brine shrimp, look closely at the cysts, then plan your experiment by answering the following questions.

(a) What steps will you take to answer the question you posed in step 1? Be specific. Remember, brine shrimp cysts are extremely tiny.

(b) What variable(s) will you change? (2D)

(c) What will you use as your control?

(d) What will you measure?

(6) (e) How will you record your measurements?

(8) (f) How will you report your findings?

SKILLS HANDBOOK: (2) Process of

Figure 2

As fresh river water mixes with the ocean, salt concentrations change.

Making Connections

1. How might your findings relate to the productivity of brine shrimp in the natural world?

Exploring

2. Design an experiment to test a different environmental condition. Check with your teacher before attempting it. Observe all safety precautions.

3. After using print and electronic resources to research appropriate aquarium conditions, set up a small aquarium to maintain your shrimp colony. How will these conditions differ from those in the investigation?

Reflecting

4. What difficulties did you experience with this investigation? How did you solve them?

Design Challenge

What did you learn from designing and conducting this investigation that might help you design a fair test for your Design Challenge?

Materials

4 Decide on the materials you will need to complete the experiment, and list them in your notebook.

Procedure

5 Show your experimental plan and list of materials to your teacher. With your teacher's approval, begin the experiment, wearing an apron.

(a) Record any changes you make to your plan as you proceed.

(b) Record all observations.

Analysis

6 Analyze your results by answering the following questions.

(a) What was the answer to your question in step 1? Explain the evidence for your answer.

(b) What variables did you keep constant during the experiment?

(c) Write a report describing your investigation.

Hi Chelsea! Boo!

People, Resources, and Water Systems

Have you ever thought that the water in a lake or stream could be traded or bought? Your generation may be the Canadians who decide whether to sell some of Canada's fresh water to other parts of the world. (See **Figure 1**.)

In Search of Plenty

Canada's abundant water is attractive to other countries for one main reason: to help grow food. Most areas with ideal conditions for plant growth are already being used for farming. Yet as the human population increases, so does the need for more farmland. Many people face starvation unless more food can be grown. Farming is one of the largest users of fresh water.

Irrigation

One way to increase the amount of food grown is to irrigate the fields. (See **Figure 2**.) **Irrigation** brings water to otherwise dry areas from rivers, lakes, or ground water. For example, in Uzbekistan (in Asia), massive systems of dams and canals diverted water that used to flow into the Aral Sea. Millions of hectares of land became productive farmland. But huge irrigation projects like this can also be disastrous. Once the fourth-largest body of inland water, the Aral Sea began to dry up. Scientists predict it will disappear completely by 2010. The fishing industry on the Aral Sea died—the last fish was caught in 1983. To make matters worse, after a few years, large sections of the irrigated fields became crusted with salt. Crop production, which had increased dramatically after the irrigation projects began, has since fallen sharply.

Despite these problems, agriculture experts still think that irrigation is an effective way to grow more food. This makes Canada's vast water supply an important resource not only to Canadians, but to the rest of the world. Two projects, the GRAND (Great Recycling and Northern Development) and Rocky Mountain Trench (**Figure 3**) schemes, suggested years ago, are being discussed again. The GRAND project, for example, proposes to dam James Bay, slowly converting it into a large, freshwater lake. This new lake would then be connected to the Great Lakes by a large canal, and its water sold south of the border. The North American Free Trade Agreement might reduce some of the political and economic barriers to water sales as fewer restrictions are placed on goods traded.

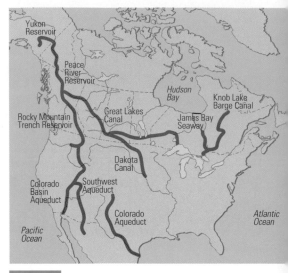

Figure 1
Several huge projects, including canals and aqueducts, are proposed to divert water south.

Figure 2
Ground water, dug wells, lakes, and rivers are all potential sources of water for irrigation.

Figure 3
The Rocky Mountain Trench, beginning near Cranbrook, B.C., extends 1400 km to the northwest. Thirsty farms in California could benefit from a proposal to dam and flood part of the trench. This would result in a huge freshwater canal, carrying water from the Mackenzie River southward.

Understanding Concepts

1. How is water physically diverted in an irrigation project?

2. What problems can large-scale irrigation projects cause?

Role Play — Water for Sale (8D)

Your town is considering a local company's proposal to sell water to the United States. The project could give the town's economy a much-needed boost. The resulting changes in climate could also affect the rich ecosystem that surrounds the area, currently a major tourist draw.

The town council has called a public meeting so that interested townspeople and other parties can discuss the pros and cons of accepting the proposal. Playing one of the roles below, you will participate in this town meeting. Are you in favour of selling Canada's water through projects like the GRAND? Consider the economic, environmental, and social impact the project may have.

The Roles

- The businessperson who got the idea and would like to divert the water only to places where it is truly needed

- The mayor of the town, who knows that the project could generate significant new income for the town, but is worried that the tourist trade may suffer

- A wildlife biologist who has evidence that the project would have a major impact on wildlife

- A vegetable grower who would consider buying Canadian fresh water, but not before knowing more about the issues

- A climatologist who has evidence that diverting water southward would change regional weather patterns

How Would You Act?

- In your role, prepare to form and express an opinion of the water sale project.

- Identify which other players you would agree with. Who would you have a harder time convincing?

- To support your position, search newspapers, a library periodical (4A) index, the Internet, and other sources for information on water projects like the GRAND.

- Prepare to present your opinion and evidence to others in your class. (8) Consider, too, how you would act on your opinions. Would you start a petition? Conduct further studies? Develop a poster campaign?

Design Challenge

SKILLS MENU
- Identify a Problem
- Planning
- Building
- Testing
- Recording
- Evaluating
- Communicating

Design and Build a Device to Live Safely with Water

Human beings face many challenges in safely using and maintaining water systems. We have the power to influence—and often damage—Earth's water systems. Water also has the power to harm us, as well as sustain us. Creative use of technology can help us preserve healthy water systems and protect ourselves, other living things, and the environment.

1 A Device to Make Safe Drinking Water

Problem situation

Most Canadians have clean, safe drinking water available at the turn of a tap. This is not true in many areas of the world. Millions of people use water that contains disease-causing organisms and other impurities. Many live at the edge of an ocean, undrinkable because of its high salt content.

Figure 1
Visible salt signals undrinkable water.

Design brief

- Design and build an inexpensive device for separating and collecting fresh water from sea water or polluted water.

🛑 Never drink or even taste anything from a science class.

Design criteria

- Sunlight must be the only source of energy.
- The device must have a collection system for gathering the fresh water from an impure sample provided by your teacher.
- Make a plan for disposal of the salt or residue that remains.

2 Structures to Prevent Damage from Water

Problem situation

Why do some trees growing along a river bank have exposed roots? As the water moves past the soil and rock at the river's edge, it carries small amounts away. Wave action along the shores of lakes and oceans can cause similar problems. The sand and silt carried in the water may harm fish and other aquatic organisms. If banks slide, trees and even homes may fall into the water.

Figure 2
Moving water can cause considerable land damage.

Design brief

- Design a product that will stabilize shorelines and reduce the erosion effects of wave action. Build a working model of your erosion control.

Design criteria

- Your model must include: (a) a soil- or sand-based shoreline; (b) water, with waves striking the shore at different angles; and (c) a scale model of the structure(s) used to stabilize the shore.
- The model must visibly demonstrate wave actions.

The 1989 oil spill of the *Exxon Valdez*

3 Cleanup for Oil Spills

Problem situation

As the world's population increases, the need for crude oil will increase as well. So too will the risk of oil spills, whether from cargo ships, from offshore drilling rigs, or from shore-based industrial plants. If humans want to maintain healthy water systems, we need to develop products, techniques, and safety practices that will help us prevent oil spills and minimize any damage from them.

Design brief

- Design a product that will surround and absorb a simulated oil spill. This challenge might involve two steps: a model of the containment device and the clean-up process itself.

Design criteria

- The model device must be able to contain a simulated oil spill and remove as much of the oil and as little of the water as possible.

When preparing to build or test a design, have your plan approved by your teacher before you begin.

Assessment

Your model will be assessed according to how well you:

Process
- understand the problem
- develop a safe plan
- choose and safely use appropriate materials, tools, and equipment
- test and record results
- evaluate your model, including suggestions for improvement

Communication
- prepare a presentation
- use correct terms
- write clear descriptions of the steps you took in building and testing your model
- explain clearly how your model solves the problem
- make an accurate technical drawing for your model

Product
- meet the design criteria with your model
- use your chosen materials effectively
- construct your model
- solve the identified problem

Unit 4 Summary

In this unit you have learned how Earth's water in all its forms makes up a system that shapes our world, sustains life, and deserves respectful treatment by humans.

Reflecting

- Reflect on the ideas and questions presented in the Unit Overview and in the Getting Started. How can you connect what you have done and learned in this unit with those ideas and questions? (To review, check the sections indicated in this Summary.)
- Revise your answers to the Reflecting questions in ❶,❷,❸ and the questions you created in the Getting Started. How has your thinking changed?
- What new questions do you have? How will you answer them?

Understanding Concepts

- identify the different states of water, giving specific examples from nature 4.1, 4.3

- describe how water moves through the water cycle 4.1, 4.3, 4.5

- compare the formation of geological features on land with those on the ocean floor 4.9

- describe how currents redistribute nutrients and dissolved oxygen 4.12

- describe wave formation and the positive and negative effects of waves 4.14

- explain, using specific examples, how bodies of water affect climate 4.10, 4.12, 4.13

- compare the diversity of organisms in saltwater and freshwater environments 4.18

Applying Skills

- compare the physical characteristics of salt water with those of fresh water 4.2

- demonstrate how changes in temperature affect water movement 4.11

- explain, using simulations, how geological features affect tides 4.15

- design, plan, and conduct investigations to describe relationships between environmental factors and productivity of organisms 4.19, 4.20

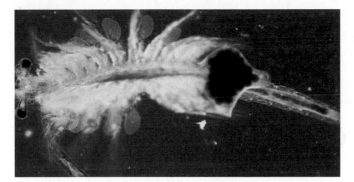

- Understand and use the following terms:

acid precipitation	irrigation
aquifer	overturn
aquitard	percolation
basin	precipitation
capillary action	productivity
chlorination	runoff
condensation	salinity
Continental Divide	saturated zone
continental shelf	seamount
convection current	sediment
current	seiche
diversity	system
erosion	tidal range
estuary	tide
evaporation	trench
flocculation	tributaries
flood plain	tsunami
fresh water	water cycle
glacier	watershed
ground water	water table
guyot	wavelength
gyre	

Making Connections

- identify methods developed to limit damage caused by water 4.4, 4.8, 4.14, 4.17

- describe how the water cycle affects the water table 4.5, 4.8

- explain how water is processed before and after being used by people 4.7

- describe at least two careers related to water systems 4.8, 4.16, 4.17

- describe how new technologies have helped improve ocean exploration 4.16

- evaluate how human use of natural resources has affected water systems 4.4, 4.17

- evaluate how human use of water affects water systems 4.6, 4.7, 4.8, 4.21

Unit 4 Review

Understanding Concepts

1. Which of the following is ranked correctly from greatest salinity to least salinity?
   (a) Dead Sea, ocean, estuary, Lake Winnipeg
   (b) ocean, estuary, Dead Sea, Lake Winnipeg
   (c) Lake Winnipeg, estuary, ocean, Dead Sea
   (d) ocean, Dead Sea, estuary, Lake Winnipeg

2. When you compared salt water and fresh water in Investigation 4.2, you rinsed your slides with distilled water. How does distilled water differ from fresh water?

3. Copy **Table 1** in your notebook. Write where each item can be found in water systems. The first one is done for you.

4. Complete the table begun in section 4.1, "Water in Our World."

5. The ship on the Welland Canal shown in **Figure 1** is fully loaded and sailing for England. What level do you think the waterline will be at once the ship is on the ocean? Explain your answer.

7. Which of the following statements are not true? Explain why.
   (a) Acid precipitation includes snow.
   (b) Acid rain causes lake water to become cloudy.
   (c) Acid rain can dissolve some buildings.
   (d) Acid rain has no effect on trees.

8. Compare the urban and rural treatment of water after it is used in the home. List the similarities and differences between these treatments.

Table 1

Item	Location
liquid water	rivers, streams, lakes, oceans, estuaries, marshes, precipitation, taps, living things
solid water	?
water vapour	?
salt water	?
brackish water	?
saturated zone	?
sediment	?

9. Draw a series of simple sketches to show how the Mid-Atlantic Ridge (**Figure 2**) is being formed. Label each sketch.

Figure 1

6. Explain the connection between bacteria and beach closures in the summer.

Figure 2

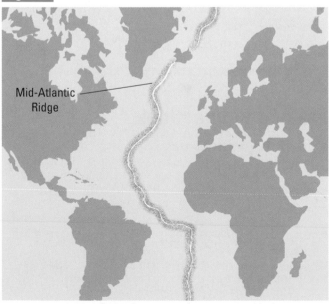

Mid-Atlantic Ridge

10. Describe how guyots are formed.

11. Use the word "basin" to explain how lakes, oceans, and mud puddles are similar.

12. Alpine and continental glaciers are similar because
    (a) both occur in mountains
    (b) both tend to flow
    (c) both contribute to polar icecaps
    (d) both are responsible for helping to cause deep ocean currents

13. If the snow and ice in glaciers are tens of thousands of years old, explain how they can be part of the water cycle.

Figure 3

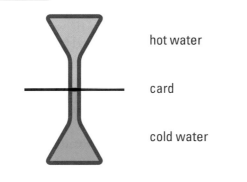

14. Describe how the waters in **Figure 3** above would mix once the card is removed. What would happen if the hot and cold water samples were reversed?

15. Design a chart to compare river currents with ocean currents. Discuss the characteristics of each and the effects of each on their surroundings.

16. Why do waves "fall forward" when they reach a beach? Explain using a diagram.

17. How are deep-sea submersibles designed to protect researchers from the pressure of the ocean?

18. Describe the purpose of a wildcat drill.

19. Which of the following are true about marshes?
    (a) Grass is the dominant plant species.
    (b) Trees are the dominant plant species.
    (c) Marshes are only saltwater bodies.
    (d) Marshes are low in diversity.

20. In the upper levels of the ocean,
    (a) diversity of marine life is greater because the surface is warmer than the deeper levels
    (b) diversity of marine life is greater because the ocean bottom does not have enough food to support more life forms
    (c) diversity of marine life is the same as in deeper levels
    (d) diversity of marine life is greater because more light penetrates than in the deeper levels

21. Describe briefly each of the following:
    (a) the GRAND project, and
    (b) the Rocky Mountain Trench project

22. For each statement below, if it is true, copy the statement and mark a (T) after it. If it is false, rewrite it so that it becomes true.
    (a) Lakes usually heat up more slowly than land, but cool down more quickly.
    (b) Without oceans to moderate the climate, humans could not live on Earth.
    (c) Since air absorbs a lot of moisture as it passes over cold currents, a great deal of rain falls on nearby coasts.
    (d) It is not possible to have two wells beside each other, one with water and the other dry, because the water table for each well is at the same level.
    (e) During water treatment, chlorine is added to help prevent flocculation.

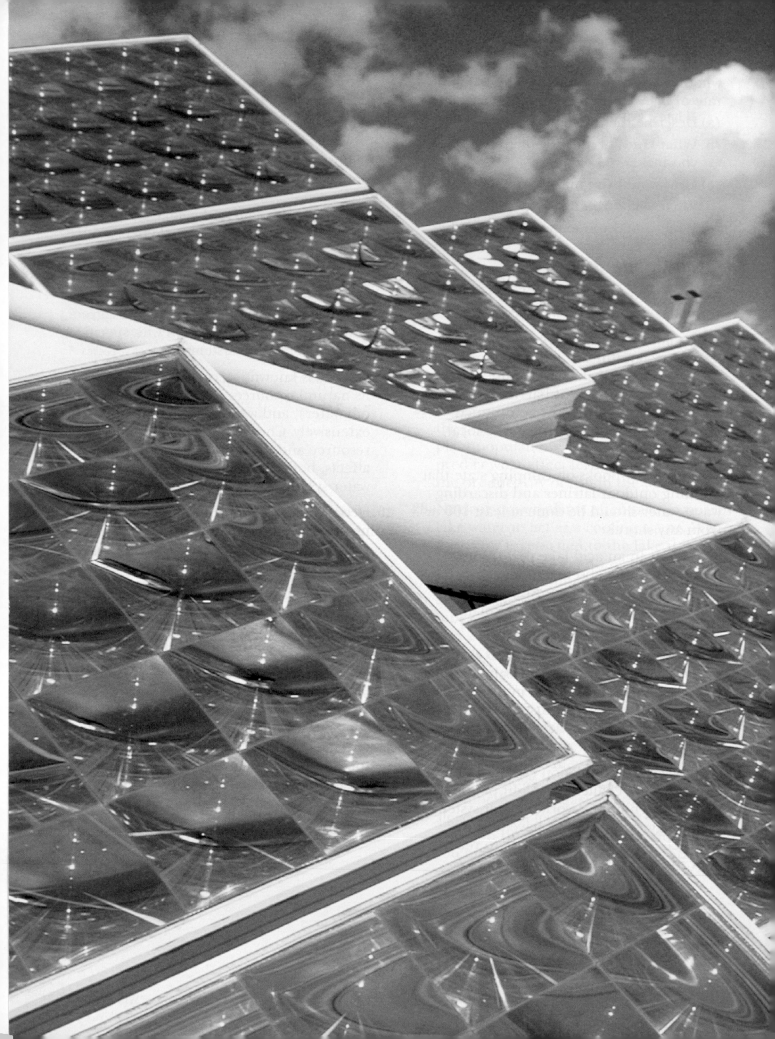

Unit 5

Optics

Unit 5 Overview

Getting Started: Viewing Light Energy

5.1   Light Energy and Its Sources

5.2   Inquiry Investigation: Watching Light Travel

5.3   Getting in Light's Way

5.4   Describing Images

5.5   Inquiry Investigation: Reflecting Light Off a Plane Mirror

5.6   Reflecting Light Off Surfaces

5.7   Inquiry Investigation: Viewing Images in a Plane Mirror

5.8   Inquiry Investigation: Curved Mirrors

5.9   Using Curved Mirrors

5.10   Inquiry Investigation: The Refraction of Light

5.11   Refracting Light in Lenses

5.12   Inquiry Investigation: Investigating Lenses

5.13   The Human Eye and the Camera

5.14   The Visible Spectrum

5.15   The Electromagnetic Spectrum

5.16   Case Study: A Telescope for Every Wave

5.17   Inquiry Investigation: Mixing the Colours of Light

5.18   Additive Colour Mixing

5.19   Career Profile: Light Entertainment

5.20   Design Investigation: Pigments and Filters for the Stage

5.21   Subtractive Colour Mixing

5.22   Explore an Issue: Solar Panels

Design Challenge: Design and Build a Device or System That Controls Light

Unit 5 Summary

Unit 5 Review

Unit 5 Overview

Think about how important light is to your life. Without this form of energy, plants would not grow, so animals, including humans, could not survive. Without light we would not be able to see and appreciate the beauty of the world. How is light produced? How does it get from one place to another? What is it made of? How can we apply the properties of light to design devices that help us see better and see more?

Sources and Properties of Light

The most important source of light for everything on Earth is the Sun.

You will be able to:

- describe how various sources, both natural and artificial, produce light

- evaluate the efficiency of light sources

- identify the properties of visible light through experiment

- compare the properties of visible light with those of other types of radiation

- investigate how objects or materials reflect, transmit, absorb, or refract light

Colour and Vision

You can discover the composition of light through experimentation.

You will be able to:

- identify the spectral colours

- explain how we see colours

- predict the colours that will result when sets of light colours overlap

- record observations to check your predictions

Mirrors and Lenses

The effects of reflection and refraction are used to design a variety of optical devices.

You will be able to:

- investigate the characteristics of mirrors and lenses
- communicate the results of investigations using diagrams and appropriate terminology
- identify ways mirrors and lenses are used in optical devices
- compare the functions of the human eye to the functions of the camera

Design Challenge

You will be able to ...

demonstrate your learning by completing a Design Challenge.

A Device or System That Controls Light

Whether you're looking at a star in the sky, a star on stage, or the star in your mirror, light and optical devices can improve how well you see it.

In this unit you will be able to design and build:

1 **An Aid to Vision**
Design and build an optical instrument that will let you see an object that you can't see normally.

2 **A Fun House**
Design and build a model of a fun house that will amaze, surprise, and delight visitors.

3 **A Stage Lighting System**
Design and build a model lighting system for a play or puppet show.

To start your Design Challenge, see page 314.

Record your thoughts and design ideas for the Challenge when you see

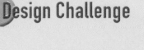

Design Challenge

Getting Started

Viewing Light Energy

1 Consider the Sun. It is so bright that it is dangerous to look at, yet thinking about it reveals a lot about light. Sunlight produces shadows in the forest and in the city. Sunlight shines through the atmosphere and through windows, but not through bricks. Sunlight glints brightly off mirrors and water, but not off asphalt. Why does sunlight, and all other light, behave in these ways?

2 We see colours in fall leaves—red, orange, yellow, green, maybe even purple. We see colours everywhere—television, video games, advertisements. But if you look at sunlight streaming through a window, it doesn't look like it has a colour. Why don't we see everything as just light or dark, like a black-and-white movie? How does colour work? Is colour a property of light? Is it a property of matter? Is there another explanation?

3 Mirrors and lenses change our view of the world. In the photo, you can see these soccer balls as they would normally appear to your eye, and as they appear after light passes through two very different lenses. What happens as light passes through a lens? How do lenses work? In the photo you can see reflections in the mirrors. What happens when light hits a mirror? How do mirrors work?

Reflecting

Think about the questions in ❶,❷,❸. What other questions do you have about light and optics? As you progress through this unit, reflect on your answers and revise them based on what you have learned.

 **Tricks of Light** (2A)

You can use mirrors to see what has been hidden.

- Hide an object behind a box or a desk, so no one can see it.

- Get some flat mirrors from your teacher. Set these up around the room so as many people as possible, while still seated, can see the hidden object by looking at reflections in the mirrors.

✋ Handle mirrors carefully to avoid breakage.

1. Draw a diagram of the classroom that
(6C) shows the locations of the object and the

mirrors. In your diagram, indicate which mirrors are used to see the object from several seats.

2. Are there places in the room where you still cannot see the object? Predict with a mark on your diagram where you could put a mirror that would allow you to see the object from one of those locations. Explain why you think this placement will work.

- Test your prediction by placing a mirror in the marked spot in the room.

3. Were you correct? If not, explain why.

Light Energy and Its Sources

What is light? Light is not something you can touch or taste. It doesn't have any mass. But you can see light, and it has other effects on matter. For example, a penny put in sunlight will get warmer than a penny placed in the shade. The penny in the sunlight gains energy from the light. Based on these observations, we can say that **light** is a form of energy that can be detected by the human eye. (After you have studied the properties of light, you will be able to state a more complex definition of light.)

You can learn more about light by looking carefully around you. For example, in a room lit by electric light, you can see the light that comes directly from the electric light to your eyes. But what about other objects in the room? How can you see them? The light energy from the electric light must spread throughout the room. Some of it bounces off objects, then travels to your eyes, enabling you to see objects and people in the room. **Figure 1** shows how light reaches your eyes.

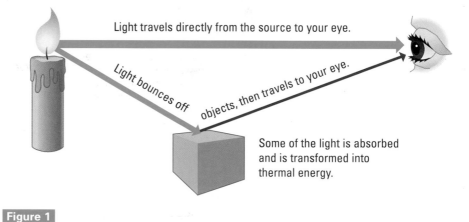

Light travels directly from the source to your eye.

Light bounces off objects, then travels to your eye.

Some of the light is absorbed and is transformed into thermal energy.

Figure 1

Light energy travels directly and indirectly to your eyes.

Sources of Light and Reflectors of Light

Light energy comes from many different sources, both natural and artificial. The Sun is the most important natural light source. Artificial sources of light are created by people. Objects that emit (give off) their own light are said to be **luminous**. The Sun is luminous; a burning candle is luminous. Objects that do not emit light, but only reflect light from other sources, are said to be **nonluminous**. Most things—this book, your desk, your classmates—are nonluminous. Even the Moon is nonluminous; it does not emit light. We see the Moon because it reflects light from the Sun.

In luminous objects, the input energy transforms into light energy. Common initial forms of energy are chemical energy, electrical energy, nuclear energy, and thermal energy.

When designing light sources, people consider not only the brightness, location, attractiveness, and cost of a light source, they also consider how effectively the source transforms the initial energy into light energy. As you read about various light sources, consider which ones produce a lot of heat—they are not efficient sources of light.

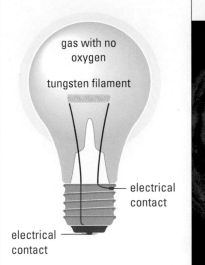

gas with no oxygen

tungsten filament

electrical contact

electrical contact

a Electrical energy transforms into heat and light energy in an incandescent light bulb. Electricity passing through a fine metal wire (the tungsten filament) makes the wire very hot when the bulb is turned on.

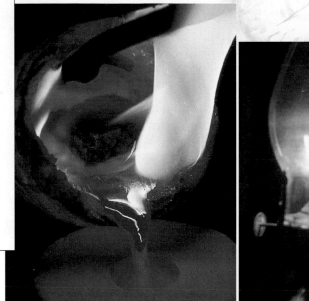

b Thermal energy can heat a metal to such a high temperature that it emits light. Such light ranges from dull red through yellow to white and blue-white as the metal gets hotter. The colour of the emitted light indicates when the molten metal is ready to be poured.

c A kerosene lamp can provide enough light to read by. The chemical energy in the kerosene fuel transforms into heat and light energy.

Figure 2
Incandescent light sources.

Light from Incandescence

Things that are extremely hot become luminous. At high temperatures, they begin to emit light. The process of emitting light because of a high temperature is called **incandescence**. Some incandescent sources of light are shown in **Figure 2**. In incandescent sources, a large amount of the input energy becomes thermal energy, so these sources are not efficient sources of light.

Light from Phosphorescence

Certain materials, called phosphors, will give off light for a short time after you shine a light on them. They store the energy and then release it gradually as light energy. The process of emitting light for some time after receiving energy from another source is called **phosphorescence**. The colour of the light and how long it lasts depend on the material used. This is a good way to make light switches that glow in the dark. **Figure 3** shows a phosphorescent light source.

Figure 3
The painted luminous dials on some watches and clocks are phosphorescent.

Light from Electric Discharge

When electricity passes through a gas, the gas particles can emit light. This process of emitting light because of electricity passing through a gas is called **electric discharge**.

Lightning is an example of electric discharge in nature. The electricity discharges through the air, from one cloud to another, or from a cloud to Earth. Artificial light sources also make use of electric discharge. Electricity is passed through tubes filled with gases such as neon. The electricity causes the gases to emit light, as you can see in **Figure 4**. Neon gas gives off a red-orange colour. Sodium vapour gives off a yellowish light. Other gases emit light of other colours.

Figure 4

An artificial light source that makes use of electric discharge.

Light from Fluorescence

Fluorescence is the process of emitting light while receiving energy from another source. Fluorescent tubes are used in schools, offices, and sometimes in homes. Fluorescent tubes take advantage of electric discharge and phosphorescence, as shown in **Figure 5**. In fluorescent tubes, the phosphors are of a kind that emits light for only a very brief time, much less than a second, after the light is turned off.

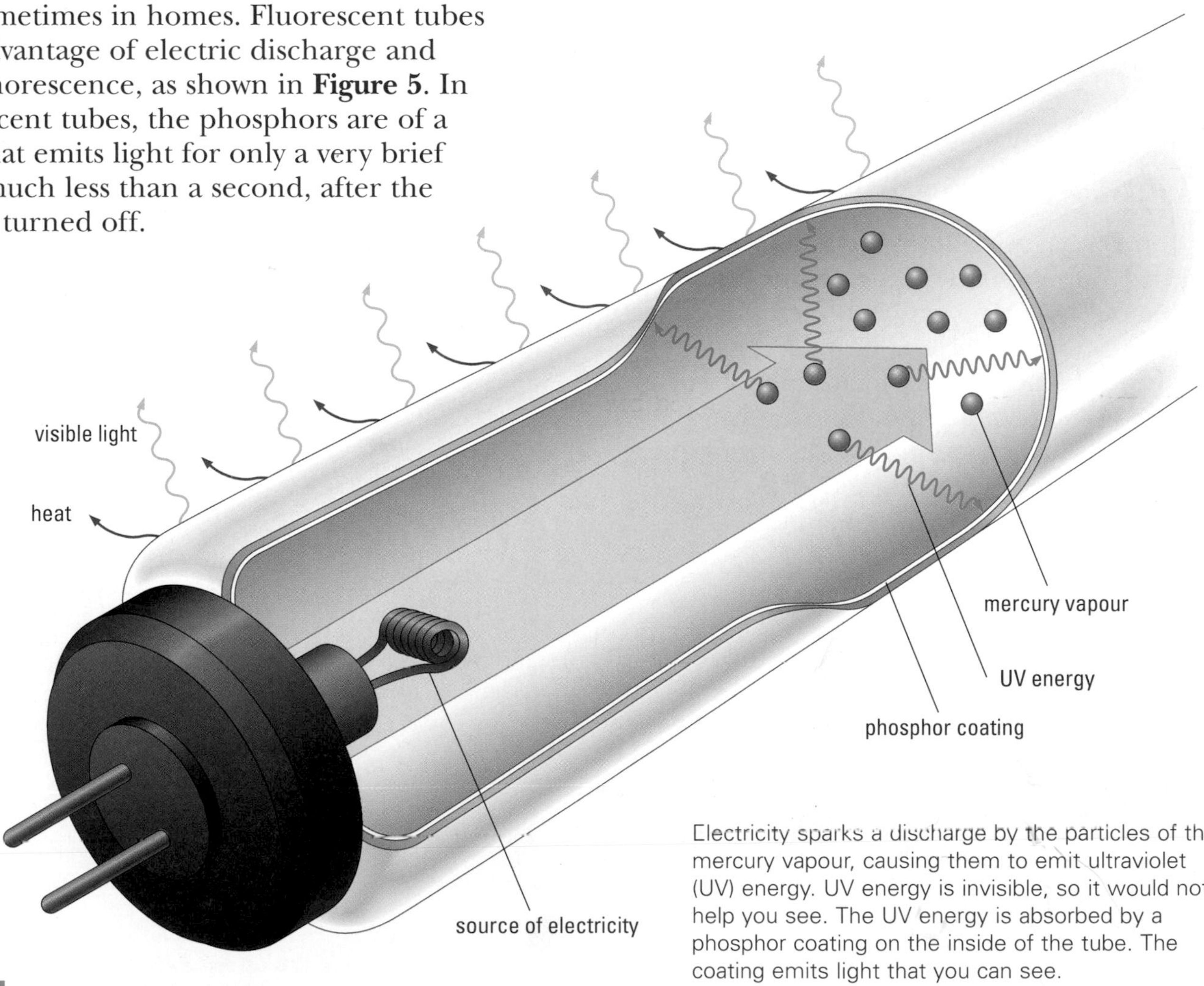

visible light

heat

source of electricity

mercury vapour

UV energy

phosphor coating

Electricity sparks a discharge by the particles of the mercury vapour, causing them to emit ultraviolet (UV) energy. UV energy is invisible, so it would not help you see. The UV energy is absorbed by a phosphor coating on the inside of the tube. The coating emits light that you can see.

Figure 5

A fluorescent light source. Fluorescent tubes do not produce as much heat as incandescent light bulbs.

Light from Chemiluminescence

Chemiluminescence is the process of changing chemical energy into light energy with little or no change in temperature.

Safety lights, or "cool lights," produce light by chemiluminescence. In these devices, a thin wall separates two chemicals, as shown in **Figure 6**. When this wall is broken, the chemicals mix and react to produce a light until the chemicals are used up.

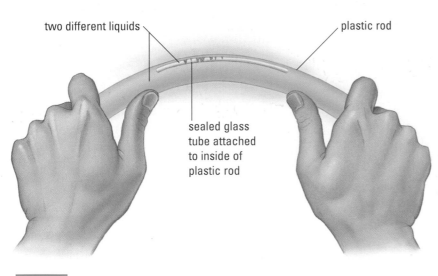

two different liquids

plastic rod

sealed glass tube attached to inside of plastic rod

Figure 6
Cool lights are chemiluminescent light sources.

Light from Bioluminescence

Some living things, such as the fish in **Figure 7**, can make themselves luminous using a chemical reaction similar to chemiluminescence. This process is called **bioluminescence**. Fireflies, glow-worms, and types of fish, squid, bacteria, and fungi all display bioluminescence.

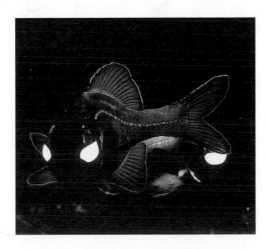

Figure 7
Many of the organisms that live deep in the ocean are bioluminescent. Scientists are not sure why so many species glow. Perhaps it allows members of the same species to find each other.

Design Challenge

Which of the sources of light discussed here could you use in your Challenge? What more would you have to learn about each source before deciding which is best for your uses?

Understanding Concepts

1. Which of the following are luminous?

   (a) campfire

   (b) the Moon

   (c) a hot toaster filament

2. For the following luminous objects, make a flow chart to illustrate the process they use to emit light and the type of energy that is transformed into light energy:

   (a) the lights in your home

   (b) a lit match

   (c) a car headlight

   (d) Day-Glo paints and fabrics

3. Explain in your own words the difference between a phosphorescent source and a fluorescent source.

4. Describe how a flashlight can be luminous. Describe how it can also be nonluminous.

Making Connections

5. While cycling, your body's efficiency is about 20%. This means your body uses about 20% of the energy available for cycling. The remaining 80% becomes heat. Incandescent bulbs have an efficiency of about 5%, fluorescent tubes about 20%.

   (a) Why does a bright incandescent bulb get much hotter than a bright fluorescent tube?

   (b) Why don't people always use the most energy-efficient type of lighting? What other factors could affect their decision?

Exploring

6. Which kind of light source would be safest to use in buildings or mines that may be filled with explosive gas?

Reflecting

7. List ways in which light energy is important in your life. What sources of light do you use?

Watching Light Travel

Have you ever tried to escape from the heat of direct sunlight on a summer day? One way is to find shade under a tree or to step into the shadow of a building. A **shadow** is an area where light has been blocked by a solid object, as shown in **Figure 1**. The dark part of a shadow is called the **umbra**; no light from the source reaches there. The lighter part of a shadow is called the **penumbra**; some light from the source reaches there. In this investigation, you will use the umbra and the penumbra to reveal an important property of light.

Materials
- rubber stopper
- paper
- pencil
- ruler
- 2 ray boxes

Question
What property of light allows shadows to form?

Hypothesis
1 Create a hypothesis that answers the question.

Procedure

Experimental Design
Using light and a solid object, you will explore shadow formation. You will create diagrams that include rays. A ray is how we represent the path taken by the light energy. It is represented by a line with an arrow to show the direction light is travelling. Light does not really travel in rays, but rays do help us to understand some properties of light.

🛑 Do not touch the ray box light bulb or look directly into the light.

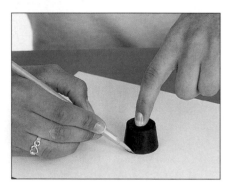

2 Put a rubber stopper on a piece of paper.
- Draw the outline of the stopper on the paper.
- Place the ray box 5 cm away from the stopper, and aim a wide light ray toward the stopper. The ray must travel on both sides of the stopper.

3 Use a pencil and a ruler to draw the outside edges of the shadow behind the stopper, and the source of light.
- Remove the stopper and turn off the ray box.
- Shade in the area of the diagram where the shadow was.

  (a) Label the light source, the object, and the umbra.

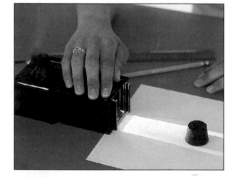

4 Repeat steps 2 and 3 using a new piece of paper, and moving the ray box to 10 cm from the stopper.

  (a) What differences do you notice in your diagram?

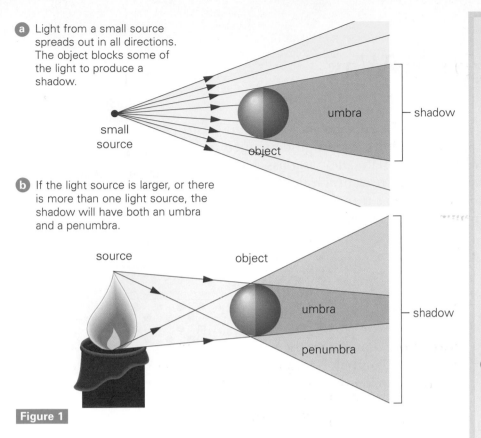

a Light from a small source spreads out in all directions. The object blocks some of the light to produce a shadow.

small source

object

umbra — shadow

b If the light source is larger, or there is more than one light source, the shadow will have both an umbra and a penumbra.

source

object

umbra — shadow

penumbra

Figure 1

5 With new paper, set up the stopper again as in step 4.
- Aim light rays from two ray boxes toward the stopper. Make sure that each ray travels on both sides of the stopper.
- Use a ruler and a pencil to outline the umbra and the penumbra. Use darker shading for the umbra than for the penumbra.

(a) Label the light sources, object, umbra, and penumbra.

Analysis

6 Analyze your results by answering these questions.

(a) In each of your diagrams, add arrows to the pencil lines to show the direction light was travelling.

(b) How accurate was your hypothesis?

(c) Explain how the property of light illustrated in this activity also prevents us from seeing around corners.

(d) Compare **Figure 1** with your ray diagrams. Does a wide light ray from a single ray box act like light from a small source or from a large source?

Making Connections

1. The position of the Sun in the sky changes during the day.

(a) **6C** Draw a diagram of the shadows cast by a building at three different times of day.

(b) Each species of plant requires different amounts of sunlight. Some need full sunlight all day, some need it part of the day, and some plants grow only in shade. Show where each of these kinds of plants will grow best around your building.

Exploring

2. **Figure 2** shows a gobo, a disc **3D** that is placed in front of a stage light to cast a shadow on the stage. Design a gobo that could be placed in front of a ray box or a flashlight. Cut it out and try it.

Figure 2
This gobo would project the shadow of a palm tree on the stage.

Reflecting

3. Shadows affect our lives in many different ways—our emotions, safety, where we place plants. Describe some situations involving shadows and how we have changed their effect.

(e) Do rays from two ray boxes act like a small source or large source? Explain your answer.

Design Challenge

Will you use shadows in your fun house or in your stage lighting system? If so, what objects will you use to cast the shadows? Where will you place them?

Getting in Light's Way

Imagine a world without glass. Your school would be very different—and very dark. When choosing materials, designers and engineers need to consider which materials block light and which, such as glass, let light pass through. **Transparency** is a measure of how much light can pass through a material. Materials are classified as transparent, translucent, or opaque, according to their transparency, as shown in **Figure 1**.

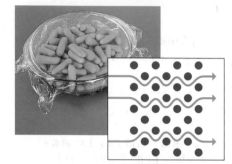

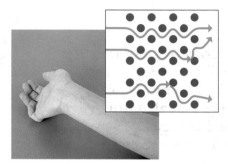

(a) Plastic wrap is transparent. Particles in **transparent** material let light transmit through easily. A clear image can be seen through the material. Plate glass, air, and shallow, clear water are other examples of transparent materials.

(b) Skin is a translucent material. Particles in a **translucent** material transmit the light, but also reflect some, so a clear image cannot be seen through it. Frosted glass, clouds, and your fingernails are also translucent materials.

(c) A glass of milk is opaque. Particles of an **opaque** material do not allow any light to transmit through. All of the light energy is either absorbed or reflected. Most materials are opaque. Building materials, such as wood, stone, and brick, are examples.

Figure 1

Transparent, translucent, and opaque materials

Handle mirrors carefully to avoid breakage.

Try This Comparing Dark and Light Surfaces

You can test how surfaces absorb and reflect light using a flashlight as a light source and a piece of white cardboard as a screen. You will also need a small flat mirror, another piece of white cardboard, and a piece of dull, black cardboard.

- In a dark room, shine the flashlight onto the mirror, as shown in **Figure 3**. Observe the effect on the white cardboard you are using as a screen.
- Replace the mirror with the second sheet of white cardboard and observe the effect on the screen.
- Replace the white cardboard with the black one and shine the flashlight on

the black card. Observe the effect on the screen.

1. Try other surfaces, some rough, some smooth, some dark, some light. In each case, predict how strong the reflection will be before testing the surface.

Figure 3

Classifying materials for transparency can be tricky. A glass of water, for example, is transparent. However, you may have noticed that you can't see the bottom of a deep lake, no matter how clear the water is. Water actually absorbs and reflects light slightly. As a result, small amounts of water are transparent, larger amounts are translucent, and great amounts are opaque. This is true of all transparent materials. It is also true in reverse. If you cut an opaque material like rock into very thin slices, the slices will be translucent, rather than opaque. Small amounts of the opaque material cannot absorb or reflect all of the light.

Absorbing and Reflecting Light

When light strikes an opaque material, none of it is transmitted through. Some of the light energy is absorbed by the material and is converted into thermal energy. For example, on a warm, sunny day, asphalt absorbs light energy and converts it into thermal energy, becoming hot. Light energy that is not absorbed is reflected from the material. This allows us to see the asphalt.

Colour, sheen (shininess), and texture are three properties that describe the amount of light energy absorbed or reflected. Black and dark-coloured material absorbs more light energy than white and light-coloured material. This is one reason builders often use dark shingles on Canadian homes.

Dull materials, such as wood, absorb more energy than shiny materials, such as aluminum siding.

A material with a rough surface, such as stucco, will absorb more light energy than a smooth surface, such as plaster.

Can you decide which of the materials in **Figure 2** would absorb more light energy?

These properties of materials are also important in the design of posters, magazines, clothing, and solar heating panels. For instance, if you were designing a poster, you might use some materials that absorb light and some that reflect light, so the contrast would allow the printing or artwork to be seen easily from far away. You might also want to avoid using shiny material that would cause glare.

Understanding Concepts

1. Are the following transparent, translucent, or opaque?
   (a) very smoky air
   (b) waxed paper
   (c) a copper plate
   (d) an ice cube

2. Give two new examples of:
   (a) transparent materials
   (b) translucent materials
   (c) opaque materials

Making Connections

3. Draw and label two leaves, one (6A) from a plant that would grow well in bright light, and one from a plant that would grow well in shade. Think about size, shape, colour, and shininess. Explain each of the features of your leaves.

Exploring

4. Many homes and other buildings (4A) use special glass for windows called low-emissivity glass. Research, using print and electronic media, to find out why.

Reflecting

5. What evidence do you have from reading this page that light travels in straight lines?

Design Challenge

Which components in your Challenge design will need to be transparent, translucent, and opaque? Will absorption of light energy be important for any of the components?

Figure 2

Two buildings that use different construction materials. An architect would choose certain materials in a hot, sunny area, and different materials for a cool area, based on their ability to transmit, absorb, or reflect light energy.

Describing Images

When your teacher shows you slides, you see an image on the screen produced by the projector. When you look at the letters in this sentence, an image of the letters forms at the back of your eyes. An image is the likeness of an object. An **optical device** produces an image of an object.

Real and Virtual

Images can be real or virtual. What does that mean? A **real image** can be placed on a screen. A **virtual image** cannot be placed on a screen. A virtual image can be seen only by looking at or through an optical device.

The four main characteristics listed in **Table 1** are generally used to study and compare images. These characteristics are used to describe an image in **Figure 1**.

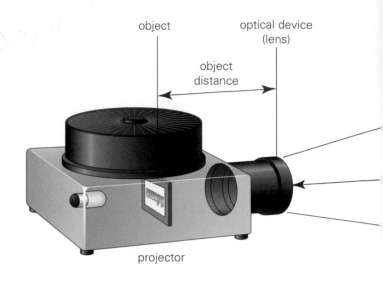

Figure 1

A slide projector shows a description of an image.

Try This Images in a Pinhole Camera

Using a homemade pinhole camera, you can investigate images. A pinhole camera is a box with a tiny hole at one end and a viewing screen at the other end. It can be as small as a shoebox or as large as a box for packing a new refrigerator. You can even stand inside a large pinhole camera to view the images! **Figure 2** shows how to make a pinhole camera.

1. What are the characteristics of the image of an object that is a few metres away from the camera?

2. What happens to the image as the camera gets closer to the object?

3. What happens if a second hole is poked about 1 cm below the first pinhole?

4. Draw a diagram to show how the image is formed in a pinhole camera.

5. Is the image seen in a pinhole camera real or virtual? Why?

✋ Do not look at the Sun or any other bright source of light with a pinhole camera. The light could damage your eyes.

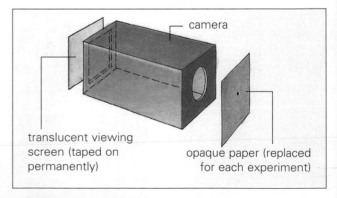

Figure 2

This type of pinhole camera is easy to make. Aim the pinhole toward the object you want to see and look at the screen.

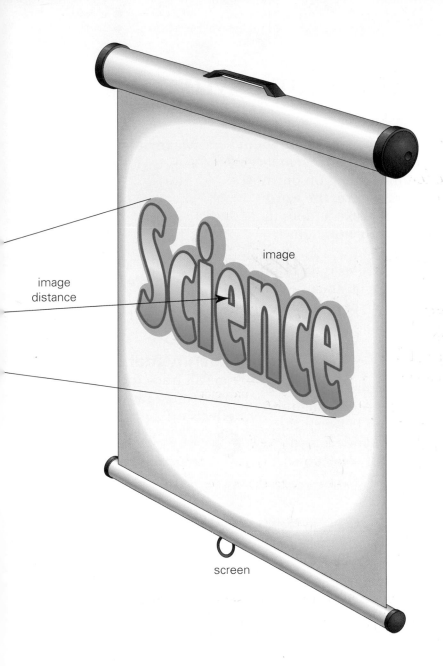

image

image distance

screen

Table 1: Characteristics of Images

Characteristic	Possible Descriptions
Size	Smaller than the object viewed Larger than the object viewed Same size as the object viewed
Attitude	Upright (right-side up) Inverted (upside down)
Location	Several choices Examples: on the side of the lens opposite the object; closer to the optical device than to the object, etc.
Type	**Real image** (can be placed onto a screen) **Virtual image** (can be seen only by looking at or through an optical device)

Understanding Concepts

1. Describe the characteristics of the image you see when your teacher uses the overhead projector.

2. In a pinhole camera used to view images, the screen must be translucent rather than transparent or opaque. Why?

Making Connections

3. An image can be either real or virtual, but not both at the same time. In games with "virtual reality," computer-controlled images appear to be real. Do you think "virtual reality" is a good name for images? Explain why or why not on the basis of what you have learned so far.

Exploring

4. A mathematical way to describe the size of an image is to state its magnification. For example, binoculars may have 10× (10 times) magnification and a microscope may have 1000× magnification. Use the equation below to calculate the magnification in each case.

$$\text{magnification} = \frac{\text{image height}}{\text{object height}}$$

   (a) A pair of binoculars makes a 9 cm–high bird look as if it is 63 cm high.

   (b) A microscope makes a thread that is 0.1 mm wide look as if it is 40 mm wide.

   (c) A lens makes lettering that is 8 mm high look as if it is 4 mm high.

5. Photography can be a hobby or a rewarding career. Find out more about this field by interviewing someone in the photographic industry and researching print and media sources. Create a poster about one area of photography that interests you.

5.5 Inquiry Investigation

SKILLS MENU
- Questioning
- Conducting
- Analyzing
- Hypothesizing
- Recording
- Communicating
- Planning

Reflecting Light Off a Plane Mirror

Mirrors. Dentists use them to examine our teeth, drivers use them to monitor traffic, decorators use them to make rooms seem larger, and we use them to check if we have doughnut filling on our noses. Regular, flat mirrors are called **plane mirrors**. (Here, the word "plane" means a flat, two-dimensional surface, just as it does in mathematics.) In this investigation, you will study how light reflects off a plane mirror.

Your skill in using a protractor to measure angles is useful in this investigation. Whenever you measure an angle, always estimate its value first, so you can check that the result of your measurement makes sense.

Materials
- ray box with a single-slit window
- plane mirror that can stand by itself
- ruler
- sharp pencil
- plain paper
- protractor

Question

1 Write a question that is being answered through this investigation.
2B

Hypothesis

2 Look at **Figure 1**. Create a hypothesis predicting the relationship between the angle of incidence and the angle of reflection.
2C

 Handle mirrors carefully to avoid breakage.

Experimental Design

You will trace the path of a ray from a ray box as it reflects off a plane mirror.

 Do not touch the ray box light bulb or look directly into the light.

Procedure

3 Aim a narrow ray of light from the ray box toward the mirror.
- Move the ray box so the incident ray hits the mirror at the same point but with different angles of incidence.
- Observe the reflected ray each time you move the ray box.

✎ (a) Record your observations.

4 Draw a straight line, AB, on a piece of paper. The line should be longer than your mirror.
- Mark a point near the middle of AB. This will be your point of incidence.
- Place the plane mirror so its reflecting surface (not the glass surface) lies along AB.

5 Aim a light ray at the point of incidence. Move the ray box until the reflected ray is lined up with the incident ray. Draw three small dots along the middle of the light ray. Remove the ray box and the mirror and use a ruler to connect the dots to the point of incidence with a broken line.

(a) What is this line? Label it.

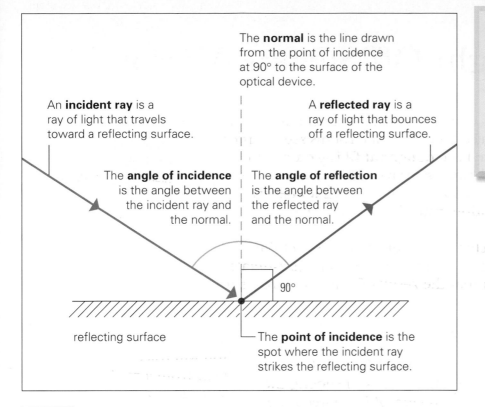

An **incident ray** is a ray of light that travels toward a reflecting surface.

The **normal** is the line drawn from the point of incidence at 90° to the surface of the optical device.

A **reflected ray** is a ray of light that bounces off a reflecting surface.

The **angle of incidence** is the angle between the incident ray and the normal.

The **angle of reflection** is the angle between the reflected ray and the normal.

90°

reflecting surface

The **point of incidence** is the spot where the incident ray strikes the reflecting surface.

Figure 1

Terms related to the reflection of light. Light travels in straight lines and can be represented using rays.

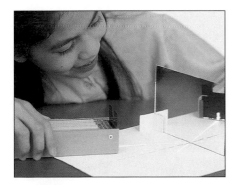

6 Return the mirror and aim a ray of light toward the point of incidence. Make sure the angle of incidence is large.

- Mark small dots along the middle of the incident and reflected rays.
- Remove the mirror and the ray box and use a ruler to join the dots of each ray to the point of incidence. Label the rays and show their directions with arrows.

- Use your protractor to
(7D) measure the angle of incidence and the angle of reflection in your diagram.

(a) Record the sizes of the angles on the diagram.

7 Repeat steps 5 and 6 on new paper for several different angles of incidence.

(a) Summarize your results in a chart.

Design Challenge

Knowing the laws of reflection means you can use mathematics to design optical devices. How will this help you place the mirrors you will use in your Challenge?

Analysis

8 Analyze your results by answering these questions.

(a) How accurate was your hypothesis?

(b) Where is the reflected ray when the incident ray travels along the normal to a plane mirror?

(c) What are the angles of incidence and reflection in this case?

(d) Scientists use two laws to describe how light reflects from a plane mirror. The first law of reflection compares the angle of incidence with the angle of reflection for light rays hitting a mirror. What does the first law of reflection say?

(e) The second law of reflection states that the incident ray, the reflected ray, and the normal all lie in the same plane. Can you support this with your observations? Explain.

Reflecting Light Off Surfaces

When shooting hoops outdoors, have you ever tried bouncing the ball on the grass instead of the asphalt? When the ball bounces off a smooth driveway or a gym floor, you can predict the direction it will travel. But when it bounces off the lawn, you can't predict where it will go. The same is true of light, as shown in **Figure 1**.

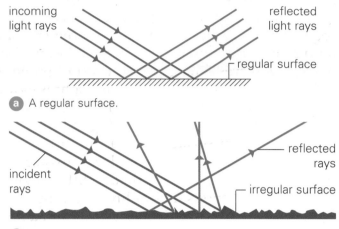

a A regular surface.

b An irregular surface. For each ray of light, the angle of incidence still equals the angle of reflection.

Figure 1

Light hitting various surfaces acts in a similar way. If the surface is smooth and regular, like a mirror, you can predict the direction of the reflected light more easily than if the surface is irregular.

Regular Reflection

You've learned that a smooth, shiny surface reflects light more predictably than a rough, dull surface. The reflection of light off a smooth, shiny surface is called **regular reflection**. When light reflects in this way, you can see an image. Regular reflection occurs off mirrors, shiny metal, and the surface of still water, as you can see in **Figure 2**.

Figure 2

Which way is up? Turn the book upside down and see if that helps you decide.

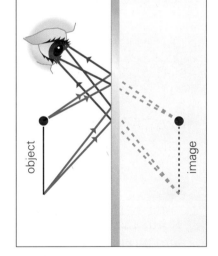

Figure 3

When you look at a mirror, you see an image that appears to be behind the mirror. If you extend the reflected rays behind the mirror, the image is where the rays appear to come from. For each set of incident and reflected rays, the angle of incidence equals the angle of reflection.

The Laws of Reflection

You have used rays to represent light as it travels from a ray box to a mirror, and then as it is reflected in a straight line off the mirror. Experiments similar to yours always yield the same results. When experimental results are consistent, scientists create "laws" to summarize their observations. They have created two **laws of reflection**:

• The angle of incidence equals the angle of reflection.
• The incident ray, normal, and reflected ray all lie in the same plane.

The laws of reflection can be used to learn why the eye sees an image in a plane mirror, as you can see in **Figure 3**.

Diffuse Reflection

Most surfaces are not regular. You can't see images in cardboard or in broccoli. When light hits an irregular surface, you see **diffuse reflection** as the reflected light scatters in many directions.

Light direct from a source, or reflected from a regular surface, strains the eyes. A room with a bright light source and mirrors on every wall would be very hard on the eyes. The glare from a transparent glass lamp would be unpleasant. Diffuse light is easy on the eyes. Homes, schools, and places of work are designed with this in mind. Ceilings are often coated with an irregular surface, such as stucco, that causes diffuse reflection. Lamps often have "frosted" bulbs that diffuse the light. Lampshades diffuse light even more. **Figure 4** shows how indirect lighting and irregular surfaces help diffuse the light in a room.

Figure 4

In indirect lighting, the light bulbs cannot be seen. The light from the bulbs reflects off the ceiling or walls before it reaches your eyes. How many examples of diffuse reflection and regular reflection of light can you find in the photograph?

Design Challenge

Will diffuse reflection be important in your Challenge? What materials could you choose to take advantage of it?

Understanding Concepts

1. In your own words describe regular reflection and diffuse reflection.

2. 6C Draw a ray diagram showing a plane mirror and an incident ray with an angle of incidence of 37°. Then draw the reflected ray. Use angles of incidence of 77° and 0° as well.

3. **(a)** What is the largest possible angle of incidence for a light ray travelling toward a mirror?

   (b) What is the smallest possible angle of incidence?

Making Connections

4. Give examples of how an interior designer might benefit from a knowledge of diffuse reflection. Choose an example of direct and indirect light in your home. Briefly summarize their effectiveness.

Exploring

5. Look closely at a glass mirror to see how it is made. Draw a diagram of the layers you see. Speculate on the functions of each of the layers.

    Do not attempt this using a large wall mirror.

Reflecting

6. Why is diffuse reflection more important than regular reflection in our every day lives? Give evidence in a short paragraph.

Try This Regular and Diffuse Reflection

Shiny aluminum foil can be used to study regular and diffuse reflection.

1. Predict what will happen when you shine a flashlight on the three pieces of aluminum foil shown in **Figure 5**.

   - Set up the material and make your observations. You will see the effect best if the room is dark.

2. 6C Explain your observations using a diagram.

   - Repeat the investigation using three different fabrics. Choose materials of the same colour that have smooth, textured, and very rough surfaces.

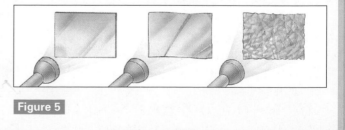

Figure 5

Viewing Images in a Plane Mirror

Dentists, drivers, decorators, and nose-checkers use mirrors. When we look in a plane mirror, we see an image of the object, not the object itself. As you learned earlier, an image can be described by four characteristics: size, attitude, location, and type.

Question
What are the characteristics of the image seen in a plane mirror?

Hypothesis

1 From your experience with mirrors, write a hypothesis. Predict (2c) what you will discover in this investigation.

Experimental Design
You will view images in mirrors and draw diagrams to complete a description of the images seen in a mirror.

Procedure

Materials
- large plane mirror
- plain paper
- flat cardboard
- ruler
- small plane mirror (or a mira)
- four pins

Handle mirrors carefully to avoid breakage.

To avoid injury, handle pins with care.

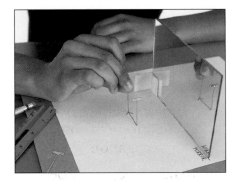

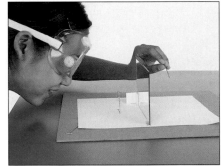

2 Look into a large plane mirror.

  (a) What is the size of the image compared with the object (you)?

  (b) What is the attitude of your image?

3 Place a piece of paper on the cardboard and draw a straight line a little longer than the small mirror. Label this line *mirror*.
- Place the reflecting surface of the mirror along this line.
- Draw an arrow about 2 or 3 cm long in front of the mirror. Label this arrow *object*.
- Stick a pin vertically through each end of the arrow.

4 Move a pin around behind the mirror until it is exactly where the image of the first pin appears to be. Check by looking at the image from several viewpoints.
- When you are sure of the location, stick the second pin into the paper and cardboard behind the mirror.
- Repeat this step using a fourth pin for the other end of the arrow.
- Draw a broken arrow between the two pins and label it *image*.

Figure 1
Because reflection in a mirror is regular, the location of each image and the total number of images of the apple can be predicted.

5 Check to see if the image of the arrow is real or virtual.

• Put a piece of paper (a screen) where the image seems to be. If you can see the image on the paper, it is real. If you cannot see the image, it is virtual.

✎ (a) Record your observations.

6 Remove the mirror and the pins.

• On your diagram,
(6C) measure and label the shortest distance from the mirror line to each end of the object. (This is the object distance.)

• Measure and label the shortest distance from the mirror line to each end of the image. (This is the image distance.)

Analysis

7 Analyze your results by answering these questions.

(a) State the four characteristics of the image in your investigation.

(b) In step 6, how does the image distance compare with the object distance?

Design Challenge

Describe how the equation given in question 3 might be useful for the fun house challenge.

Making Connections

1. In some public areas, one mirror is placed at an angle to the wall to enable people in wheelchairs to see themselves. Draw a diagram to find the image in this slanted mirror.

2. Two plane mirrors are located inside a kaleidoscope. Explain how this optical device produces patterns.

Exploring

3. If you place two plane mirrors so one edge is touching, you will see multiple images, as shown in **Figure 1**. The following equation can be used to calculate the number of images formed by two plane mirrors at an angle to each other.

$$\text{Number of images} = \frac{360°}{\text{angle between the mirrors}} - 1$$

(a) Use this equation to calculate the number of images when the angle between the mirrors is 180°, 90°, 60°, and 45°.

(b) Design an investigation
(2E) to test your answer.

4. In your notebook, use a ruler to draw a line in the middle of a page. This represents a plane mirror. Draw a letter F on one side of the "mirror." Apply what you learned in this investigation to locate and draw the image of the letter F. Label your diagram.

Reflecting

5. What problems occur when printing or writing is seen in a mirror? What could you do to read printing when looking in a mirror?

SKILLS MENU
- Questioning
- Conducting
- Analyzing
- Hypothesizing
- Recording
- Communicating
- Planning

Curved Mirrors

You may have noticed a big curved mirror high in a corner at the local store (see **Figure 1**). The storeowner uses the convex mirror to detect theft. What is it about the images that you see in that mirror that make the mirror effective for surveillance?

Next time you visit the dentist, look closely at the lamp the dentist uses (see **Figure 2**). A concave mirror in the lamp focuses the light into your mouth so that the dentist can work on your teeth. What is it about a concave mirror that makes the mirror effective for this purpose?

The images you see in curved mirrors look different from those in plane mirrors. In this investigation, you will explore those differences.

Materials
- curved mirrors for viewing
- curved mirrors for use with a ray box
- ray box with multiple-slit window and single-slit window
- plain paper
- sharp pencil
- ruler
- protractor

  Do not touch the ray box light bulb or look directly into the light.

  Handle mirror carefully to avoid breakage.

Question

(2B) **1** What question is being investigated?

Experimental Design

Using a ray box and observation, you will investigate the properties of curved mirrors.

Hypothesis

(2C) **2** Create a hypothesis for this investigation.

Procedure

3 Have a partner hold a concave viewing mirror close to your eye.

  (a) Describe the image you see.

- Observe the image carefully as your partner slowly moves the mirror farther from your eye.

  (b) Describe any changes you observe in the image.

4 Have a partner hold a convex viewing mirror close to your eye.

  (a) Describe the image you see.

- Observe the image carefully as your partner slowly moves the mirror farther from your eye.

  (b) Describe any changes you observe.

  (c) What differences do you notice in the images produced by the two mirrors?

5 Use a ray box to aim a narrow ray of light at the surface of a concave mirror. Observe where each ray is reflected. Try several different angles.

  (a) Record where each ray came from and where it was reflected from the surface.

  (b) Do the laws of reflection apply to concave mirrors?

SKILLS HANDBOOK: **(2B)** Asking a Question

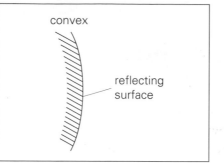

convex

reflecting surface

Figure 1

A **convex mirror** has the reflecting surface on the outside curve, like the back of a spoon.

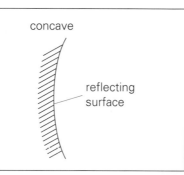

concave

reflecting surface

Figure 2

A **concave mirror** has the reflecting surface on the inside of the curve, like the inside of a spoon.

6 Use the ray box with the multiple-slit window to shine three or more parallel rays of light at once at a concave mirror.

⑥ᴄ (a) Draw a diagram of what you observe.

(b) Can a concave mirror focus light rays?

7 Repeat steps 5 and 6 using a convex mirror.

Analysis

8 Analyze your results by answering these questions.

(a) Use the characteristics of images to describe the image in

- a concave mirror when the object is close to the mirror.
- a concave mirror when the object is far from the mirror.
- a convex mirror when the object is close to the mirror.
- a convex mirror when the object is far from the mirror.

Making Connections

1. Name at least two new applications of concave and convex mirrors. Describe why you think they were chosen for this purpose.

2. Satellite dishes are used to reflect energy from a satellite so it comes to a focus. What type of reflector is a satellite dish? Draw a diagram to show how you think this device works.

● Design Challenge

Concave mirrors can be used to focus light. How might you use concave mirrors in your Design Challenge? How might you use convex mirrors?

(b) In question (a) you had to decide if the image in each of the mirrors was real or virtual. What evidence do you have
⑥ᴀ to support your choice? Describe how you could demonstrate if either of the curved mirrors produces a real image.
⑥ᴄ Draw a diagram of the setup.

Using Curved Mirrors

You may not realize it, but curved mirrors are part of your everyday life. Whether you're shopping for CDs, riding a school bus, or learning about solar heating, curved mirrors will be near. **Figure 1** shows some of the terms used when describing curved mirrors.

principal axis: a line through the centre of the mirror that includes the principal focus

principal focus: the position where reflected parallel light rays come together

focal length: the distance from the principal focus to the middle of the mirror

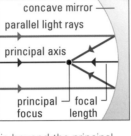

concave mirror
parallel light rays
principal axis
principal focus — focal length

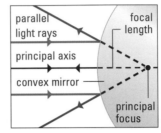

parallel light rays
focal length
principal axis
convex mirror
principal focus

principal axis: a line through the centre of the mirror that includes the principal focus

principal focus: the position where parallel light rays appear to reflect from

focal length: the distance from the principal focus to the middle of the mirror

a A concave mirror. When the object is beyond the principal focus, the type of image produced by a concave mirror will be real because it is in front of the mirror and can be placed on a screen.

b A convex mirror. Images in a convex mirror are always virtual, because they are behind the mirror and cannot be placed on a screen.

Figure 1
A concave mirror focuses parallel light rays, and a convex mirror spreads the light rays out.

Using Concave Mirrors

If you've ever looked through a reflecting telescope, you've used a concave mirror. **Figure 2** shows how a concave mirror is used to gather light from distant objects and bring it to a focus. The biggest telescopes built, including space telescopes, use this design.

Figure 3 shows how a concave cosmetic mirror is used to produce an enlarged image of a nearby object. This happens when the person using the mirror is closer to it than the principal focus.

A third use for concave mirrors is illustrated in **Figure 4**. Concave reflectors can be used in devices to send light in a beam.

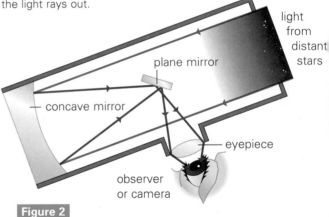

light from distant stars
plane mirror
concave mirror
eyepiece
observer or camera

Figure 2
A reflecting telescope creates an image that can be viewed, photographed, or recorded digitally.

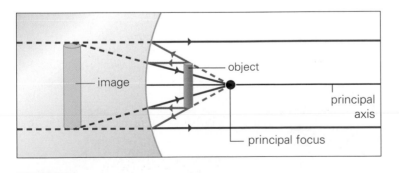

image
object
principal axis
principal focus

Figure 3
A concave mirror produces an upright, enlarged image when the person using it is closer to the mirror than the principal focus. Could this image be placed onto a screen?

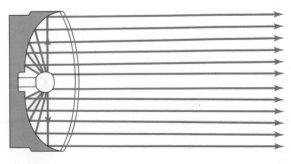

Figure 4
In this flashlight, the filament of the light bulb is near the principal focus of the concave mirror behind it. The rays that reflect off the mirror are nearly parallel. This produces a beam of light.

Using Convex Mirrors

While shopping for CDs, you probably noticed large surveillance mirrors in the store. A convex mirror can be used to monitor a very large area because its curved surface reflects light from all parts of a room to a person's eye. Images are always upright and smaller than the object, no matter where the object is located. **Figure 5** shows why a convex mirror gives a much wider view than any other kind of mirror, and how it produces an image. **Figure 6** shows another common application of convex mirrors. Can you think of others?

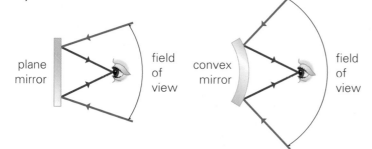

a The reflection in a convex mirror gives a much larger view than the reflection in a plane mirror of similar size.

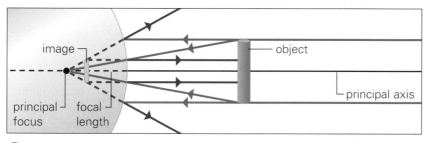

b How a convex mirror produces an image. The characteristics of the image are the same whether the object is near or far from the mirror.

Figure 5
The convex mirror.

Figure 6
A convex mirror on the front of a school bus allows the driver to see children both beside and in front of the bus. If a convex mirror is used to see behind, the driver must be careful, because the objects are actually closer than their images suggest they are.

Understanding Concepts

1. For each situation described below, state whether the image produced is real or virtual, and how you know.

   (a) A man is standing close to a cosmetic mirror while shaving.

   (b) An astronomer is looking at an image of the Moon through her telescope, which has a concave mirror.

   (c) A clerk in a drug store is looking at the image of a customer in a surveillance mirror.

2. Rewrite the following false statements to make them true.

   (a) The image in a convex mirror is always real and upright.

   (b) When an object is inside the principal focus of a concave mirror, the image is inverted and real.

   (c) Real images are always located behind the mirror.

Making Connections

3. Curved mirrors can be used to (6C) gather light from the Sun and focus it for solar heating. Draw a diagram illustrating how this might work.

Exploring

4. A helium-neon laser uses a (4A) concave mirror at each end to help create a narrow beam of light. Research this type of laser, and draw a diagram showing how the mirrors control the light.

Reflecting

5. What safety problems can occur when using convex mirrors? List situations in which a convex mirror should not be used.

Design Challenge

Which challenges would be best for using concave and convex mirrors?

The Refraction of Light

You have seen that when light travels through air, it travels in a straight line. But what happens when light travels from one material into another? Have you ever noticed when you're standing in a swimming pool that your legs look different? **Figure 1** is another example that shows this distorted view. This happens because light bends as it passes from the water into the air. The bending of light as it travels from one material into another is called **refraction**. **Figure 2** shows some terms you will find useful when discussing refraction.

Question

1 In this investigation, you will be using transparent materials. Formulate a question you will investigate on the refraction of light as it applies to transparent materials. Do all transparent materials refract light the same amount?

Hypothesis

2 Create a hypothesis for this investigation.

Experimental Design

3 Design an experiment to test your hypothesis. You should use several transparent liquids and at least one solid. You will want to explore refraction as light travels from air into another material, and when light travels from the material back into air.

4 List the materials you will require and the procedure steps you will take, and describe how you will record your data. Include the safety precautions you will take.

5 Ask your teacher to approve your design and procedure.

Procedure

6 Carry out your experiment.

Materials

- apron
- safety goggles
- thin transparent dishes (containers for liquids)
- ray box with a single-slit window

Possible transparent materials:

- water
- glycerin
- mineral oil
- salt water solution
- sugar water solution
- solid rectangular prism (an acrylic block)
- Other materials as needed

Clean up any spills immediately.

Do not touch the ray box light bulb or look directly into the light.

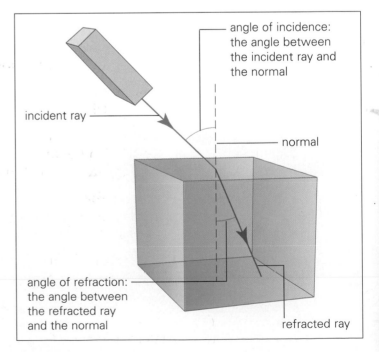

Figure 2
Some terms used to describe refraction

angle of incidence: the angle between the incident ray and the normal

incident ray

normal

angle of refraction: the angle between the refracted ray and the normal

refracted ray

Figure 1
Light refracts as it travels from water into air, causing a distorted view. Will it refract the same amount in glycerin or a block of acrylic?

Understanding Concepts

1. If you found a coin in the water, would you reach for the exact location the coin appears to be? Explain your answer.

Exploring

2. When a certain liquid is poured into a beaker that contains a block of acrylic, the block disappears from view.

   (a) Explain this phenomenon.

   (b) Based on the results of your experiment, which liquid should be used?

   (c) With your teacher's permission, test your answer to (b).

Analysis

7 Analyze your results by answering these questions.

(a) Light travels in a straight line in air. How does it travel in other transparent materials?

(b) Compare the angle of refraction for light as it travels from air into a liquid or solid to the angle of refraction for light as it travels from a liquid or solid into air.

(c) List the differences between the materials you tested. Speculate about what property of the materials you tested explains your results.

(d) In your experiment you used a container to hold the liquids. Did the container affect the results? Support your answer using a diagram.

(e) Make a chart listing the materials you tested in order of least refraction to greatest refraction for light entering from air.

Design Challenge

How could refraction of light be used to create a special effect on stage or in a fun house?

Refracting Light in Lenses

Your eyes depend on refraction. They make use of a special optical device. A **lens** is a curved, transparent device that causes light to refract as it passes through. As you read, light reflects off the page, travels to your eyes, and refracts when it enters the lens of each eye. A magnifying glass (**Figure 1**), contact lenses, the lenses in eyeglasses, and camera lenses are all examples of useful lenses.

Why Does Light Refract?

You have seen that light refracts when it travels from one material into another. Why does this happen? Using careful measurements, scientists have discovered that the speed of light differs in different transparent materials. The denser the material is, the slower light travels as it passes through. When light travels from air into denser glass, it slows down. This change in speed causes the light to change direction. The same thing happens, for the same reason, if you ride a bike from pavement into sand, as shown in **Figure 2**. The new medium causes a change in speed and direction.

Figure 1

Lenses have a variety of uses, depending on their size, shape, and other factors. As light passes through this lens it refracts to create enlarged images.

Exploring Lens Combinations

How do designers decide which lenses to use and how to set up the best combination in microscopes and other devices? You can explore this question using several glass lenses.

- Examine several single lenses. Look through them from both sides, from near and far, and at objects far away and nearby.

 Do not look at any bright light sources through the lenses.

 Handle lenses carefully to avoid breakage.

1. How do concave and convex lenses compare?

2. How does the thickness of a lens affect the image?

3. How does the distance between the lens and the object viewed affect the image?

4. Does the distance between your eye and the lens affect the image?

- Combine lenses by putting one in front of the other and looking through them.

5. What is the best combination for viewing nearby objects?

6. What combination is most useful for viewing objects far away?

7. When using a concave/convex combination, what arrangement works for viewing objects near or far?

- Try combining three lenses.

8. Did you discover any useful combinations of three lenses?

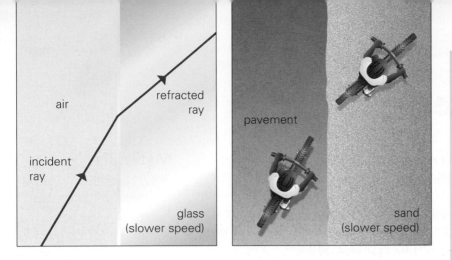

Figure 2

Light refracts when its speed changes, just as a bicycle changes direction as it slows down when moving from pavement to sand.

Lens Designs

Generally, lenses are convex or concave, as shown in **Figure 3**. A **convex lens** is thicker in the middle than at the outside edge. A **concave lens** is thinner in the middle than at the outside edge. These different designs cause different effects and images when light passes through them. However, notice that in **Figure 3** a light ray through the middle of the lens does not refract, because it meets the surface at a 90° angle. Would this happen with the bicycle?

Combining Lenses

Devices often use more than one lens. A microscope, for example, has two lenses—the objective lens close to the object viewed, and the eyepiece lens that you look through.

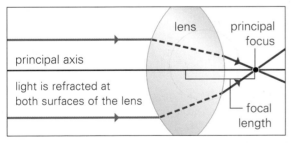

principal focus: the position where parallel light rays come together

focal length: the distance from the principal focus to the centre of the lens

(a) A convex lens bulges outward. It causes light rays to come together.

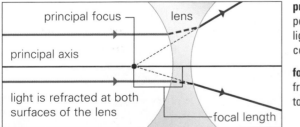

principal focus: the position where parallel light rays appear to come from

focal length: the distance from the principal focus to the centre of the lens

(b) A concave lens is caved inward. It causes light rays to spread apart.

Understanding Concepts

1. Explain why light bends as it travels from air into water.

2. Light speeds up when it passes from glass to air. Redraw **Figure 2**, showing what would happen if light were travelling from glass into air.

3. Describe the attitude and approximate size of the image when the object is very close to and far from

   (a) a convex lens

   (b) a concave lens

4. Explain, using a diagram, whether a thick or a thin lens would have a greater focal length in

   (a) a convex lens

   (b) a concave lens

5. Is a convex lens more like a convex mirror or a concave mirror in the way it produces images? Explain your answer.

Making Connections

6. Light refracts more when passing from air to diamond than to any other common material. (This is one of the reasons diamonds sparkle.) What can you conclude about the speed of light in diamond?

7. Make a list of devices that use at least one lens.

Exploring

8. Not all lenses are concave or convex. For example, one type of lens has one side concave and the other convex. Find some examples of other shapes of lenses and report on interesting combinations of lenses that you discover.

Figure 3

Convex and concave lenses. The characteristics of these lenses determine how they are used in different optical devices.

Investigating Lenses

Have you ever looked through a peephole to see who is on the other side of the door? Or through binoculars at a ball game? Have you ever used a microscope to look at cells? Whether used to make faraway objects appear clearer or to enlarge small objects, various shapes of lenses can produce interesting results (**Figure 1**). In this investigation, you will use light rays to discover how lenses are used to produce images.

Materials

- ray box with multiple-slit window and single-slit window
- convex and concave lenses for use with the ray box
- plain paper
- sharp pencil
- ruler

Question

2B **1** Write a question about images and lenses that you can investigate.

Hypothesis

2C **2** Based on what you have learned, predict an answer to the question.

Experimental Design

Using a ray box you will find images created by lenses and determine if your hypothesis is correct.

Look at **Figure 2** to see how to use two rays, one at a time, to locate the top of the image of an object that has been placed in front of a convex lens. Using two more rays you can use a similar technique to locate the bottom of the image.

3 Design an investigation that will allow you to find the image and decide what type of image it is for the following cases:

Convex lens
(a) an object that is 2 times the focal length from the lens.
(b) an object that is 1.5 times the focal length from the lens.
(c) an object that is exactly the focal length from the lens.
(d) an object that is half the focal length from the lens.

Concave lens
(e) an object that is 2 times the focal length from the lens.
(f) an object that is exactly the focal length from the lens.

4 Make a list of the procedure steps you will take.

5 Have your teacher approve your

 Do not touch the ray box light bulb or look directly into the light.

 Handle lenses carefully to avoid breakage.

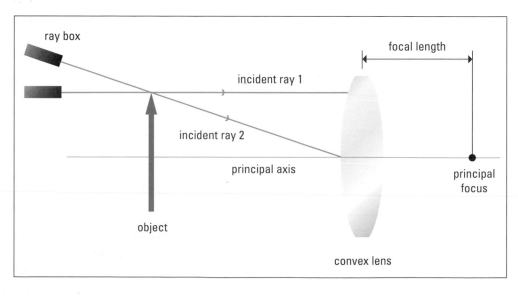

Figure 1

This image was created using a fisheye lens.

Procedure

6 Carry out your procedure.

(6C) (a) For each of cases (a) to (f) listed in 3, draw a diagram showing what you discover. (If the rays are spreading apart, extend the rays with a ruler to find out where they appear to come from.)

Figure 2

How to find the top of the image

Analysis

7 Analyze your results by answering these questions.

(a) Describe the steps you would take to determine the focal length of

- a convex lens.
- a concave lens.

(b) Under what conditions can a convex lens produce

- a real image?
- a virtual image?
- no image?

(c) Does a concave lens produce a real or a virtual image? Explain.

Making Connections

1. Compare what you observed in this investigation with what you discovered in Try This in 5.11. Describe any patterns you notice.

Reflecting

2. How would you improve your (7F) procedure if you were going to do this investigation again?

3. Write a paragraph summarizing your observations about images formed by concave and convex lenses.

Design Challenge

Combinations of lenses may be useful in your Challenge. Explain how you will set up and test the lens combinations you choose to use.

The Human Eye and the Camera

The human eye is an amazing optical device that allows you to see objects near and far, in bright light and in dim light. Although the details of how we see are complex, we can compare the eye to an ordinary camera.

Figures 1 and **2** show the basic structures of the human eye and of the camera.

c pupil
the hole in the iris that light passes through to reach the retina

d lens
helps focus light onto retina

e ciliary muscles
control the thickness of the lens, to adjust for near and far objects

b iris
makes the pupil large when light is dim, small when light is bright

f retina
the area where the image is produced and converted into nerve signal

a cornea
helps focus light onto retina

g optic nerve
carries nerve signals to the brain

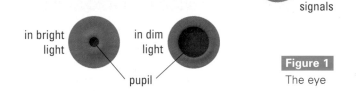

signals

in bright light

in dim light

pupil

Figure 1
The eye

The Cornea and Lens: Gathering Light

Both the human eye and the camera use a convex lens to gather light from an object and produce an image of the object. In the eye, the light also passes through the cornea, a transparent layer at the front of the eye. Light refracts a large amount when it passes through the cornea, then it refracts more as it passes through the convex lens.

The camera uses a set of lenses to achieve the same effect.

The Iris: Controlling the Amount of Light

You have likely walked into a dark room or theatre before. At first you cannot see well, but your eyes "become adjusted to the dark," and you begin to see better. What actually happens is your pupils become larger. The pupil of the eye is the "window" through which light enters the lens. It looks black because most of the light that enters the eye is absorbed inside.

In a camera the diaphragm has the same function as the iris. Photographers must consider both the diameter of the diaphragm and the exposure time (how long the shutter is open) to get a high-quality photograph.

Ciliary Muscles: Controlling the Focus

If you look at printing held a few centimetres from your eye, you will notice that it is blurred; the printing is out of focus. Your eye can focus clearly on objects as near as about 25 cm and as far away as you can see. When you look at objects far away, the lens is in its normal shape and the ciliary muscles are relaxed. When you look at a close object, the muscles force the lens to become thicker to keep the image focused. As people get older, their lenses and muscles become less flexible, which reduces their ability to control the focus and see close objects clearly.

Instead of changing the shape of the lens, the camera moves the whole lens system to focus. The lens system can be moved back and forth to be the correct distance from the recording medium to produce a clear image.

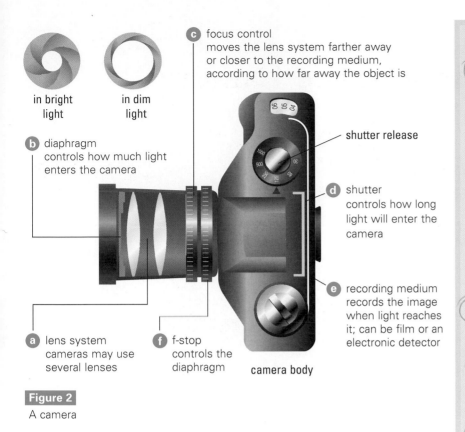

c focus control
moves the lens system farther away or closer to the recording medium, according to how far away the object is

in bright light

in dim light

b diaphragm
controls how much light enters the camera

shutter release

d shutter
controls how long light will enter the camera

e recording medium
records the image when light reaches it; can be film or an electronic detector

a lens system
cameras may use several lenses

f f-stop
controls the diaphragm

camera body

Figure 2
A camera

The Retina: Producing an Image

In the eye, the image is produced on the retina, the light-sensitive layer on the inside of the eye. This area has many blood vessels, nerves, and two types of light receptor cells, called rods and cones because of their shape when examined under a microscope. In most eyes there are about 120 million rods, which are sensitive to the level of light, and about 6 million cones, which are sensitive to colour. The rods and cones transform the light into nerve signals, which are sent to the brain to interpret.

In the camera, the image is produced either on a chemical film, to be developed later, or on a digital device that can be transferred to a computer.

Images in the Eye and the Camera

As you can see in **Figure 3**, in both the eye and the camera, the image is real and inverted. You may think it strange that the images are inverted in your eye, but your brain has had lots of practice flipping them.

Understanding Concepts

1. Copy **Table 1** into your notebook, then fill in the blank spaces.

Table 1 Function Table

Function of Parts	Camera Parts	Eye Parts
?	?	convex lens
controls the amount of light entering	?	?
?	?	ciliary muscles
records the image	?	?

2. Compare and contrast the image that is formed on the film of a camera and the retina of the eye.

3. Where does refraction occur in the human eye?

Making Connections

4. When your eyes feel tired from looking at close objects, it is good to look at distant objects for a few minutes. Why do you think this would help?

Exploring

5. Lenses can be used to correct problems of human vision. Research one of the problems listed below. Prepare a visual presentation illustrating the problem and how it can be corrected.
   (a) myopia (near-sightedness)
   (b) hyperopia (far-sightedness)
   (c) astigmatism
   (d) presbyopia

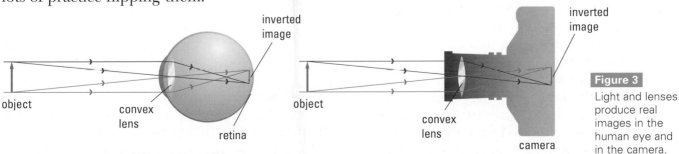

inverted image

object

convex lens

retina

inverted image

object

convex lens

camera

Figure 3
Light and lenses produce real images in the human eye and in the camera.

The Visible Spectrum

You have investigated and studied several properties of light. You know light is a form of energy; it travels in straight lines; it can be reflected, absorbed, transmitted, and refracted. But none of these properties explains an important fact: we can see colours.

You have probably seen a rainbow, like the one in **Figure 1**. The rainbow gives an important clue in the search for an explanation of colour. The band of colours visible in the rainbow is called the **visible spectrum**. It has six main colours, called the spectral colours. Starting at the top, the spectral colours are red, orange, yellow, green, blue, and violet.

Figure 1
For you to see a rainbow, the Sun must be behind you and the water droplets (in the rain and the clouds) in front of you.

Try This Viewing the Visible Spectrum

You can create your own mini-rainbow. For this activity, you will need two solid triangular prisms (blocks of acrylic) and a ray box or similar light source.

 Do not touch the ray box light bulb or look directly into the light.

- Place one prism on a sheet of white paper and trace its outline.

- With the room lights dim, aim a ray of white light from the ray box toward the prism, as shown in **Figure 2**. Move the ray box to adjust the position of the ray, until you obtain the brightest possible spectrum.

1. Draw a diagram of your observations.
6C Include the white light ray and the colours.

- Position the second prism as shown in **Figure 3** and aim the ray as you did earlier.

2. Draw a diagram of what you observe.

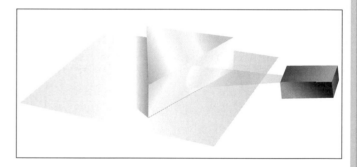

Figure 2

Figure 3

The Discovery of the Composition of White Light

Hundreds of years ago, scientists thought they could see colours in objects because the objects added colour to white light. Then, in the year 1666, an important discovery was made. A brilliant scientist named Isaac Newton hypothesized that light from the Sun might be made up of several colours. To test his hypothesis, he passed a beam of sunlight through a triangular glass prism, as in **Figure 2**. Newton discovered that white light is made up of the spectral colours red through violet.

Those who opposed Newton's explanation were quick to argue that the different colours were produced by the prism. They reasoned that the colours must be inside the glass. The light just allowed the colours to escape.

Recombining the Visible Spectrum

To end the controversy, Newton decided to collect the separate colours of light with a second prism, as in **Figure 3**. As he had predicted, when the six colours were added together, the light became white again.

Newton's experiments provided evidence that white light is composed of colours, and each colour acts differently inside a prism. Many years after Newton's discovery, scientists found that the colours of light actually travel at different speeds in the prism, causing each colour to refract a slightly different amount when the light reaches the surface of the glass. The colour that refracts the most (violet) slows down the most.

Understanding Concepts

1. Explain which statement below you believe to be correct.

   Statement A: White light is made up of the spectral colours. The rainbow colours appear when light passes through water droplets.

   Statement B: Water droplets add colour to white light to produce the rainbow.

2. Explain in your own words the expression "recombining the visible spectrum."

3. Which colour of light changes direction the most when it leaves the triangular prism? Which changes direction the least?

4. Predict what you would observe if you aimed red light at the triangular prism instead of white light.

Making Connections

5. List as many places that you can where you have seen the visible spectrum.

Exploring

6. On a clear day you can create your own rainbow. With your back to the Sun, spray a fine mist of water from a garden hose into the air. Change the angle of spray until you see a rainbow. Draw a diagram of the arrangement you used.

Reflecting

7. Explain how coloured light can be produced from white light. Speculate on what you would observe if white light is passed through coloured filters.

Design Challenge

You have learned that white light is really a band of spectral colours. How does this information affect the solution to your Challenge?

The Electromagnetic Spectrum

Light is a form of radiant energy that you can see. But the visible spectrum that you saw through the prism is only a small part of the range of radiant energies. Other radiant energies you may have heard of include microwaves, ultraviolet (UV) radiation, and X rays. These forms of energy are invisible to our eyes, but they are of the same kind as light. The entire range of radiant energies is called the **electromagnetic spectrum**.

Radiation in Space

We know that light from the Sun and other stars reaches us after travelling great distances, mostly through the vacuum of space. Other parts of the electromagnetic spectrum can also travel through space. One important property of all electromagnetic radiation is that it can travel in a vacuum; no particles are needed to transmit it.

Light and other parts of the electromagnetic spectrum travel at an extremely high speed. In a vacuum, that speed is 300 000 km/s. At this speed, it takes light about 1.3 s to travel from Earth to the Moon. Light from the Sun takes about 8 min to reach Earth. Light from the nearest star beyond the solar system takes over 4 years to reach us, even at its high speed.

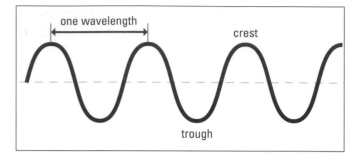

Figure 1

Energy can be transmitted as a wave. One **wavelength** is the distance from one crest to the next, or from one trough to the next.

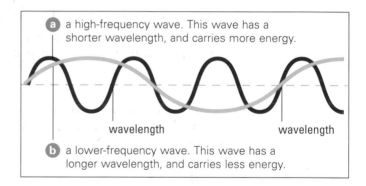

a a high-frequency wave. This wave has a shorter wavelength, and carries more energy.

b a lower-frequency wave. This wave has a longer wavelength, and carries less energy.

Figure 2

Waves with short wavelengths have more energy, because more energy is needed to create them.

Figure 3

Segments of the electromagnetic spectrum

radio waves
- AM radio waves are about 1 km long
- research is being done to determine the effects of cell phone frequencies on the human brain

Uses
- ship and boat communication
- AM radio
- cellular telephones
- television
- FM radio

microwaves
- one wave can fit into about 1 cm

Uses
- microwave ovens
- communication

infrared radiation (IR)
- about 1000 waves can fit into 1 cm
- can be detected by the skin as heat
- emitted by living things and warm objects

Uses
- thermal photographs of houses and diseased areas on the surface of the human body
- remote control for television

visible light
- up to 500 000 waves can fit into 1 cm
- red has the longest wavelength, lowest frequency, and lowest energy
- violet has the shortest wavelength, highest frequency, and highest energy

Uses
- artificial lighting
- lasers

very long wavelengths, very low frequencies, very low energy

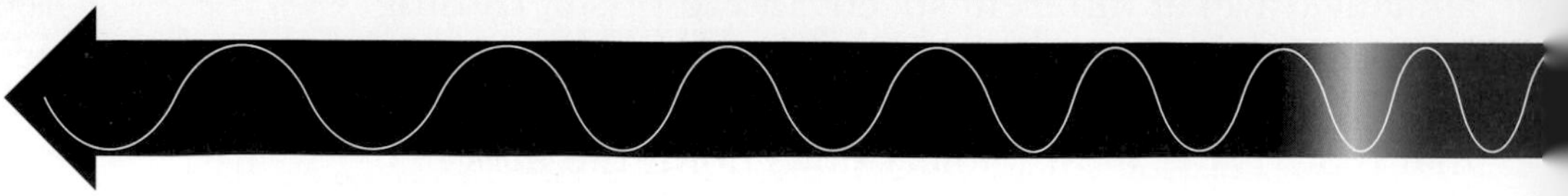

Making waves with a rope will help you understand how the parts of the electromagnetic spectrum travel.

- With a partner holding one end of the rope, stretch the rope tightly along the floor. To create waves on the rope, move your hand back and forth sideways.

- Stand a folded piece of paper beside the rope, between you and your partner. Use the rope to knock the paper over.

1. It took energy to knock over the paper; where did it come from?

2. How did the energy get to the paper?

- Move your hand back and forth slowly, at a constant speed. (This represents a low, constant frequency.) Now gradually move your hand faster (you are increasing the frequency of vibration).

3. (6C) What happens to the wavelength of the waves as the frequency increases? Use diagrams to illustrate your answer.

Waves, Energy, and Light

Waves transfer energy. Waves in a piece of rope (see Try This above) transfer mechanical energy, and electromagnetic waves transfer electromagnetic energy through space and transparent materials. **Figure 1** shows some terms that are used to describe waves.

The parts of the electromagnetic spectrum have common properties, such as their high speed and ability to travel through a vacuum. They also have different properties, related to wavelength, frequency, and energy, as shown in **Figure 2**. People take advantage of these differences and have invented uses for each part of the spectrum, as shown in **Figure 3**.

Understanding Concepts

1. Place these electromagnetic waves in order from lowest to highest energy: blue light; microwaves; X rays; orange light; infrared radiation.

2. Make a chart listing all of the electromagnetic waves you have experienced in the past year and which part of the spectrum they are part of.

Exploring

3. (8C) Research and prepare a visual presentation about the hazards of one part of the electromagnetic spectrum.

Reflecting

4. How does visible light differ from the rest of the electromagnetic spectrum?

ultraviolet radiation (UV)	X rays	gamma rays
• a million waves can fit into 1 cm	• 100 million waves can fit into 1 cm	• 10 billion waves can fit into 1 cm
• can cause sunburns, skin cancer, and cataracts in the eye	• can pass through skin, but not through bones	• dangerous energy given off by radioactive materials
• can be detected by the skin and special instruments	• can damage body cells	**Uses**
Uses	**Uses**	• studying what matter is made of
• suntanning	• X-ray photographs of parts of the human body	• studying unusual events in distant galaxies
• "black lights" in shows	• checking thicknesses in manufacturing	

Design Challenge

Some theatre groups use "black light" (actually ultraviolet radiation). When UV radiation strikes some substances, they gain energy and emit visible light. Can you use this information in your fun house or stage lighting challenge?

very short wavelengths, very high frequencies, very high energy

A Telescope for Every Wave

Just as there are many different wavelengths in the electromagnetic spectrum, there are almost as many telescopes with which to view the objects that emit them. No matter how different an X-ray telescope may look from Galileo's original model, the optical principles that operate them are the same.

The First Telescopes

The principles of light refraction and magnification that make telescopes possible were known in the time of the ancient Greeks. The modern telescope first made its appearance in the early 1600s. **Figure 1** shows two early designs by Italian scientist Galileo Galilei and German astronomer Johannes Kepler.

(a) How would you increase the magnification on Galileo's telescope without changing the basic design? What limitations to the design does this suggest?

(b) Imagine that you are looking at an oncoming car through Kepler's telescope. What would be odd about the image? Suggest a way to modify Kepler's design to correct that oddity.

(c) Under what circumstances would the oddity you observed not matter?

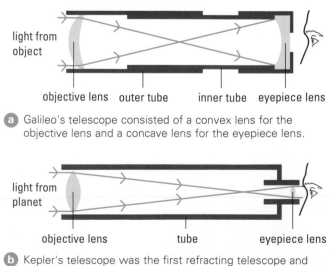

a Galileo's telescope consisted of a convex lens for the objective lens and a concave lens for the eyepiece lens.

light from planet

objective lens   tube   eyepiece lens

b Kepler's telescope was the first refracting telescope and used convex lenses for both the objective and the eyepiece.

Figure 1

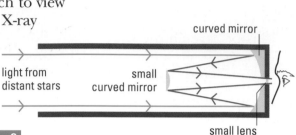

Figure 2

This design was invented by James Gregory, a Scottish mathematician who lived in the 17th century. Another refracting telescope design, still used today, was invented by Isaac Newton.

The Reflecting Telescope

If a glass lens is too big, its edges may break under heavy weight. To overcome this problem, designers began building reflecting telescopes that used a concave mirror rather than a convex lens to gather light (**Figure 2**).

(d) What advantages would a concave mirror have over a convex lens in the construction of a telescope?

Radio Telescopes

Radio waves can be detected by concave reflectors called radio telescopes (**Figure 3**). Recall that radio waves have longer wavelengths than waves of visible light, so radio telescopes tend to be much larger than telescopes that gather visible light.

(e) Radio waves can penetrate even a thick cloud cover. What might interfere with the radio wave reception capabilities of a telescope?

Figure 3

Since a large mesh is not transparent to radio waves, the radio telescope isn't as solid as a light telescope.

Figure 4
Even when gamma rays are properly caught in crystal to produce an image, that image will tend to be fuzzy.

X-Ray and Gamma-Ray Telescopes

X-ray wavelengths are so short that they penetrate ordinary mirrors. X-ray mirrors must be coated with heavy metals such as gold or beryllium to reflect the rays. Gamma-ray wavelengths are even shorter than X-rays and penetrate any mirror, no matter how heavy the metal. Gamma rays must be "caught" in a special crystal in order to obtain an image (**Figure 4**).

Figure 5

Gemini North is a part-Canadian observatory built at an altitude of 4300 m atop Mauna Kea in Hawaii. The mirror in the Gemini North reflecting telescope has a diameter of about 8 m.

Location is Everything

Today, the most powerful Earth-based telescopes are found in observatories (**Figure 5**). The telescope tracks objects in the sky as Earth rotates. The digital images it records are later analyzed by astronomers using computers.

(f) Why are observatories usually built on mountaintops?

Stars only seem to twinkle. The twinkle effect is caused by Earth's atmosphere, which also interferes with certain kinds of radiation. The Hubble Space Telescope (**Figure 6**) was launched into space to avoid this interference.

(g) What sorts of telescope must operate in space to be effective?

Understanding Concepts

1. What advancement in design led to an improvement over Galileo's magnifier?

2. What is a major disadvantage of using a lens to gather light in a telescope?

3. Do all telescopes detect visible light? Explain your answer.

Making Connections

4. When an object is viewed through Galileo's or Kepler's telescope, the object appears to be encircled by several rings of different colours. This effect does not occur when the same object is viewed through Gregory's or Newton's telescope. Why? (**Hint:** remember that white light is actually made up of many different wavelengths.)

5. Compare the structure and use of a classroom microscope with the structure and use of an astronomical refracting telescope.

Exploring

6. What effect might the hole in the ozone layer have on the receptivity of a UV telescope?

7. Canada has part ownership of (4A) large observatories in Hawaii and Chile. Research the features, uses, and discoveries of one of those observatories. Report on what you discover.

Design Challenge

Reflecting and refracting telescopes are optical devices that let us see objects far out in space. Which combination of lenses will help in your design and construction of an optical device to see into the bird's nesting box?

Figure 6

The Hubble Space Telescope, in orbit around Earth, still uses Newton's basic telescope design.

SKILLS MENU
- Questioning
- Conducting
- Analyzing
- Hypothesizing
- Recording
- Communicating
- Planning

Mixing the Colours of Light

Earlier you learned that Isaac Newton discovered that white light can be split into spectral colours and that spectral colours can be added together to produce white light. These discoveries led to other questions about light and colour. One place where these scientific facts have practical applications is the theatre: colour spotlights change what you see on the stage.

Question

2B **1** Read the procedure and create a question for this investigation.

Hypothesis

2C **2** Write a hypothesis for this investigation.

Experimental Design

By making and checking predictions, you will learn how to predict the result of any colours of light being overlapped. **Figure 2** shows the colours you will use in this investigation.

3 Read the procedure and
6D design a chart to record your predictions and observations.

4 Have your teacher approve your chart before beginning.

Materials

- 3 ray boxes
- 6 colour filters (red, green, blue, yellow, cyan, and magenta)
- white screen

 Do not touch the ray box light bulb or look directly into the light.

Procedure

5 Set up two ray boxes so the light from each box will overlap on the screen.
- Obtain red, green, and blue filters.
- Predict the colour that will result when the following light colours overlap:
Set A: green and red
Set B: green and blue
Set C: blue and red

(a) Record your predictions in your chart.

6 In a darkened room, put the filters for each set in the ray boxes.
- Observe the result when each set of colours overlap.

(a) Record your observations in your data chart.

7 Remove the colour filters from the ray boxes.
- Add a third ray box to your setup. Make sure the light from the new box shines on the same spot as the other two.
    Predict the colour that will result when the following colours of light overlap:
Set D: red, blue, and green

Figure 1

Figure 1

What mood do you think the set designer is trying to achieve?

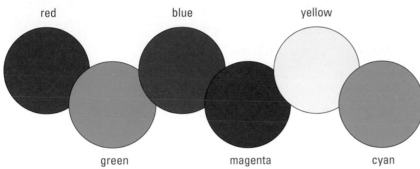

red   blue   yellow

green   magenta   cyan

Figure 2

You will overlap light of these colours in your investigation.

Making Connections

1. The lighting crew for a rock band has red, green, and blue spotlights. Which spotlights should the crew use to make a white outfit appear red? to make it appear magenta?

Reflecting

2. There are combinations of the six colours of light that you did not test in this investigation. Predict the results you would obtain for some of those combinations. With the approval of your teacher, test your predictions.

Design Challenge

The result of mixing colours of light changes slightly if one of the lights being mixed is brighter than the others. You may want to experiment with the brightness of lights and colour combinations for your fun house or stage lighting Challenges.

(a) Record your prediction.
- Use the three ray boxes and filters to test your prediction.

(b) Record your observations.

8 Obtain yellow, cyan, and magenta filters.
- Predict the colour that will result when the following colours of light overlap:
  Set E: blue and yellow
  Set F: red and cyan
  Set G: green and magenta

(a) Record your prediction.
- Test your predictions using two of the ray boxes.

(b) Record your observations.

Analysis

9 Analyze your results by doing the following.

(a) Summarize your observations using a diagram.

(b) Which of your sets of combinations produced white light?

Additive Colour Mixing

You have seen that only three overlapping colours—red, green, and blue—are needed to produce what we see as white light. It seems orange, yellow, and violet are not needed, but they are all part of natural white light. Why is this?

The explanation is in the design of the human eye.

Figure 1

Cone cells in our retinas tell us what colour of light is entering our eyes.

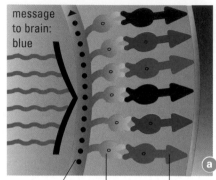

message to brain: blue

nerve fibre   nerve cells   cone cells

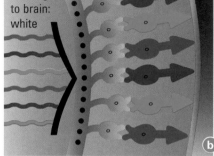

message to brain: white

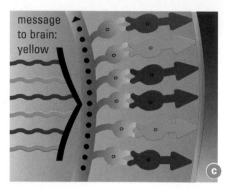

message to brain: yellow

Colour Vision

You have learned that in the retina of our eyes there are colour detectors called cones. There are three types of cone cells. One type of cone is sensitive to red light, one to blue light, and one to green light (**Figure 1**). Our eyes combine signals from each of these cones to construct all of the other colours. When our eyes receive light that contains only red, blue, and green light, we see it as white.

You can observe evidence that your cones detect red, blue, or green. When you stare at a blue object for a long time, the cones sensitive to blue become tired. If you then look at a white surface, the tired, sensitive-to-blue cones do not react to the blue in the white light. However, the cones sensitive to red and green do react. As a result, you see a combination of red and green instead of white. You see yellow.

Figure 2

Combining any two primary light colours produces a secondary light colour. Combining all three primary light colours produces white light.

Primary and Secondary Colours of Light

The process of adding colours of light together to produce other colours is called **additive colour mixing**. Studying this type of mixing will help you understand human vision.

For human vision, the **primary light colours** are the three colours of light that our cones can detect. These colours—red, green, and blue—are seen overlapping in **Figure 2**.

When any two primary light colours are combined, the resulting colour is called a **secondary light colour**. Cyan, yellow, and magenta are the secondary colours of light. For example, when blue light and green light overlap, we see cyan.

Complementary light colours are any two colours of light that produce white light when added together. For example, magenta and green are complementary colours. Magenta is created by mixing blue and red light, so when magenta and green light overlap, all three of the primary light colours are present, and we see white light.

Try This — See What Your Cones See

Test your cones.

Copy the outer box and black square of the rectangle in **Figure 3**. Stare at the black square on this page for at least 45 s. Then stare hard at the black square in your copy for the same length of time.

1. Indicate on your copy of the rectangle the colours that you saw and roughly where they appeared.

2. Explain what you saw.

Figure 3

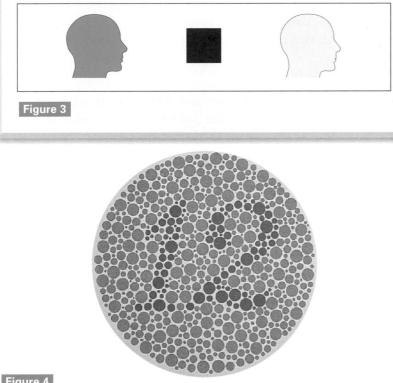

Figure 4
This pattern is a test of red-green colour blindness.

Colour Blindness

When you look at the pattern of coloured dots in **Figure 4**, do you see a number? Do any members of your group see something different? This pattern is a test of colour blindness.

A person with colour blindness is not blind to colours, but is unable to distinguish certain shades of colours clearly. Some of the cones at the back of the person's eye do not respond to the light received. One example is red-green colour blindness. A person with this condition may have difficulty distinguishing something red against a green background, especially from a distance. Consider the difficulties a person with colour blindness would have observing traffic lights.

Understanding Concepts

1. What are the primary light colours and the secondary light colours?

2. What is the complementary light colour of:
   - **(a)** red
   - **(b)** green
   - **(c)** magenta
   - **(d)** yellow

3. Explain, using a diagram, why overlapping two complementary colours would produce white light.

4. Which cones in the human eye must be activated in order to see the following colours?
   - **(a)** yellow
   - **(b)** cyan
   - **(c)** white

5. **(a)** If you stare intently at a bright green square, then look at a white surface, what will you see? Explain why this happens.

   (b) Predict and explain what will happen if you stare at a bright cyan square, then look at a white surface.

Making Connections

6. Scientists have evidence that certain animals, such as bees, can see ultraviolet radiation, which is invisible to our eyes. Create an imaginary additive colour theory for an animal that can see much more of the electromagnetic spectrum than we can.

7. The design of colour TV screens (8C) and computer monitors is based on additive colour theory. Research, using electronic and print media, the process used to produce colours in these devices. Describe what you discover.

Design Challenge

Knowing more about light and how our eyes detect it, should you change your design for your stage lighting or fun house challenge? How many lights will you need to produce all of your colour effects?

Light Entertainment

In the entertainment industry, science, technology, and art come together to take advantage of the properties of light. Brad Dickson works as a lighting director/lighting instructor for CBC Television. When asked about his career, he was glad to share his experiences.

Question: What are your job responsibilities?

Brad: I design the lighting plot for a show, order equipment, and instruct the crew on its installation. I interpret the mood and create the artistic look the producers want for the show.

Question: What skills are important in your career?

Brad: A technical understanding of light is important, because many times we mix various light sources together. This is fine for our eye, because it adapts to these different sources, but the camera does not. Colour correction is often necessary, using filters on the lights, known as "gels."

We must manipulate the light to achieve the desired effect. Knowing the effect various materials—colour gels, diffuse materials, etc.—have is critical, because you cannot waste time on the set.

Diplomacy is another important skill, because everyone involved in the production has an artistic vision of how the show should look. It is my responsibility to combine their visions with my own. An image is created by a team of people, and you have to get that team working with you if you want it to look like you had planned.

Question: How does a knowledge of optics, light, and colour help in your career?

Brad: They are the brushes we use in the entertainment industry to "paint" the image. Without a good background in these elements, you will never be able to get the desired lighting effect quickly.

Question: How are science and technology combined in your career?

Brad: Video transforms light into an electrical signal that can be broadcast. Without science and technology the art of lighting design would be limited to theatre and only those attending the production could see the show.

Try This Lights, Camera, Lights

8C You can get a better idea of the kinds of problems Brad has to solve by shooting your own scene. You will need a video camera.

- Write a script for a 2-min scene of two people sitting at a table.
- Using a video camera, shoot your scene using available light.
- After viewing the results, plan how you will change the lighting to make it look as though the scene is taking place early in the morning.
- Shoot your scene again and evaluate the results.
- Keep shooting the scene until you are satisfied with the results.

1. What technique seems to be most effective at producing an "early-morning" look?

Question: What educational background is needed to be successful in your field?

Brad: You need a technical understanding of the media, either film or video. Television goes everywhere, so you should have a wide knowledge of lighting styles from theatre to sports arenas. Computers play a big role in the process. In fact, software programs allow the lighting director to visualize the lighting before any lights are hung.

Question: What is your most interesting memory from your career?

Brad: Working with various performers is always interesting, but my work takes me to interesting locations. I have been in a helicopter without doors, circling the CN Tower; I have been near special-effect explosions; I have been on top of a lighting truss high above large crowds.

Question: How important will your career and related careers be in the future?

Brad: Multimedia is becoming a very large business, and lighting plays a major role in every aspect of it. Even if you are creating a video game scene, creating a realistic environment depends on a knowledge of lighting.

Question: What advice do you have for students?

Brad: I would encourage you to "try." Whatever your goal is, you will never achieve it if you hold yourself back by not trying. Don't be afraid of making mistakes; no one does it perfectly the first time.

Pigments and Filters for the Stage

Even in small theatres, lighting technicians use as many as 150 different lights to illuminate a show (see **Figure 1**). Different-coloured filters can be slipped in front of these lights. In this way, the stage lighting can create the illusion of a certain time of day or year, a kind of weather, a mood. The colours of paint in the set, the colour of the clothing, and the colours of makeup of the actors must all look right under the lights. Imagine you are the lighting director for a play with limited funding. The play requires three different moods: mysterious; joyful; romantic. You must work with the set designer to ensure that your work combines in such a way that the different moods can be created whenever needed.

Materials
- plain white paper
- red, green, blue, yellow, cyan, and magenta water-based colour markers
- red, green, blue, yellow, cyan, and magenta colour filters
- black pencil
- colour splotches
- materials as needed for storyboard and model or simulation

Problem

3B **1** What problem(s) can you identify in the introduction above?

Design Brief

3D Design a storyboard and a model or simulation of one of the
3E three moods required.

Design Criteria

- The storyboard must provide details of the colours of the filters used, suggested costume colours, and suggested pigment (paint) colours for the mood you are trying to create. These three sets of colours must work well together.
- The working model or simulation must demonstrate the mood depicted in your storyboard.

2 Design a chart to record your predictions and observations for parts 1 and 2 of the Build.

Build Part 1: Mixing Pigments

3 Choose two of the colour markers and predict the colour that will result when you overlap the pigments on white paper.

✏ (a) Record your prediction.

- Test your prediction by making overlapping marks with each colour of marker.

✏ (b) Record your observations.

4 Repeat step 3 using various colour combinations.

- Predict which set of three pigments produce black (or nearly black) when mixed and which sets of two pigments produce black when mixed.

✏ (a) Record your predictions.

- Test your predictions.

✏ (b) Record your observations.

SKILLS HANDBOOK: **3B** Identifying a Problem **3D** Planning a Prototype **3E** Building a Prototype

Figure 1

Lighting designers control the colours of lights by choosing coloured filters called gels. The intensity of each light can be controlled by computer, which is part of a feedback system.

cyan   magenta   yellow

blue   green   red

Figure 2

Use these colour splotches with the filters.

Design Challenge

In this investigation, three different moods were created for a scene. Can you apply any of the design features used to the stage lighting system?

Part 2: Looking Through Filters

5 Predict what colour you will see when you look at each of the splotches in **Figure 2** through the red filter.

🖉 (a) Record your predictions.

- Check your predictions by viewing each of the colour splotches in **Figure 2** through the red filter.

🖉 (b) Record your observations.

6 Repeat step 5 with the other filters, one at a time.

🖉 (a) Record your predictions and observations.

Part 3: Colours for the Set

7 For the mood your group is creating, design a combination of costume pigments, set pigments, and colour filters.

- Prepare your storyboard.
- Prepare a working model or simulation.

Test

8 Study the storyboards presented by the other groups.

- Predict which will best create the desired mood.

🖉 (a) Record your prediction.

9 View the models or simulations in action.

🖉 (a) Record your observations for each presentation.

Understanding Concepts

1. What colours are produced when the following pigments are mixed?
   (a) yellow and cyan
   (b) yellow and magenta
   (c) magenta and cyan
   (d) yellow, cyan, and magenta
   (e) red and green
   (f) magenta and green

Making Connections

2. As a set designer, your task is to create a scenery backcloth for a school play. The backcloth must include a circle that will represent the Sun in one scene and the Moon later. What colours would you paint the circle, and what colour filters would you use on the stage lights so the circle looks like the Sun? like the Moon?

Exploring

3. Design an investigation to discover how a colour printer produces its large number of colours. Have your teacher approve your design before proceeding. View samples of colour using a microscope. Make a presentation showing the results of your investigation.

Reflecting

4. For each of the terms below, list the pigment colours you think the term refers to.
   (a) primary colours
   (b) secondary colours
   (c) complementary colours

Evaluate

10 Evaluate the results by answering these questions.
(a) Do the models or simulations create a mood that could be used in a real stage setting?
(b) What colours would you change and where would you change them to improve the final result for each presentation?

Subtractive Colour Mixing

A chemical that absorbs certain colours of light, but reflects others, is a pigment. You mixed two pigments when you overlapped two colours of marker. When you mix pigments the results are predictable. For example, if you mix yellow paint with cyan paint, you get a greenish colour.

The theory used to explain how pigments mix to obtain new colours is called **subtractive colour theory**, because each pigment absorbs (subtracts) different colours from white light. Just as additive colour theory applies to the mixing of coloured lights, subtractive colour theory applies only to the mixing of pigments.

The Colour of a Rose

Why is a red rose red? A red object has particles of pigment that absorb the other two primary light colours, blue and green, and reflect red light.

The pigment in the petals of a yellow rose absorbs blue light and reflects both red and green light, as you can see in **Figure 1**.

An object's colour is determined by which light colours are absorbed and which are reflected.

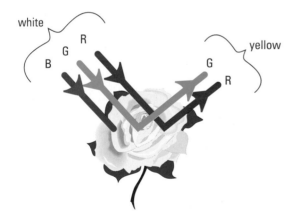

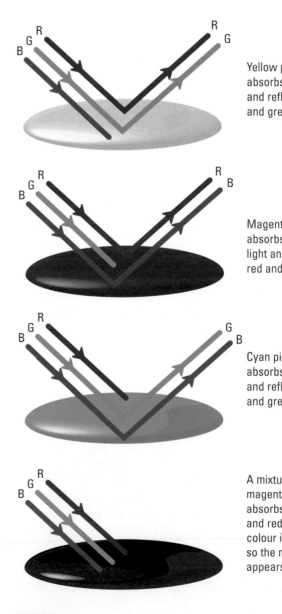

Yellow pigment absorbs blue light and reflects red and green light.

Magenta pigment absorbs green light and reflects red and blue light.

Cyan pigment absorbs red light and reflects blue and green light.

Figure 1

Red roses appear red, and yellow roses appear yellow because of the pigments in their petals.

Primary Pigments

Three colour pigments can be mixed to obtain black (or almost black). As you have discovered, these three **primary pigment colours** are yellow, cyan, and magenta. Each of these pigments absorbs one primary colour from white light, as shown in **Figure 2**.

A mixture of yellow, magenta, and cyan absorbs blue, green, and red light. No colour is reflected, so the mixture appears black.

Figure 2

Each of the three primary pigment colours absorbs a different primary light colour.

Subtractive Colour Theory

When any two primary pigments are mixed, a secondary pigment colour results. As shown in **Figure 3**, the **secondary pigment colours** are red, green, and blue. A secondary pigment colour absorbs two primary light colours, but reflects only one.

Notice the difference between light colours and pigment colours. The primary light colours (red, green, and blue) are the secondary pigment colours; and the secondary light colours (yellow, cyan, and magenta) are the primary pigment colours.

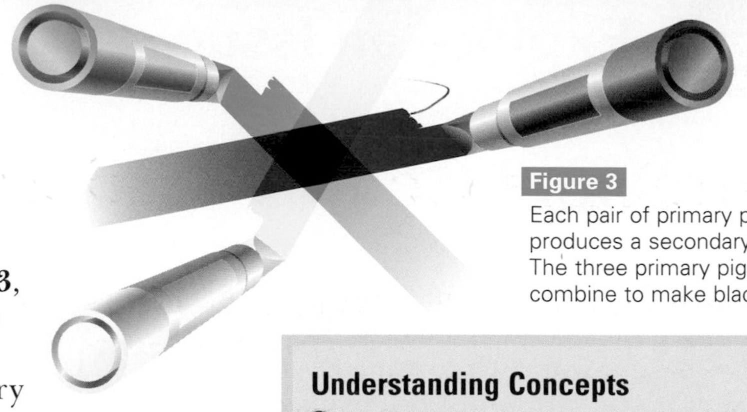

Filters and Subtractive Theory

Filters contain pigments. As light is transmitted through the filter, these pigments absorb some light colours, but not all. For example, a blue filter absorbs red and green light and transmits blue light. What light colours would a cyan filter absorb and transmit?

Colour Printing

The theory of the subtraction of light colours is applied in many situations, including colour photography and colour printing. For example, the colour printers attached to computers use three colours of ink—yellow, cyan, and magenta—to produce colours. Using these three colours and black, the printer is able to produce more than a million different colours.

Figure 3

Each pair of primary pigments produces a secondary pigment. The three primary pigments combine to make black pigment.

Understanding Concepts

1. Explain why a magenta sweater is magenta.
2. Use a diagram to explain the colour you see for each situation below:
   (a) a mixture of yellow and cyan pigments
   (b) a mixture of yellow and magenta pigments
   (c) a yellow object through a green filter
   (d) a magenta object through a yellow filter
3. What colour would you expect to see if you shine white light through a cyan filter at a
   (a) white object? (c) yellow object?
   (b) green object? (d) red object?
4. You need some green icing to frost a cake but have run out of green food colouring. However, you have red, yellow, and blue left. What could you do?

Making Connections

5. Give three examples of colours that can be produced using the inks available in a colour computer printer. What percentage of each pigment do the colours include?
6. Explain why some fabric detergents include "bluing agents" to "brighten up" older white clothes.
7. In a stage performance, half the actors on stage appear to be invisible. Later the effect is reversed. Use the diagrams to explain how this effect can be achieved with only white lights and filters of the three primary light colours.

Reflecting

8. Black is not a colour. Explain this statement.

Try This Using a Light Sensor

Computer sensors can provide evidence to support subtractive colour theory.
- Use a light sensor connected to a computer to measure the intensity of a red light aimed toward a leaf.
- Measure the intensity of the red light reflected off the leaf.
- Repeat the activity using various other colours, including secondary light colours.

1. Prepare a visual presentation showing what you discover.

Design Challenge

How can you apply your information about pigments and filters in your Challenge design?

Solar Panels

Wouldn't it be great if you could just leave your computer, the TV, or the toaster in sunlight to make it work? Unfortunately, it's not that simple. Sunlight must be changed into electrical energy first before it can be used to operate electrical devices.

A **solar cell** is a device that converts light energy into electrical energy. Solar cells are often used in calculators and watches. Light energy strikes crystals, commonly made of silicon, causing electricity to flow. Wires coming from the crystals are connected to the appliance.

Solar cell technology was developed in the 1950s when space scientists realized that the Sun was the best source of energy for satellites and spacecraft. To obtain more electricity, scientists developed **solar panels**, collections of solar cells (**Figure 1**).

Figure 1

Solar cells are packed close together in this solar panel.

Understanding Concepts

1. What are the names and functions of the components of a solar panel system?

2. Assume that the solar cells of a certain panel have an efficiency of 18% and solar energy hits the panel at a rate of 1000 watts (W) in full sunlight.

   (a) What is the output of the panel?

   (b) How many 60-W light bulbs can be operated using this panel?

Solar Panel Technology

Solar panels can be installed on a roof to provide power (**Figure 2**). Because the Sun may be hidden by clouds and is not available at night, energy collected during sunny periods must be stored for use at other times. Rechargeable batteries can be used for this purpose.

Three main factors affect the technological design of solar panels:

- the efficiency of the solar cells
- the amount of solar energy striking the cells in the panel
- the capacity of the rechargeable batteries

From the 1950s onward, the efficiency of solar cells gradually rose to about 14% in the mid-1990s. The efficiency was boosted to about 18% with the use of mirrors or lenses to focus the Sun's light onto the solar cells. But this technology requires the Sun's rays to hit the solar panel directly all day long, so a tracking system must be used. The mechanical system to track the Sun is expensive and could be a problem during periods of cold or windy weather. Rechargeable batteries used to store electrical energy are being improved continually.

Figure 2

This solar panel is installed on a south-facing roof. A tracking system allows light energy from the Sun to hit the solar cells as directly as possible.

Role Play — The Solar School

A new school is being planned for an area near where you live. To discuss possible sources of electricity for the new school, a meeting is planned at which four specialists will give presentations on solar power to concerned citizens. The specialists are described below.

The Roles

- An environmentalist who thinks that installing a solar panel system to provide all the electrical needs will help protect the environment and set a good example for other building construction.

- A manager from a power utility who is concerned that using solar power will reduce the need for electricity produced at generating stations, causing job losses.

- A school board official who is determined to keep construction costs of the new school to a minimum.

- A scientist working for a solar panel manufacturer who argues that over several years the money saved by using solar energy will pay for the installation.

Advantages of Using Solar Panels

- As technology improves, it will cost less to install a complete system, but the costs of purchasing electricity from power companies will continue to rise. From this point of view, installing a solar system is an investment rather than an expense.

- Using more solar energy will put less demand on nonrenewable sources of energy, such as fossil fuels and uranium.

- A school with solar panels would not have to worry about electric power outages caused by failures in external power lines or generators.

Disadvantages of Using Solar Panels

- The cost of installing a solar panel system is high (up to about $10 000 for a typical home, and more for larger buildings with greater power needs). Rechargeable batteries may last for only about 10 years, and then have to be replaced at a cost of about $1500.

- Repairs may be costly if some parts of the system, such as the Sun tracker, fail.

- Heavy snowfall could block the panels or overload the Sun tracker; in some regions, especially in winter, there may not be enough sunlight to produce the needed power.

Your Task

(8D) You will assume the role of one of the specialists. Prepare for your role by considering the advantages and disadvantages of solar panels above and any more you can think of. When preparing your presentation, consider the following questions:

- What arguments support your opinion?
- Will your ideas be practical in the short term?

- Will your ideas be appropriate in the long term?
- How can you justify your suggestions to the community?

(4A) Do research to help improve your arguments. Be prepared to answer questions from "concerned citizens" in your class.

Design Challenge

SKILLS MENU
- Identify a Problem
- Planning
- Building
- Testing
- Recording
- Evaluating
- Communicating

Design and Build a Device or System That Controls Light

Light does more than just let you see. Light sent through the fine glass threads of fibre-optic cables delivers information to telephones, computers, and televisions. All of the entertainment industries manipulate light to create moods and effects.

1 An Aid to Vision

Problem Situation

You are interested in studying birds as they grow in a nest. You've constructed a nesting box. You hope two parent birds will build a nest inside the box and lay eggs. You want to check periodically to see how the young birds develop. However, if you climb up and look in the box, it might scare away the parent birds.

Design Brief

Design and build an optical device that would allow you to look into the nesting box, without disturbing the birds.

Design Criteria

- Your device can use mirrors, lenses, and prisms. It must include at least two of these, used in combination.
- As a test, your optical device must allow you to see and read print from a newspaper classified advertisement that has been placed faceup on a ledge or shelf at least 1 m above your eyes.
- Your design must include a plan for connecting the device to a nesting box.

Figure 1
How can you see what is hidden?

2 A Fun House

Problem Situation

A fun house, sometimes called a hall of mirrors, uses curved and flat mirrors, lenses, and prisms to make distorted and multiple images and to create weird effects with colour. A hall of mirrors is carefully designed to make visitors laugh or cry out and become confused about where they are, what is real, and where they can go.

Design Brief

Design and build a model of a fun house that will amaze, surprise, and delight visitors.

Design Criteria

- Your fun house must include mirrors, lenses, and prisms, but it can also use other optical devices.
- You must include a plan for the layout of your fun house with a description of the different effects and how they are created.
- The fun house must be safe for visitors.

Figure 2
In a fun house, what you see may not be what is.

Figure 3
Stage lights can produce many interesting effects.

3 A Stage Lighting System

Problem Situation

In a theatre, getting the light right for a play is often difficult. For each play, the set designer and lighting technicians must create a system that can provide the proper effects for each scene. You have a play to light. The play has three scenes that take place outside on a balcony: one on a warm, sunny day; one on a cold, cloudy day; and one in moonlight. The play also has three indoor scenes. One takes place in the morning, one around sunset, and one at night. The indoor scenes are set in the same room, which has windows.

Design Brief

Design and build a model of a lighting system to create effects for the stage play.

Design Criteria

- The model must create the effects needed to stage each scene in the play.
- Your plan must include a description of how the lighting system will be used in each scene.
- The stage lighting system must be safe for actors, technicians, and the audience.

Assessment

Your model or device will be assessed according to how well you:

Process
- Understand the problem
- Develop a plan
- Choose and safely use appropriate materials, tools, and equipment
- Test and record results
- Evaluate your model, including suggestions for improvement

Communicate
- Prepare a presentation
- Use correct terms
- Write clear descriptions of the steps you took in building and testing your model
- Explain clearly how your model solves the problem
- Make an accurate technical drawing for your model

Produce
- Meet the design criteria with your model
- Use your chosen materials effectively
- Construct your model
- Solve the identified problem

 When preparing to build or test a design, have your plan approved by your teacher before you begin.

Unit 5 Summary

In this unit, you have learned that the Sun is the primary source of light on Earth, but that artificial sources produce light too. The composition of light allows us to see colour, and the human eye and the camera share common properties.

Reflecting

- Reflect on the ideas and questions presented in the Unit Overview and in the Getting Started. How can you connect what you have done and learned in this unit with those ideas and questions? (To review, check the sections indicated in this Summary.)
- Revise your answers to the Reflecting questions in ❶, ❷, ❸ and the questions you created in the Getting Started. How has your thinking changed?
- What new questions do you have? How will you answer them?

Understanding Concepts

- describe how light sources produce light 5.1
- recognize that materials react differently to light: some transmit, some reflect, and some absorb 5.3
- identify which characteristics of mirrors and lenses make them useful in optical instruments 5.9, 5.11, 5.16
- describe how light refracts in different materials 5.10
- compare the properties of visible light and other types of electromagnetic radiation 5.14, 5.15
- explain colour vision and why objects appear to have colour 5.17, 5.18
- describe how coloured filters and pigments interact with light 5.20, 5.21

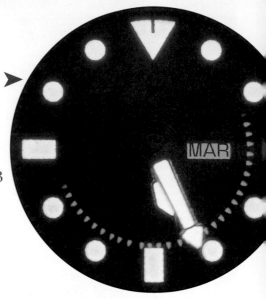

Applying Skills

- formulate a hypothesis and conduct an investigation to determine what property of light allows shadows to form 5.2
- investigate how light rays reflect off surfaces and describe the laws of reflection using diagrams of your findings 5.5, 5.7, 5.8

- design, plan, and carry out an investigation to explain images seen in lenses 5.12
- plan and carry out investigations to explore colour 5.17, 5.20

- understand and use the following terms:

  additive colour mixing
  angle of incidence
  angle of reflection
  angle of refraction
  bioluminescence
  chemiluminescence
  complementary light colours
  concave lens
  concave mirror
  convex lens
  convex mirror
  diffuse reflection
  electric discharge
  electromagnetic spectrum
  focal length
  fluorescence
  incandescence
  incident ray
  laws of reflection
  lens
  light
  luminous
  nonluminous
  normal
  opaque
  optical device
  penumbra
  phosphorescence
  plane mirror
  primary light colours
  primary pigment colours
  principal axis
  principal focus
  real image
  reflected ray
  refraction
  regular reflection
  secondary light colours
  secondary pigment colours
  shadow
  solar cell
  solar panels
  subtractive colour theory
  translucent
  transparency
  transparent
  umbra
  virtual image
  visible spectrum
  wavelength

Making Connections

- evaluate the efficiency of energy transformations in light sources 5.1

- recognize that knowledge of how light interacts with materials is important in design 5.3, 5.5, 5.6, 5.8, 5.18, 5.21

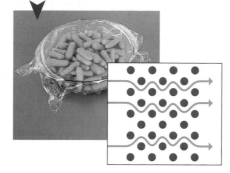

- identify how reflection is used in everyday life 5.6, 5.9

- describe how the properties of multiple lenses or mirrors can be used to design optical instruments 5.11, 5.16

- compare the human eye and the camera 5.13

- describe the electromagnetic spectrum and how radiant energy reaches Earth 5.15

- recognize the costs and benefits of converting light from the Sun into electrical energy 5.22

Applying Skills

23. You are asked to put on a "light show" to demonstrate that light travels in a straight line. How would you do it?

24. A manufacturing company has hired you to design lamps that have a special feature: the on/off switch must be visible in the dark, and it must not consume any electrical energy directly.

    (a) What design would you use?

    (b) How would you test your design to see how effective it is?

25. Draw a top-view diagram to show how you would place a mirror that would allow you to see around a corner.

26. The pinhole camera shown in **Figure 4** is a simple design. How would you redesign the camera so:

    (a) its length can be adjusted.

    (b) it could be used to take a photograph.

27. Design a sundial so that a person standing at a set position creates a shadow that indicates the time of day. How can you ensure that your sundial would be accurate?

28. Describe ways to determine the focal length of a concave mirror.

29. How could you use a curved mirror to start a campfire on a sunny day? Draw a diagram to illustrate your answer.

30. When you press a button on a TV remote control, infrared radiation is emitted. Design an investigation to determine the transparency of the following materials to infrared radiation: glass, plastic, wood, the human body.

31. Describe how you would investigate several coloured light bulbs to determine which visible colours each emits.

32. Only a small percentage of the energy emitted by the Sun strikes Earth. Use a diagram to explain why.

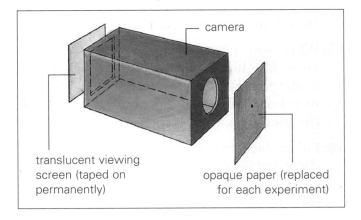

camera

translucent viewing screen (taped on permanently)

opaque paper (replaced for each experiment)

Figure 4

Figure 5

Making Connections

33. Meteoroids are nonluminous chunks of rocky material travelling through space. Meteoroids that fall into Earth's atmosphere become meteors or "shooting stars." Why are meteors luminous?

34. Assume you are buying one of the following: a telescope, a microscope, a pair of binoculars, or a camera. Make a list of questions you would ask the salesperson in order to help you decide.

35. How are transparent and translucent materials used in practical applications? Consider home, school, transport, clothing, packaging, and sports products. Which of the uses you identified are for appearance and which are functional?

36. Identify 10 ways that the reflection of light is used in everyday situations.

37. Why is the lettering on the front of the ambulance in **Figure 5** printed backward?

38. Energy must be used to produce artificial light, usually electrical energy. Electricity generation is expensive and sometimes damaging to the environment. Identify a common use of light that you think we could do without. Explain why.

39. Many streetlights turn on and off automatically (**Figure 6**).

(a) Identify the input, output, and feedback features of this system.

(b) How might fog affect the stability of the system?

40. What optical instruments could you design using the sets of components listed?

(a) two convex lenses

(b) a concave mirror and a convex lens

(c) two plane mirrors

(d) three convex lenses

41. Using a diagram, describe how eyeglasses correct near-sightedness and far-sightedness.

42. Describe how our lives would be different if there were no mirrors or lenses.

43. Compare the automatic functions of the human eye to the automatic functions of the camera.

44. Draw a concept map with yourself in the middle, showing all the ways that light can reach your eyes.

45. Sometimes the colour of something you buy in a store looks different in sunlight. This happens because stores often use fluorescent lights, which emit more blue light than red light. How would fluorescent light affect the colours of such items as clothing, cosmetics, and decorating supplies? Design a system that would avoid this problem.

46. Some of our emotional responses to different colours have been identified through research. Think of commercials and advertisements that capture your interest. How is colour used to influence you? What are the benefits and abuses related to the use of colour?

Figure 6

Skills Handbook

1. Safety in Science & Technology

2. Process of Scientific Inquiry
   2A   Process of Scientific Inquiry
   2B   Asking a Question
   2C   Predicting and Hypothesizing
   2D   Identifying Variables and Controls
   2E   Designing an Inquiry Investigation

3. Process of Design
   3A   The Problem-Solving Cycle
   3B   Identifying a Problem
   3C   Selecting the Best Alternative
   3D   Planning a Prototype
   3E   Building a Prototype
   3F   Testing and Evaluating a Prototype
   3G   Patents, Trademarks, & Copyrights

4. Researching
   4A   Research Skills
   4B   Interviewing and Survey Skills
   4C   Critical Thinking

5. Using Equipment in Science & Technology
   5A   Using the Microscope
   5B   Working with Scales and Balances
   5C   Using Other Scientific Equipment
   5D   Using Technology Equipment
   5E   Fabrication Techniques

6. Observing and Recording Data
   6A   Obtaining Qualitative Data
   6B   Obtaining Quantitative Data
   6C   Scientific & Technical Drawing
   6D   Creating Data Tables

7. Analyzing Results
   7A   The Need to Graph
   7B   Reading a Graph
   7C   Constructing Graphs
   7D   Using Math in Science & Technology
   7E   Reaching a Conclusion
   7F   Reflecting on Your Work

8. Communicating
   8A   Writing a Report
   8B   Creating a Design Folder
   8C   Multimedia Presentations
   8D   Exploring an Issue

9. Study Skills
   9A   Setting Goals and Monitoring Progress
   9B   Good Study Habits
   9C   Using Your Computer Effectively
   9D   Working Together
   9E   Graphic Organizers

① Safety in Science & Technology

Safety Conventions in *Nelson Science & Technology 7/8*

The investigations in *Nelson Science & Technology 7/8* are challenging, interesting, and safe. However, accidents can happen. In all of the investigations, potential hazards are identified by a caution symbol and described in red type (**Figure 1**).

Figure 1	✋ (octagon symbol)	Be careful when cutting. Always cut away from your body.

Always read the cautions carefully and make sure you understand what they mean before you proceed. If you are in doubt about anything, ask someone who knows (i.e., your teacher or a parent).

You should also look for caution symbols on the materials and products you use in your investigations. The symbols in **Figures 2 and 3** are often found on the labels of hazardous products.

Hazardous Household Product Symbols (HHPS)

You are probably familiar with the warning symbols in **Figure 2**. They appear on a number of products that are common in most households. These warning symbols indicate exactly why and to what degree a product is dangerous.

Workplace Hazardous Materials Information System (WHMIS) Symbols

The Workplace Hazardous Materials Information System (WHMIS) symbols in **Figure 3** were developed to standardize the labelling of dangerous materials used in all workplaces, including schools.

Preventing Accidents

Most accidents in the Science & Technology classroom are caused by carelessness. Following these general procedures can help you prevent them.
- Pay careful attention to instructions and take your work seriously.
- Be prepared for every investigation.

Figure 2
Hazardous Household Product Symbols (HHPS)

Figure 3
Workplace Hazardous Materials Information System (WHMIS) Symbols

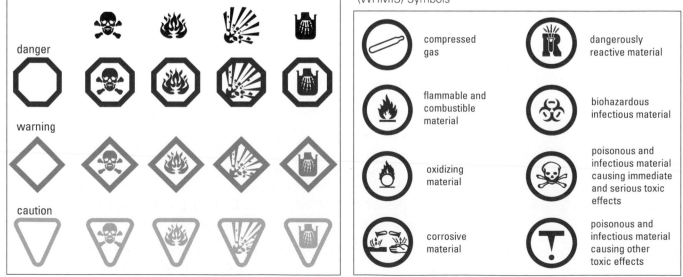

- Keep your working space clean and organized.
- Tie back long hair and don't wear loose clothing or jewellery.
- Measure and mix chemicals correctly.
- Handle hot equipment with care.
- Do not apply too much pressure to glass equipment (including microscope slides, cover slips, and thermometers).
- Use all tools, especially sharp tools, with proper care.
- Wear safety goggles.

Getting Off to a Safe Start

1. Learn the location and proper use of safety equipment, such as:
   - safety goggles
   - protective aprons
   - heat-resistant gloves
   - eye-wash station
   - broken-glass container
   - first-aid kit
   - fire extinguishers
   - fire blankets
   - water station

   Locate the nearest fire alarm.

   Know the procedures to follow in case an accident does occur.

2. Inform your teacher of any allergies or medical conditions that you may have. Do not wear contact lenses when conducting investigations—if a foreign substance became trapped beneath the lens, it would be difficult to remove it.

3. Read the procedure of any investigation carefully before you start. If there is anything you do not understand, ask your teacher to explain. Check all materials for warning labels. Make sure all tools and equipment are in good working condition and are properly secured. Clear your work area of all materials except those you will use in the investigation. If you are designing your own investigation, have your teacher check your design before you proceed.

4. Wear safety goggles and appropriate protective clothing, and tie back long hair

(**Figure 4**). Remove jewellery and neckties. Wear closed shoes, not open sandals. Beware of loose clothing.

5. Return all equipment and tools to the appropriate storage facility.

6. Only use power tools if a qualified adult has trained you in their safe use.

7. Never work alone.

Figure 4

a Ready to conduct a safe inquiry investigation

b Ready to conduct a safe design investigation

Working with Chemicals

1. Do not taste, touch, or smell anything unless you are asked to do so by your teacher. Do not chew gum, eat, or drink in the Science & Technology classroom.

2. Be aware of where the Material Safety Data Sheet (MSDS) manual is kept. Know any relevant MSDS information for the chemicals you are working with.

3. Label all containers. When taking something from a bottle or other

container, double-check the label to be sure you are taking exactly what you need.

4. If any part of your body comes in contact with a chemical or specimen, wash the area immediately and thoroughly with water. If your eyes are affected, do not touch them but wash them immediately and continuously with cool water, moving from the bridge of the nose toward the outside corner of the eye, for at least 15 min. Inform your teacher.

5. Handle all chemicals carefully. When you are instructed to smell a chemical, wave the vapour toward your nose (**Figure 5**). This way, you can smell the substance without inhaling too much into your lungs. Never put your nose close to a chemical.

Figure 5
Safe smelling

6. Place test tubes in a rack before pouring liquids into them. If you must hold a test tube, tilt it away from you (and others) before pouring in a liquid (**Figure 6**).

Figure 6
Safe pouring

7. Clean up any spilled or dropped materials immediately, following instructions given by your teacher.

8. Do not return unused chemicals to the original containers, and do not pour them down the drain. Dispose of chemicals as instructed by your teacher.

9. Ensure the area is well ventilated when using chemicals.

10. Clean all equipment thoroughly after use.

Working with Heat

1. Whenever possible, use electric hot plates for heating materials. Use a flame only if instructed to do so. If a Bunsen burner (**Figure 7**) is used in your Science & Technology classroom, make sure you follow the procedures listed below.
   • Obtain instructions from your teacher on the proper method of lighting and adjusting the Bunsen burner.
   • Do not heat a flammable material (for example, alcohol) over a Bunsen burner. Make sure there are no flammable materials nearby.
   • Do not leave a lighted Bunsen burner unattended.
   • Always turn off the gas at the valve, not at the base of the Bunsen burner.

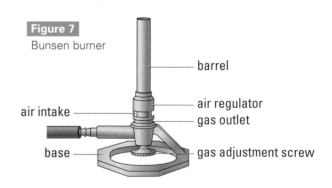

Figure 7
Bunsen burner

barrel
air regulator
gas outlet
air intake
base
gas adjustment screw

2. When heating liquids in glass containers, make sure you use clean Pyrex or Kimax. Do not use broken or cracked glassware. Never allow a container to boil dry.

3. When heating a test tube over a flame, use a test-tube holder. Hold the test tube at an angle, with the opening facing away from

you and others (**Figure 8**). Heat the upper half of the liquid first, then move it gently in the flame, to distribute the heat evenly.

Figure 8
Heating using a test-tube

4. Be careful when handling hot objects and objects that might be hot. Hot plates can take up to 60 min to cool completely. Test that they are cool enough to move by touching first with a damp paper towel. If you hear sizzling or see steam, wait a little longer! If you burn yourself, immediately apply cold water or ice, and inform your teacher.

5. Always have an inspected and certified fire extinguisher at hand.

Working with Light

1. Never look directly into a light source (including the Sun). Do not use magnifying lenses to observe light directly.

2. Use mirrors with care. If a mirror is broken, dispose of glass in the appropriate receptacle.

3. Since ray boxes are used in the dark, be careful when moving from place to place. Allow your eyes to become accustomed to the dark prior to beginning an activity.

Working with Sharp Tools

All tools must be used below waist level. Always wear safety goggles.

1. Saws (**Figure 9**):
   • Always use the correct type of mitre box to match the saw you are using. Be sure

that the mitre box is secured to the work surface.
   • Make sure the saw blade is properly in place (the teeth of the saw should be angled away from your body).

Figure 9
The safe use of a saw

2. Drills:
   • Change drill bits carefully. To reduce breakage, always use high quality drill bits.
   • Drill on a solid, flat, secured surface. Be sure to secure the object you are drilling.
   • Always drill downwards.

3. Paper Drills:
   • Secure the cutting end.
   • Drill on a solid, flat, secured surface.
   • Use light pressure only.

4. Utility Knife:
   • Always use a metal safety ruler.
   • Cut on a solid, flat, secured surface.
   • Keep work area clear.
   • Always cut by pulling the knife toward you. Keep your other hand well out of the way. Work carefully and slowly. Use light pressure. Thicker materials may need several cuts (not more pressure).
   • Always retract the blade when finished.

5. Snips and Scissors:
   • Always carry these by the blade end.
   • Place the material being cut close to the pivot point so that it is easier to cut.
   • Snip materials so that they fall down onto the working surface.
   • When snips are not in use, secure the safety catch.

6. Hammer:
   - Hammer only the nail head. Never bang two hammers together.
   - Work on a solid, flat, secured surface.

7. Screwdriver:
   - Use a screwdriver only for its intended purpose, turning screws. Do not use as a punch, wedge, etc.

Working with Adhesives and Fasteners

1. Always read the label to ensure that what you are using is not toxic.

2. Follow directions for safe use. Be aware of first aid precautions and treatment.

3. Always use glue guns and adhesives in a well-ventilated area.

4. Glue Guns (**Figure 10**):
   - Wear safety goggles.
   - Always use a glue gun in a low traffic area of the room, near an electrical outlet. Ensure that glue gun cords are out of the work area.
   - Your work surface should be protected.
   - Always glue down to the object. Gluing should take place at the level of the work surface area.
   - To avoid burning fingers, always use a stick to position an object being glued. Never use a foreign object to force the glue through the barrel of the glue gun. Have cool water available in case of burns. Immerse burn for at least 10 min and inform your teacher.

Figure 10
Using a glue gun safely

5. Fasteners: Always use caution when putting metal fasteners in or through various materials. Whenever possible, precut the hole.

Other Hazards

1. Keep water and wet hands away from electrical cords, plugs, and sockets. Always unplug electrical cords by pulling on the plug, not the cord. Report any frayed cords or damaged outlets to your teacher. Make sure electrical cords are not placed where someone could trip over them.

2. Place broken and waste glass in the specially marked containers.

3. Follow your teacher's instructions when disposing of waste materials.

4. Report to your teacher all accidents and injuries (no matter how minor), broken equipment, damaged or defective facilities, and suspicious-looking chemicals.

5. Wash your hands thoroughly, using soap and warm water, after every inquiry or design investigation. This practice is especially important when you handle chemicals, biological specimens, and microorganisms.

6. Store chemicals and solvents in a secure, well-ventilated area.

7. Store tools and equipment in a safe place after use.

 **Safety Posters**

In groups, create safety posters for your classroom. These may include a map of the route your class should follow when the fire alarm sounds, a map of where the safety materials (fire extinguisher, first aid kit, etc.) are located in your classroom, information about the safe use of a specific tool, or an illustrated poster outlining specific safety rules, etc.

2A Process of Scientific Inquiry

Science is knowledge of the world around us. It's also a way of learning about the world around us by observing things, asking questions, proposing answers, and testing those answers. Science is also about sharing information that encourages others to discover more. All scientists use a similar process to find answers to their questions. Let's look at an example of how this process is used before examining the specific steps.

Using the Process of Scientific Inquiry

From Curiosity to a Testable Hypothesis

After observing plants for some time, you may observe that they grow upward (**Figure 1**).

Figure 1

Why do plants grow upward?

If you're curious, you may ask yourself "Why?" You can probably think of some possible answers. For example, maybe plants grow upward because they grow toward the light. This is a hypothesis. From your hypothesis, you can make a prediction that you can test through experimentation. You could test the following prediction: "As the angle of light shining on plants steadily increases, the angle of the plants' growth should also steadily increase."

The Investigation

Once you have a prediction, you can design a test. You can think of your prediction as a statement of cause and effect. The effect you identified is the angle of plant growth. The cause you identified is the angle of light shining on the plant. Your investigation should test whether the cause will produce the effect you predict. The cause and effect can change or vary—so they are known as variables. To plan a careful, accurate investigation, you need to control the cause variable as much as possible. For example, you could investigate the growth of five identical plants, ensuring that all growing conditions—water, nutrients, temperature, kind of light, etc.—are the same (**Figure 2**). You would then change one variable, the angle of light shone on one plant, and measure the results.

Figure 2

Does changing the angle of light change the angle of growth?

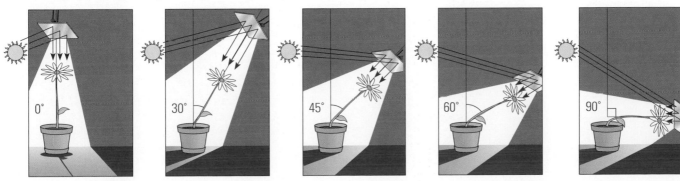

The Results

When you design your investigation, you need to think about what you are going to measure and how you are going to record your results. For instance, you might create a data table like the one in **Table 1**.

Table 1	Record of Angle of Growth					
Angle of Light	**Day 1**	**Day 3**	**Day 5**	**Day 7**	**Day 9**	**Day 11**
Sample A (0º)	?	?	?	?	?	?
Sample B (30º)	?	?	?	?	?	?
Sample C (45º)	?	?	?	?	?	?
Sample D (60º)	?	?	?	?	?	?
Sample E (90º)	?	?	?	?	?	?

Once you have completed the investigation, you will have to analyze your results to see whether or not they support your hypothesis. You may create graphs based on the data you collect that will help you make sense of your results. Ultimately, your conclusions will be communicated to others in a report.

Unfortunately, you can never be sure that all possible causes of the effects have been controlled. This means that you can never be absolutely sure that your conclusions are true. However, the more closely the results match the prediction, the more confident you can be that your hypothesis was sound. If you communicate your procedure and conclusions clearly, the experiment can be repeated and the hypothesis re-evaluated. New questions may arise, and new evidence may be gathered.

The Steps in the Process of Scientific Inquiry

It is important that you follow this process and use the related skills whenever you are asked to design and conduct an experiment, if you expect to find reliable answers to the questions you pose. You can use the flow chart in **Figure 3** as a checklist. You can also refer to the more detailed sections in the *Skills Handbook* that deal with each of the specific skills necessary for each part of the process.

 **Detective as Scientist**

Read a mystery story and describe which of the steps in the inquiry process were used by the detective to solve the crime. Use the flowchart in **Figure 3** as a checklist. The following list of questions may help you:

1. What question did the detective have to answer?

2. How did the detective reach a hypothesis? Were observation, research, or prediction used?

3. How was the hypothesis tested? Were variables controlled? Were clues observed? Were scientific instruments used?

4. How were the results of the investigation analyzed? How were observations recorded? What trends or patterns emerged? What conclusions were drawn? What new questions emerged?

5. How was the conclusion communicated?

① Asking a Question

- Ask a question that interests you or express an idea that can be tested.

② Making a Hypothesis

- Research information and previous discoveries that might help you answer your question.
- Develop an educated guess that answers your question. This is your hypothesis.
- Make a prediction based on your hypothesis and state it as a cause-effect relationship.

③ Designing the Experiment

- Identify all your variables.
- Decide what materials and equipment you will need to perform your experiment.
- Write a procedure that explains how you will conduct your experiment. Be sure to take safety into account.
- Draw a labelled diagram that visually explains your procedure and the material and equipment you will use in your experiment.
- Create a rough draft of tables for recording your data.

④ Conducting the Experiment

- Follow the steps in the procedure carefully and thoroughly.
- Use all equipment and materials safely, accurately, and with precision.
- Record the variable(s) you are measuring, manipulating and controlling.
- Remember to repeat your experiment at least three times. If you are collecting quantitative data, take an average. This increases the accuracy and reliability of your results.

Figure 3

The Steps in the Process of Scientific Inquiry

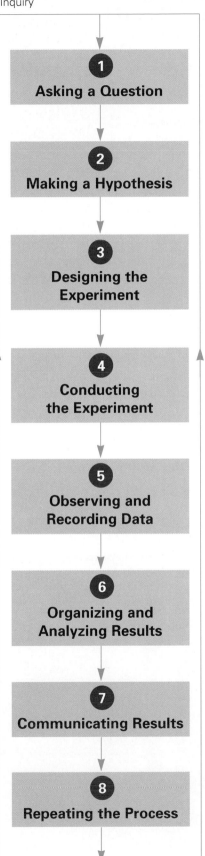

1. Asking a Question
2. Making a Hypothesis
3. Designing the Experiment
4. Conducting the Experiment
5. Observing and Recording Data
6. Organizing and Analyzing Results
7. Communicating Results
8. Repeating the Process

⑤ Observing and Recording Data

- Make careful notes of everything that you observe during the experiment.
- Record numerical data in tables.

⑥ Organizing and Analyzing Results

- When appropriate, create graphs to make better sense of data from your tables.
- Study all of your observations.
- Identify patterns and trends.
- Make a conclusion. Be sure that your results support, partially support, or reject your hypothesis.
- Develop an explanation for your conclusion.
- Apply your findings to your life today. Think about who will want to know about your discovery, how it will affect our lives, who it will benefit, and whether or not it could harm our world if used in a certain way.
- Reflect on your experiment. Explore any sources of experimental error in your process. Think about what changes you would make if you were to conduct this experiment in the future.

⑦ Communicating Results

- Write a report to summarize your investigation. In order to have their investigations repeated and validated, it is common for scientists to publish details of their research, results, and conclusions.

⑧ Repeating the Process

- If your experiment did not answer the question you initially asked, revise it and repeat it until the question is answered. Most scientists must complete an experiment many times before making important discoveries (e.g., a cure for cancer).

②B Asking a Question

Wondering About the World Around You

All scientific questions are asked by people who are curious about the world around them. Our curiosity is fed by observation, experience, and research. You may have noticed, for example, that balloons stick to walls if you rub them on your head (**Figure 1**). This observation might lead you to wonder about a number of things: Does a balloon stick better if you rub it more times? Does the length or texture of a person's hair affect how well a balloon sticks? Does it matter how inflated the balloon is or what colour it is?

Each of these questions is the basis for a sound scientific investigation. With a little rewording, it will become clear how these questions can be tested. Not every question that you will want an answer for *can* be tested: some are too general or too vague. Learning to ask questions that can be tested takes time and is a fundamental skill in scientific inquiry.

Questions About Cause and Effect

The first balloon-related question could be stated more usefully: "What is the effect of increasing the number of times that a balloon is rubbed on a person's head on the time that the balloon stays stuck to a wall?" You can probably already begin to plan an experiment that would answer this question. A testable question is often about cause-effect relationships. These questions often take the form: "What causes the change in variables?" and "What are the effects on a variable if we change another variable?" As you know, a variable is something that can change or vary in an investigation.

Variables and Questions You Can Test

Scientists call the cause variable the independent variable. This is the one thing in the experiment that you purposely change. For instance, increasing the number of times that a balloon is rubbed on a person's head is something you control: you are changing the independent variable.

Figure 1

What affects how well the balloon sticks to the wall?

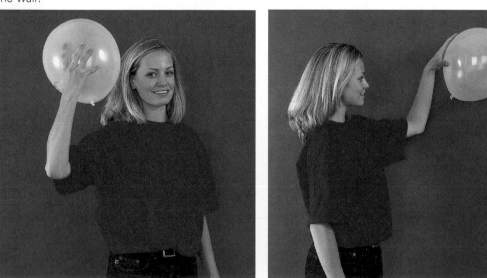

The effect variable is called the dependent variable. This is what you measure in your experiment (e.g., time, distance) and "depends" on what variable you purposely change (independent variable). The amount of time the balloon stays on the wall is the dependent variable.

A scientific question that asks what happens to a dependent variable when we change the independent variable is a question you can test. Some examples appear in **Table 1**.

Table 1 Testable Questions

Question	Independent (cause) variable	Dependent (effect) variable
How do fertilizers and phosphates affect the productivity of algae?	fertilizers and phosphates	rate of algae growth
What happens to the volume of a liquid when it is heated?	applying heat	volume of the liquid
Do all transparent materials refract light the same amount?	kind of transparent material	amount of light refracted
Does stirring affect how quickly a solute dissolves in a solvent?	stirring the solvent	rate at which the solute dissolves

Try This What's the Question?

Have you ever kicked a ball during the winter? It almost feels like kicking a brick.

1. Place a tennis ball in a refrigerator overnight.

2. Reproduce **Table 2** for recording your observations.

Table 2

Temperature of ball	Height of ball (cm)	Trial 1	Trial 2	Trial 3	Average
cold	?	?	?	?	?
room temperature	?	?	?	?	?

3. Hold a metre stick vertically with the zero end on the floor.

4. Drop the cold tennis ball from the upper end of the metre stick (**Figure 2**).

Figure 2

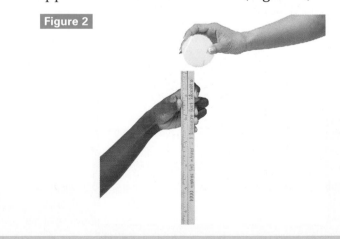

5. Measure the height that the tennis ball bounces back (**Figure 3**).

Figure 3

6. Do this three times (each time is called a test or a trial).

7. Repeat steps 3–6 with a ball that is at room temperature.
   • What question is being investigated in steps 1–6?
   • What question is being investigated in step 7?
   • What evidence is being gathered to answer the questions?

2C Predicting and Hypothesizing

The Hypothesis

A suggested answer or reason why one variable affects another in a certain way is called a hypothesis. Often you have some idea about this even as you ask your question. Having noticed, for instance, that a balloon sticks to the wall after you rub it in your hair, you might predict that rubbing it more will make it stick longer. You might be wrong, of course, but your prediction is probably based on past observations, on logic, and on bits of scientific theory you may remember. If you're really interested, you may even do some research based on what you already know. If you then pull everything you know together and express it, you would have a hypothesis. For instance, you might posit that the balloon sticks to the wall because it is attracted by static electricity, and that rubbing the balloon more produces a greater static electric charge on the balloon.

The Relationship Between Hypotheses and Predictions

Predictions and hypotheses go hand in hand (**Table 1**). The hypothesis is how you can explain a prediction. The prediction is what you test through your experiment. And, if the experiment confirms the prediction, you can have more confidence that your hypothesis is correct. Naturally, your experiment will not always confirm your prediction. In this case, you may need to re-evaluate your hypothesis and design a new experiment.

Answer These Questions

Support a plank with some books, so it forms an inclined plane (**Figure 1**). When you roll a jar down the plane, which will roll farther: an empty jar, or one filled with water? Write a hypothesis and a prediction to answer that question. Then carry out the experiment. How accurate was your prediction?

Now empty half of the water from the jar (**Figure 2**). How far will it roll? Write a hypothesis and prediction to answer the question, and try the experiment.

Do you need to change your hypothesis in either case?

Figure 1

Figure 2

Table 1 Sample Hypotheses and Predictions

Hypothesis (possible reason for cause-effect relationship)	Prediction	
	Possible cause (independent variable)	Possible effect (dependent variable)
Candy contains sugar that is used for energy by germs in the mouth, and these germs produce an acid that decays the teeth.	As the amount of candy that a person eats increases…	…the number of tooth cavities increases.
A larger sail traps more air, which then provides a greater force to a boat.	As the size of the sail increases…	…the top speed of the sailboat increases.
Salt helps oxygen in the air combine with iron in the metal of a bicycle to form rust.	As the amount of salt on a road increases…	…the amount of rusting of the metal parts of a bicycle increases.

② Identifying Variables and Controls

You may notice that milk has a different taste if it is left out on the table for more than 3 h. What additional factors, other than the time that it has been left on the table, do you think might affect the taste of milk? You have just identified variables!

Identifying Variables

Identifying variables is extremely important to the process of scientific inquiry: it allows you to ask good scientific questions, make predictions, and design a meaningful experiment. As you know, anything that can change in an experiment is a variable. Any variable that can be changed by the experimenter is called an independent variable. For example, you might predict that if a jar has a greater mass, then it will roll farther after it leaves a ramp. The mass of the jar is the independent (or cause) variable. There are other independent variables in this experiment, shown in **Figure 1 a–c.**

The effect of changing the independent variable is called the dependent variable. The distance that the jar travels is the dependent variable.

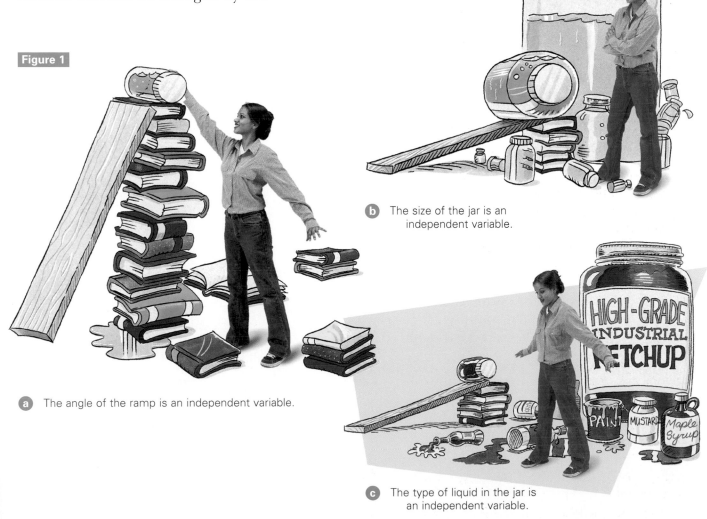

Figure 1

a   The angle of the ramp is an independent variable.

b   The size of the jar is an independent variable.

c   The type of liquid in the jar is an independent variable.

Identifying Controls

Scientists attempt to test only one independent variable at a time. That way the scientist knows which cause produced the effect. Controls are used to eliminate the possibility of an unknown variable.

In the jar experiment, you need to control the independent variables. To isolate the mass of the jar as the cause, you must try to change only the mass. The angle of the ramp, the size of the jar, and the type of liquid you use must always be the same—only the amount of liquid can change. If you try the experiment, you may find that the results with a half-filled jar surprise you. As a half-filled jar rolls down the ramp, water sloshes back and forth, creating friction. The friction inside the jar slows it down, and it doesn't travel as far. Friction is another independent variable that needs to be controlled. The jar in **Figure 2** with no water in it isn't affected by this variable: it is the control.

Figure 2
The empty jar on the ramp is a control.

Why Do Scientists Use Controls?

The following experiment shows why scientists use a control. A student notices spots of rust on the frame of her bike after riding all winter. The student hypothesizes that the rust was caused by the salt on the roads. But is salt the only variable (**Figure 3a**)? It is possible that the rusting was not caused by the salt alone. For example, the roads were also wet a lot of the winter. By comparing the amount of rusting with and without salt, you can determine just how much rusting is caused by the salt (**Figure 3b**).

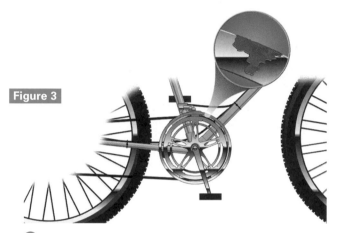

Figure 3

a Your prediction: As metal is exposed to more salt, more rusting will occur.

no salt

control

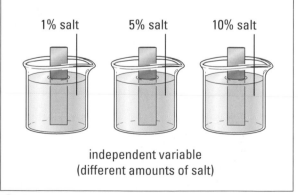

1% salt   5% salt   10% salt

independent variable
(different amounts of salt)

b The experiment: Metal placed in different solutions

Try This   Don't Get Burned!

Do sunscreens really prevent sunburn?

1. State a related hypothesis and prediction.

2. Identify the dependent and independent variables in your experiment.

3. What would your controls be?

②E Designing an Inquiry Investigation

Once you have asked a testable question and developed a hypothesis, you can design an investigation that will test that hypothesis. To design an inquiry investigation, you need to think of all the steps in the process of scientific inquiry outlined in section ②A. You need to visualize the investigation from beginning to end and plan for everything you'll need and every step you'll take.

Variables

Let's imagine that your question is: "Does mass affect the swing of a pendulum?" Your prediction may be: "As the mass of the pendulum increases, the number of swings per second will increase." The first step in designing your inquiry investigation is to identify your variables. Remember that an independent variable is the possible cause and a dependent variable is what the effect will be. You know you will be using different masses in your experiment (which you will have to record), and you will be measuring the number of swings per second. But you must also identify other possible independent variables so that you can control them. As you picture yourself testing the pendulum (**Figure 1**), you can probably list some of these possible causes. For instance, the length of the string, the length of the arc, the materials from which the pendulum is made—all of these may affect the swing. You must design your experiment so that these variables are kept constant.

Observations

You also need to think carefully about what you are going to measure—in this case, mass and number of swings of the pendulum. What mass are you going to start with? And how are you going to increase the mass? What unit of time arc you going to use? And how long will you observe the pendulum in each case? Then you need to design a table to record your data (**Table 1**).

The effect of mass on number of swings per second (based on 15 s of observation)	
Mass	**Number of swings per second**
1 g	?
2 g	?
3 g	?
4 g	?

Equipment and Materials

Obviously, you must also decide what materials and equipment you will use (**Figure 2**). It is useful to create a labelled diagram that illustrates the materials and equipment you will need, and the procedure you are going to use.

Figure 1
What are the independent variables?

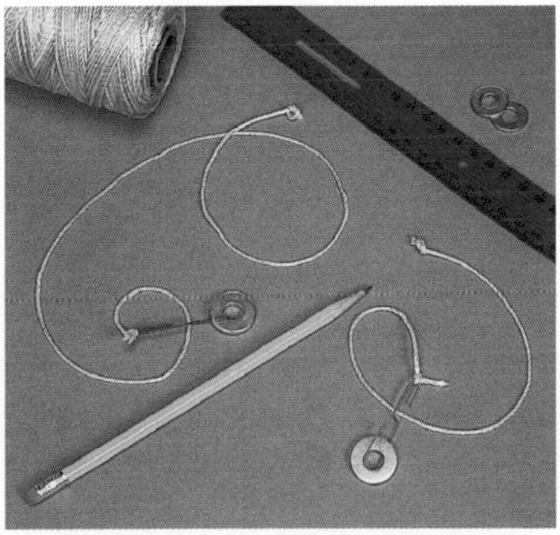

Figure 2
What materials will you need?

The Procedure

This is an essential component of an experimental design. Anyone who is interested in learning about your experiment needs to be able to understand how it was performed, so that it can be duplicated exactly (**Figure 3**). Therefore, it is important that you be able to write an experimental procedure clearly, concisely, and accurately. When writing a procedure, you should use:

- numbered steps
- passive voice (avoid using pronouns)
- past tense

Figure 3

Record every step you will take.

For example, the first two steps of a procedure could look like **Figure 4**.

Don't forget to consider all possible safety issues!

Figure 4

Procedure

1. The experiment was set up as shown in the diagram.

2. In each case, the pendulum was observed for 15 s.

 **Write a Procedure**

Think about how you would conduct the pendulum experiment. Write a procedure for this experiment, using the format explained above.

ⓐ The Problem-Solving Cycle

The major goal of technology is to improve the world by creating products that satisfy human needs. For example, while scientists try to explain why and how the mosquito finds its prey, technologists try to create products to protect us from these annoying pests (**Figure 1**).

Figure 1

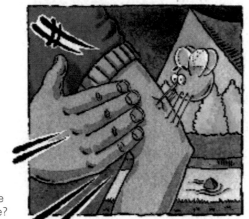

ⓐ Why does the mosquito bite?

ⓑ How can we stop the mosquito from biting?

For example, consider automobiles, computers, plastics, or the process for making decaffeinated soft drinks. Most of us are most creative when we're trying to satisfy a need. Imagine, for instance, that you and a few friends are alone at home. You're hungry, but there's not a lot of food in the refrigerator that you're really interested in. You all agree that hotdogs would be acceptable, but the power is out. Your problem is to design a method of cooking hotdogs without electricity. Luckily, your friends are with you. Working together to brainstorm possible solutions and to identify the advantages and disadvantages will help you come up with a good solution to your problem (**Figure 2**).

Figure 2

Technologists use a process of design to solve problems. Let's look at an example of how this process is used before examining the specific steps.

Using the Process of Design
What Are You Designing?

Things are usually designed in response to needs and to try to improve the quality of life.

Creating the Solution

You decide to use the energy from the Sun to cook your hotdogs. You know that aluminum foil reflects heat, so you will use it to get the most from the Sun's heat. And you want to make sure the hotdog cooks evenly. You jot down ideas and sketch out possible designs, considering all the tools and materials that you will need. You talk through how to build your hotdog cooker and realize there are a couple of things you hadn't thought of. When you think you're ready to build, you gather everything you need and go to work. Together you have built a prototype hotdog-cooker that is designed to solve your problem (**Figure 3**).

Figure 3

The Sun cooks lunch.

What Have You Learned?

The first hotdog you cook may not have turned out perfectly. Maybe the wire wasn't turning freely, and you had trouble cooking your hotdog evenly. That first hotdog was a test of your prototype, and you discovered that your design could be improved. You need to back up a few steps and modify your prototype. Once you get it working right, you may want to show some of your other friends how to make a solar hotdog cooker. Communicating the steps of the process is a very important part of the process.

The Steps in the Process of Design

The steps in the process of design are very similar to the steps used in the process of scientific inquiry. The flow chart in **Figure 5** identifies those steps. Use it as a checklist when you are required to design and test a prototype you construct in your Science & Technology class this year.

Try This Design a Mould

It's your little sister's birthday, and she loves strawberry gelatine (**Figure 4**). You've bought the powder and are trying to find something to make it in. You'd like the end result to look fun and festive. All you have are three bowls, and none of them is the right size. You've used one of the bowls in the past, and it was hard to get the gelatine out once it was set.

* Write a problem statement, choose a solution, and plan a prototype for a jelly mould that you think would solve your problem.

Figure 4

Figure 5
The Steps in the Process of Design

❶ Identifying a Problem

- Identify and record the problem.
- Identify any limits posed by the problem.
- Research possible solutions to the problem and record new ideas.
- Restate the problem so that it clearly states what needs to be solved.

❷ Selecting the Best Alternative

- Identify the constraints (e.g., human resources, time, money, environmental issues).
- Develop the design criteria (e.g., cost, reliability, safety, size, materials).
- Brainstorm all possible solutions to the problem.
- Rate the possible solutions.
- Select the alternative with the highest rating.

❸ Planning the Prototype

- Draw sketches and/or schematics of your prototype.
- List materials and tools that will be needed to construct the prototype and gather them.

❹ Building the Prototype

- Refer to "Safety in Science & Technology" for a review of safety precautions when using tools.
- Construct a working prototype.

❺ Testing and Evaluating the Prototype

- Use the design criteria to develop a test.
- Test the prototype to evaluate its ability to solve the identified problem.
- Quantify and record your test results.

❻ Communicating

- Create a Design Folder that describes your process and product, and communicates your evaluation of how well the product satisfied the design criteria.

❼ Repeating the Cycle

- Revise and reconstruct the prototype in order to make it more effective.
- Repeat the process until an effective solution to the problem has been developed.

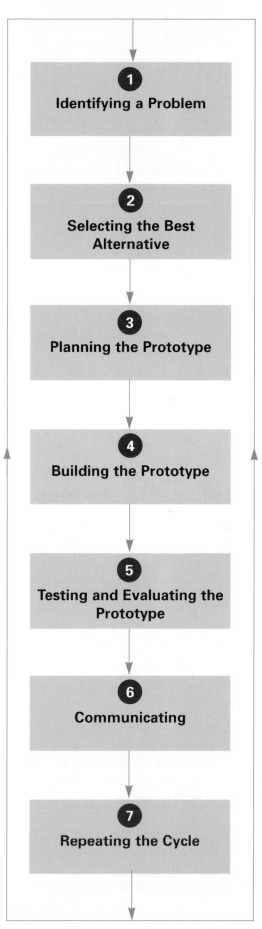

Identifying a Problem

Identify and Record the Problem

It is important that, as you start the design process, you understand and specify the nature of the problem. Start by writing down what you believe the problem is, based on the information you have gathered. Often the problem is the need of a client. The problem may be written as a question or a statement.

Let's assume that your neighbours have a need and that they are your clients. They have ten goldfish that they dearly love. Occasionally, they go away for week-long vacations. Your neighbours are worried about how to feed the fish. They would like you to design and build a device that drops a small quantity of goldfish food into the goldfish tank twice a day (**Figure 1**).

Figure 1

Goldfish require daily feeding.

Your stated problem could be:

A device is necessary to automatically feed ten goldfish two times a day for a period of one week.

Examine and Redefine the Problem

It is important to fully understand this problem statement and to redefine the problem so that it is as clear and objective as possible. The following steps may lead you to rephrase your problem statement:

- **Be sure you fully understand the terms stated in the problem.** You may have to clarify terms or make them more precise. For example, in the given problem it is not clear how much goldfish food is to be released—the amount of food should be specified. The problem could be restated:

  *A device is necessary to automatically feed ten goldfish **0.5g** of food, two times a day, for a period of one week.*

- **Identify limits posed by the problem as stated.** For instance, the problem may have been expressed by someone who already has an idea about the "best" solution. In the problem statement above, it is obvious that your clients think that an automatic device is necessary to feed the goldfish. It may, however, be possible to hire a person to come in and feed the fish. Therefore, the problem may be refined to say:

  *A **method** or device is necessary to feed ten goldfish 0.5g of food, two times a day, for a period of one week.*

- **Research possible solutions to the problem and record new ideas.** You may find an appropriate solution that already exists. Or you may get new ideas that will help you focus your problem-solving.

 **Listing Needs**

Generate a list of 10–15 needs that could be met through technology. Categorize the needs under the headings in **Table 1**:

Table 1

Personal needs	Class needs	School needs	Community needs
?	?	?	?
?	?	?	?
?	?	?	?

③C Selecting the Best Alternative

Identifying Constraints

For every design problem there will be factors that limit or constrain a solution. If you are designing an automatic goldfish-feeder, for instance, your clients will probably give you a limited amount of money and time to complete the project. The money and time factors are limits or constraints.

General Constraints

General constraints that should be considered for most technological designs are listed below:
- **Natural Constraints:** Will the laws of nature let me do this?
- **Time Constraints:** How long will this take? Is this a major project involving years of development and testing or a relatively short endeavour?
- **Financial Constraints:** How much money do I have to pay for the development of this?
- **Material Constraints:** What materials and tools are available to complete this project?
- **Societal Constraints:** Is there actually a need or demand for this product?
- **Ethical Constraints:** Should we be doing this? Is this harmful for society in any way?
- **Environmental Constraints:** What impact will this have on the environment?

Evaluating these constraints will influence what solutions are available and affect the specific design criteria for a project (**Figure 1**).

Developing Design Criteria

Design criteria clearly outline what your product needs to achieve if it is to successfully solve the problem for which it was designed. After answering the questions in the list of general constraints you may come up with some of the design criteria for your project. For instance, your clients may be going on vacation in three weeks. In this case, one of your design criteria would be that the automatic goldfish-feeder must be complete in three weeks.

Other design criteria will be determined by the specific nature of the problem you are trying to solve. Reliability, size, appearance, strength, durability, safety, efficiency, and maintenance are just some of the factors that may be relevant to your design.

It is useful to brainstorm a list of criteria, judging how important each is to the success of the design. For an automatic goldfish-feeder, for instance, you might consider the following design criteria:
- **Time:** The goldfish-feeder must be complete in three weeks.
- **Money:** It must cost $120 or less.
- **Reliability:** It must be completely reliable, or the fish will die.
- **Ease of use:** It is of medium importance that the device be easy to use. It has to be set up correctly, but the owner can take time to ensure that it has been correctly set up before leaving the fish unattended.
- **Appearance:** It is of low importance for the device to be attractive since it is in use only when people are away.

Brainstorming Solutions

It is now time for you to brainstorm a list of possible solutions to your problem (**Figure 2**). This may involve coming up with an idea for a new product, a modification to a device that already exists, or a new or modified process.

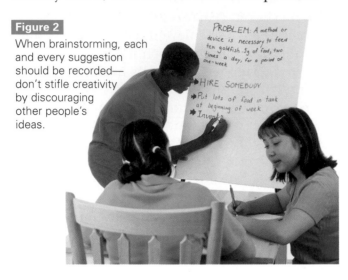

After you have completed your brainstorming exercise, vote for and list the best alternatives.

Rating the Alternatives

We now need a method for choosing the very best alternative. There are different ways of rating alternatives, but it is important you measure each alternative against your design criteria.

The problem-solving matrix in **Table 1** is one way you can rate alternatives. **Table 2** provides an example of how the matrix can be used to rank alternatives to the automatic fish-feeder challenge. In this example, the lower the number, the worse the rating. Note that the criteria are measured according to different scales, depending on the relative importance of each criterion.

Table 1 **Generic Problem Solving Matrix**

Alternatives	Design Criteria					Totals
	Criterion A rating scale	Criterion B rating scale	Criterion C rating scale			
Alternative A	?	?	?	?	?	?
Alternative B	?	?	?	?	?	?
Alternative C	?	?	?	?	?	?

Table 2 **Problem Solving Matrix – Fish-Feeder Example**

Alternatives	Design criteria					Totals
	Time (0-10)	Cost (0-10)	Reliability (0-10)	Ease of Use (0-5)	Appearance (0-3)	
7-day dissolving fish feeder tablet	5	10	5	5	1	26
Put a whole lot of fish food in at the beginning of the week	10	10	1	5	0	26
Hire a person to feed the goldfish	10	10	4	2	3	29
FishFeeder Timer Device (an original device using a timer and gravity feed of premeasured food)	9	5	9	5	2	(30)

Another system uses the following rating scale:
+ = good or better than other alternatives or positive influence
0 = fair or at par with other alternatives or neutral influence
● = poor or worse than other alternatives or negative influence

Try This — What are the Criteria?

Brainstorm design criteria for the problems listed in **Table 3**.

Table 3

Problem	Design Criteria
A device or process is needed that will make polluted water safe to drink.	?
A device is needed to keep a can of soda cold from breakfast until noon.	?
An optical device is needed that would allow a person to observe hatching birds in their nest.	?
A process or device is needed for watering hanging baskets of flowers.	?

3D Planning a Prototype

Once you know what alternative you want to design and build, it's time to plan a prototype. A prototype is an original model that exhibits the essential features of the solution you chose. It can be a device or it can be a method that demonstrates a new or an improved process.

- **Start by making sketches and detailed drawings of your prototype.** Initially, these may be hand-drawn sketches with approximate dimensions, but you may find it worthwhile to produce a prototype drawing that shows specific measurements and working parts. (Refer to 6C "Scientific & Technical Drawing" for more details.)

  You may want to use computer-aided design programs to help you in the design process.

- **Make a list of the materials and tools you will need to build your prototype.** Examine your drawings carefully to ensure that your list is as complete as possible.

- **Write out the instructions you will follow to build the prototype.** Think this through carefully. As you set down each step in the building process, you may think of additional materials and tools to add to your list. You may also uncover potential difficulties or problems that require you to make design changes. This is not a design failure! Regular evaluation and modification of your design is an important part of the process.

- **Have others review your plan.** A fresh pair of eyes will often discover small flaws or visualize slight improvements that will enhance your design. In your Science & Technology class, you will often be asked to have your teacher approve your plan before you begin building.

 **Planning**

Choose one of the problems in **Table 3** in section 3C and plan a prototype.

Building a Prototype

Before you begin construction, review the safety precautions for using the tools you'll need. Be sure that you have access to all the necessary materials and tools. If you are gathering these in advance, consider how you will store them for use throughout the project.

General Building Tips

- Read through your building instructions before you begin.
- If you need to, review specific tools (5D "Using Technology Equipment") or specific fabrication techniques (5E "Fabrication Techniques").
- Measure and cut materials to prepare for assembly. (Remember: Measure twice, cut once.)

- Temporarily join parts to test and evaluate their effectiveness. You may wish to use elastics, Plasticine, tape, string, and plastic tubing to assist you.
- Once you are satisfied with the components and their ability to operate, then you are ready to join the components permanently. It is important to consider methods of assembly that allow the parts to be added in such a way that they can be moved slightly, if needed.

 **Deconstruction**

One way of learning how to build things is to take things apart (**Figure 1**). Take apart one of the things listed below and jot down anything you learn about how it is put together.

- a flashlight
- a pen

- a chocolate box
- a bicycle wheel

Figure 1

Consider the construction materials, how things are held together, the shape of the various parts, what tools would have been required, etc.

🛑 Do not take apart small appliances or electronics. You may receive an electric shock.

③F Testing and Evaluating a Prototype

What to Test

It is important to find out how well your prototype works. You need to develop a good test that will answer three basic questions:
1 Does the prototype solve the problem?
2. Does the prototype satisfy the design criteria?
3. Are there any unanticipated problems?

Does the Prototype Solve the Problem?

Let's assume you have built an automatic fish-feeder to solve the following problem:

A method or device is necessary to feed ten goldfish 0.5g of food, two times a day, for a period of one week.

To determine whether or not your prototype solved the problem, your test-period would have to be at least one-week long, you would have to record how many times a day food actually made it into the tank, and you would have to record the amount of food that was deposited at each feed.

Does the Prototype Satisfy the Design Criteria?

Let's assume that you identified and rated the importance of the design criteria in **Table 1**:

Table 1		
time:	maximum importance	(rated between 0-10)
cost:	maximum importance	(rated between 0-10)
reliability:	maximum importance	(rated between 0-10)
ease of use:	medium importance	(rated between 0-5)
appearance:	low importance	(rated between 0-3)

To determine whether the prototype meets the design criteria, your test must measure against them. In some cases, the measure will be quantitative (e.g., time and cost). In other cases, your measure will be qualitative (e.g., appearance). In any case, your evaluation must be carefully recorded.

Are There Any Unanticipated Problems?

Your test may also show you weaknesses that you hadn't considered. For instance, does the position of the fish-feeder on the tank affect how much light is reaching the water? Do you need to adjust the position? Do you need to reconsider the materials you have used?

Testing Tips

The following tips will help you design and conduct your tests:
• Decide how long the test should last.
• Decide how many times the test should be done.
• Consider whether the test needs to be done in different circumstances or conditions.
• Rate each of the design criteria.
• Make and record all quantitative measurements.
• Record all qualitative observations.
• Consider potential problems that may not be related to the design criteria.
• Have other people make use of the prototype and get their feedback.
• Keep a log of your test information.

Modifying Your Design

Your test will probably give you ideas about how your design can be improved. This doesn't mean that you are a bad designer. The design process is a repeating cycle, not a step-by-step path to the perfect solution. You will need to go through as many repetitions of the problem-solving cycle as needed in order to come up with the best working solution. Once you have tested your prototype, it is time to re-address the problem statement, redefine your design criteria, and work on improving your device or process.

Try This   Building the Best Papercopter

A babysitter is told that his young charge can unexpectedly become very unhappy. When this happens, the only thing that will console him is watching things, like paper airplanes, fly. The babysitter can only make one kind of paper airplane, and it doesn't fly very well. The child is unimpressed. So, the babysitter's problem is to design a device that would fly long enough to amuse the child (about 10 s).

The design criteria include ease of construction, speed of construction, reliability, and accessibility of materials.

1. Follow the babysitter's plans (**Figure 1**) and build his prototype: the papercopter.

2. Now test the papercopter.
    *   Make a list of things to measure and observe.
    *   Conduct the test.
    *   Summarize what needs to be improved.
    *   List modifications to try.
    *   Modify the papercopter until it solves the problem.

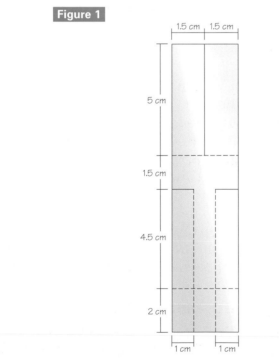

Figure 1

1.5 cm 1.5 cm
5 cm
1.5 cm
4.5 cm
2 cm
1 cm 1 cm

1. Cut a piece of writing paper 3 cm x 13 cm.
2. Cut along the two middle horizontal (solid) lines, and fold in.
3. Fold the bottom flap along the bottom dotted line.
4. Cut the solid vertical line at the top to create two flaps.
5. Attach a paperclip to the bottom.
6. Drop and watch the copter fly.

Patents, Trademarks, and Copyrights

What would you do if you invented an innovative product or process? Imagine you invented a "Landsurfer" and wanted to develop, sell, and market your invention. In our society, the law protects your intellectual property for a certain period of time. Anyone designing new products or processes should know the differences between and the uses of patents, trademarks, and copyrights.

Patents

A patent gives an inventor the exclusive rights to make, use, and/or sell a certain product, device, or process for a period of 17 years. The inventor must apply for the patent through the Canadian Patent Office. It is usually necessary to contact a Patent Attorney or Agent in order to search for other existing patents on your product and then to file the legal application. The inventor must prove that the invention is original, beneficial to society, and "not obvious" (i.e., something that is in common use, but has never previously been patented). The patent itself includes a number, title, and a short description. You may have noticed the words "Patent Pending" on a product or device. Because the patent process can be a lengthy one, inventors can let others know that they have applied for a patent by printing these words on the device.

Trademarks

A trademark is any name, symbol, picture, or design that an inventor or company may use to identify their products or affairs (**Figure 1**). Trademarks are often indicated by the following symbol: ™. Some well known and much used trademarks often become the actual name of a product and thus lose their legal status as trademarks. For example, aspirin and escalator were originally trademarks and have since become generic product names.

Figure 1

Copyright

A copyright protects the work of artists, composers, and authors from reproduction and/or distribution by others without permission (**Figure 2**).

Figure 2

Copyright © 2000 Nelson, a division of Thomson Learning. Thomson Learning is a trademark used herein under license.

ALL RIGHTS RESERVED. No part of this work covered by the copyright hereon may be reproduced, transcribed, or used in any form or by any means—graphic, electronic, or mechanical, including photocopying, recording, taping, Web distribution or information storage and retrieval systems—without the permission of the publisher.

 **Find Examples**

- List 10 inventions, devices, or products that would most likely already have a patent. You may want to visit the Canadian Patent Office's web site to see some examples of current patents.
- List 10 trademarks with which you are familiar.
- List 10 things that might be copyrighted.

4A Research Skills

Sources of Information

There is an incredible amount of scientific and technological information available to you. Before you can use it, however, you have to know how to gather it efficiently. First, you need to know where to find information.

Look at the list of information resources in **Table 1**. Some resources are more useful than others in certain circumstances. Pick one or two resources that you seldom use and think of how you might use them in your Science & Technology class.

Before you start any research, brainstorm a list of the best resources for your purpose. Rank the list, starting with the most useful resource. Always use a variety of resources.

General Research Tips

Once you've decided where to look for information, you need to find the best information in the least amount of time. Using these tips will help:

- Clearly define the topic or the question you will be researching. Ask yourself: "Do I clearly understand what I'm looking for?"
- List the most important words associated with your research, and use them to search for related topics.
- Ask yourself: "Do I understand what this resource is telling me?"
- Check when the resource was published. Is it up-to-date?
- Keep organized notes while doing your research.
- Keep a complete list of the resources you used, so you can make a bibliography when writing your report. (See 8A "Writing a Report" for proper referencing formats.)
- Review your notes. After your research, you may want to alter your original problem or hypothesis.

Table 1 **Information Resources**

Information Consultants
(people who can help you locate and interpret information)

teachers	business people
nurses	scientists
public servants	librarians
volunteers	politicians
lawyers	farmers
parents	doctors
members of the media	senior citizens
veterinarians	

Reference Materials (sources of packaged information)

encyclopedias	bibliographies
magazines/journals	newspapers
videotapes	slides
data bases	almanacs
yearbooks	dictionaries
textbooks	maps
filmstrips	charts
biographies	films
pamphlets	records
television	radio

Places (sources beyond the walls of your school)

public libraries	shopping malls	art galleries
parks	colleges	museums
universities	government offices	hospitals
historic sites	zoos	volunteer agencies
research laboratories		
businesses		
farms		

Electronic Sources

world wide web (www)
CD-ROMs
on-line search engines
on-line periodicals
computer programs

Some Specific Research Tips

Using a Library

School libraries use an organizational system, known as the Dewey Decimal Classification System, which organizes books into the major subject areas shown in **Table 2**.

Table 2	Dewey Decimal Classification System		
Catalogue #	Subject Area	Catalogue #	Subject Area
000	Generalities	500	Natural Science & Mathematics
100	Philosophy & Psychology	600	Technology (Applied Sciences)
200	Religion	700	The Arts
300	Social Science	800	Literature
400	Language	900	Geography/History

You can usually search a library database by title, author, and/or subject area. If you have access to a computer, many library databases can be accessed online.

Always ask the librarian for help if you are having trouble finding the information you need.

Using On-line Sources

The Internet is a vast network of information that is continually growing. Many Internet navigation programs make use of several search engines. Search engines are on-line tools that find web sites (or hits) based on key words you enter into the search. When researching on-line, consider these additional research tips.

- If you have a specific web site address, go to the direct source first.
- If you need to use a search engine, find two good search engines, bookmark them, and use them. While the "Search" buttons in navigation programs are useful, they will not always give you the best search engine for your purposes.
- Learn about the features of the search engine. The better search engines make use of Boolean logic, operations that are used to combine key words when searching the

Internet. In these cases, adding the word "AND" can let you narrow your search by combining two key words. Adding the word "OR" can let you expand your search by joining together two key words. Lastly, adding the word "NOT" enables you to disregard a key word. Be sure to refine your search as you continue. For example, entering the word "music" may give you 1 678 243 hits but adding "AND guitar" will reduce your search results to 18 860 hits. Including "NOT classical" will further reduce your number of hits to 2340.

- Familiarize yourself with the advanced search option within each search engine.
- Look over the first few pages of hits before you start exploring each web site. Be patient and look for the sites that seem most relevant to your topic.
- Bookmark all useful sites so you can access them readily. Put these in a specific folder if your browser allows you to do this.

Try This Research This!

Use the General Research Tips to research one of the following topics:
- the discovery of insulin
- eco-tourism in Costa Rica
- the invention of the telescope
- the most recent seismic activity on Earth
- the tides in the Bay of Fundy
- how pneumatics and hydraulics can be applied to everyday life
- how valves and pumps work
- the physical properties of plastics
- the manufacturing process of the product of your choice

Be prepared to communicate the information you find, bibliographic references (see 8A "Writing a Report"), how reliable your information is, and your research process.

4B Interviewing and Survey Skills

When to Use Surveys and Interviews

Surveys and interviews give you access to a very important information resource: people. If you need specialized information, interviewing experts (for example, engineers or researchers) is useful. If you want to find out if your design idea fills a common human need, a survey is an excellent tool. Surveys and interviews are both useful for learning about people's reactions to controversial scientific and technological issues.

Generally, surveys are better if you need specific information from a lot of people. Interviews are better if you need more detailed information from fewer people.

Effective Interviews

Use the following suggestions to help you decide who you are going to interview, and how to prepare and conduct the interview.

- *Research your topic.* Clarify what you need to learn through your interview(s).
- *Choose your interview candidate(s).* For instance, if you are researching water quality issues in your community, you might want to interview the municipal waterworks engineer, the health inspector, a member of a local environmental group, and a journalist who has written articles on the topic. Make contact with these people: explain your purpose clearly and arrange a convenient time and place.
- *Prepare your interview questions in advance.* Try to avoid simple yes/no questions— questions that require explanations will provide more information.
- *Conduct your interview in a comfortable, quiet place.*
- *Be prepared to ask questions that are not on your list.* You want to make sure all of your questions are answered, but some answers will lead to other important questions. For example, if your interviewee said "The water quality is well within set specifications and much better than it was after that incident ten years ago," you may want to ask about the "incident." A good interviewer learns when to let the interview follow its own course and when to bring it back to the prepared questions.
- *Choose an appropriate way of recording the information.* You may want to take notes or use a tape recorder. Be sure to ask if it is okay to tape record the interview. If you take notes, be sure that this does not distract you or the person you are interviewing. If you do not understand an answer, be sure to politely ask for clarification.
- *Be aware of your own biases as well as the biases of the person you are interviewing.* Remember every person has opinions that have been shaped by personal experience— these are called biases. These will influence the information you get and how you respond to it.
- *If you quote people, use their exact words and make sure you have their permission.*
- *Be respectful of the person you are interviewing.* End your interview on time and express your thanks in person and later with a thank-you note.

Effective Surveys

Planning the Survey

An effective survey requires careful planning. Try to think it through from beginning to end, using the following questions to help you:

- What exactly are we trying to find out?
- Who should we be surveying?
- How many people should we survey?
- Should we ask the survey questions in person and fill in the forms or send the surveys out to be filled in by the people being surveyed?
- How will we use the information? How will we want to present the data?

Answering these questions will affect how you design your survey questions.

Writing the Survey Questionnaire

Writing a good questionnaire requires skill and practice. Consider the following:

- *Design your questionnaire so that it can be completed easily and quickly.* The questions should be precise and concise, and the instructions should be easy to understand. Start with questions that can be answered by checking off options or giving a numbered rating, and leave the more open-ended questions to the end.
- *Design your questionnaire so that it is easy to collate and present the results.* It should be possible to present your results in meaningful charts and graphs. Using an appropriate software program can help you design your questionnaire and collate your results.
- *Begin your questionnaire with questions about the respondent.* Be sure that these questions are relevant to the topic you are studying.
- *Write clear questions that are easy to answer.* In order to quantify your results easily, you may want to use the Likert scale, developed by Renis Likert (1932). Start by writing positive or negative statements that relate to the issue being explored. Be sure to minimize any bias in your statements. For example, "CFCs should be banned in Canada" might be better than "Harmful CFCs should be banned in Canada."

Then, attach a five-point scale to rate public reaction to this statement. For example:

Circle the number that best describes your reaction to the following statement:

CFCs should be banned in Canada.

1   2   3   4   5

where

1 = strongly agree, 2 = agree,
3 = undecided, 4 = disagree, and
5 = strongly disagree

- ***Be courteous.*** If you are sending your survey in the mail, you may want to write a covering letter that explains your research and thanks the respondent in advance. If you are conducting the survey in person, use common courtesy.

Testing the Questionnaire

It is often a good idea to try your questionnaire on three or four people before sending it out to everyone on your list. You may need to modify the questionnaire after you have considered the following questions:

- How well did the respondents understand the questions?
- Did they give the kind of information you need?
- How long did it take to complete?

Try This **Interview or Survey?**

Consider the following research questions. Would you use interviews, surveys, or both to find the answers?

- What kind of training do you need to be a water resource engineer?
- How satisfied are e-mail users with their Internet service provider?
- Should we ban the use of CFCs?
- How much of Ontario's land should be set aside as protected park land?
- Should safety ever be compromised to lower costs?
- How well is the local recycling program working?
- What technology do most people feel has the greatest impact on their daily lives?

Critical Thinking

Science & Technology in the News

Understanding and evaluating the results of your research is extremely important. When you do research, you can find information using the Internet, textbooks, magazines, chat lines, television, radio, and many other forms of communication. Is all of this information reliable? How do we know what to believe and what not to believe?

Every day you see and hear extraordinary claims about objects and events (**Figure 1**). Often scientific or technological evidence is used to convince us that these claims are true. This method of reporting is sometimes used to catch your attention or to make you buy something. Even serious stories on scientific research or technological innovation can be difficult to interpret, especially when they are reported in a way that makes the work sound important, official, and somewhat mysterious.

To analyze information, you have to use your mind effectively and critically. When you encounter a report that uses scientific or technological evidence, analyze the report carefully. You might ask yourself, for instance:
- Was the investigation conducted by a reputable laboratory or firm?
- How many times was the design or inquiry process repeated?
- What are the possible sources of error? Are they addressed?
- What do other experts say about these claims?

Figure 1

There are scientific and technological stories in the news every day.

STUDY LINKS DIET AND MEMORY LOSS

NEWLY DESIGNED SKATE BLADE IMPROVES SPEED

New Technology Makes Oil Spill Fears Obsolete

New Laser May Cure Cancer

Never Have a Flat Tire Again

 **Try This** **Reading Critically**

Analyze a scientific report or story from one of the following magazines by answering the questions listed above:
- *Scientific American*
- *Popular Mechanics*
- *Discover Magazine*
- *Eureka: The Canadian Invention and Innovation Newsletter*
- or a magazine of your choice

Using Critical Thinking Skills

A lot of research has been done to help people develop critical thinking skills. One very good, practical framework is known as PERCS (which comes from the word perquisite, meaning a benefit). It was founded out of Central Park East Secondary School in New York City. To prepare themselves for their world, the students at CPESS use a series of questions to help them think critically about information and arguments. These questions will help you build an educated and critical opinion about an issue.

The PERCS Checklist:

P = Perspective

- From whose viewpoint are we seeing or reading or hearing?
- From what angle or perspective?

E = Evidence

- How do we know what we know?
- What's the evidence and how reliable is it?

R = Relevance

- So what?
- What does it matter?
- What does it all mean?
- Who cares?

C = Connections

- How are things, events, or people connected to each other?
- What is the cause and what is the effect?
- How do they "fit" together?

S = Supposition

- What if…?
- Could things be otherwise?
- What are or were the alternatives?
- Suppose things were different?

 **Using PERCS**

Try exercising your critical thinking skills. Choose any article from today's newspaper or from a popular magazine and analyze it using the PERCS checklist.

5A Using the Microscope

Because cells are small, you must make them appear larger than they really are in order to see and study them. To view cells closely, you will use a compound light microscope (**Figure 1**). It employs two lenses and a light source to make the object appear larger. The object is magnified by a lens near your eye, the ocular lens (sometimes called the eyepiece), and again by a second lens, the objective lens, which is just above the object. The comparison of the actual size of the object with the size of its image is referred to as magnification.

The parts of the microscope are described in **Table 1**.

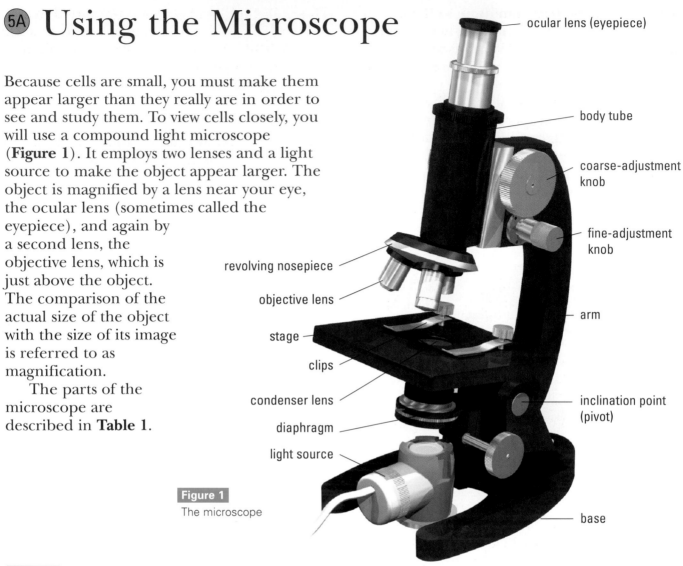

Figure 1
The microscope

Table 1   **Parts of the Microscope**

Structure	Function
body tube	Contains ocular lens, supports objective lenses.
clips	Found on the stage and used to hold the slide in position.
coarse-adjustment knob	Moves the body tube up or down so you can get the object or specimen into focus. It is used with the low-power objective lens only.
condenser lens	Directs light to the object or specimen.
diaphragm	Regulates the amount of light reaching the object being viewed.
fine-adjustment knob	Moves the tube to get the object or specimen into sharp focus. It is used with medium- and high-power magnification. The fine-adjustment knob is used only after the object or specimen has been located and focused under low-power magnification using the coarse adjustment.
objective lenses	Magnifies the object. Usually three complex lenses are located on the nosepiece immediately above the object or specimen. The smallest of these, the low-power objective lens, has the lowest magnification, usually four times (4X). The medium-power lens magnifies by 10X, and the long, high-power lens by 40X.
ocular lens	Magnifies the object, usually by 10X. Also known as the eyepiece, this is the part you look through to view the object.
revolving nosepiece	Rotates, allowing the objective lens to be changed. Each lens clicks into place.
stage	Supports the microscope slide. A central opening in the stage allows light to pass through the slide.

Care of the Microscope

The microscope is an important and expensive scientific instrument. It should always be used with care and patience. Here are some points to remember when using your microscope.

1. Always keep a microscope in an upright position.

2. When carrying a microscope, grasp its arm with one hand and support its base with the other (**Figure 2**).

Figure 2
How to carry a microscope

3. Once you have the microscope at your workstation, turn the coarse adjustment knob to lower the objective lens to its lowest point. Focus by using the knob to move the objective lens slowly upward to bring an object into focus. You must always remember to use both knobs when adjusting your microscope or you will strip the adjustment gears.

4. Microscope lenses are made of optical glass, which is soft and scratches easily. Use special lens paper to remove any dust or dirt.

5. When you complete an investigation using the microscope, follow these steps:
   - Rotate the nosepiece to the low-power objective lens.
   - Remove the slide and cover slip (if applicable).
   - Clean the slide and cover slip and return them to their appropriate location.
   - Return the microscope to the storage area.

Basic Microscope Skills

The skills outlined below are presented as sets of instructions. This will enable you to practise these skills before you are asked to use them in the investigations in *Nelson Science & Technology 7/8.*

Materials

- newspaper that contains lower-case letter "*f*" or similar small object
- scissors
- microscope slide
- cover slip
- dropper
- water
- compound microscope
- thread
- compass or petri dish
- pencil
- transparent ruler

Preparing a Dry Mount

This method of preparing a microscope slide is called a dry mount, because no water is used. A dry mount can be used for any specimen that won't dry out while you are examining it.

1. Find a small, flat object, such as a lower-case letter "*f*" cut from a newspaper.

2. Place the object in the centre of a microscope slide.

3. Hold a cover slip between your thumb and forefinger. Place the edge of the cover slip to one side of the object. Gently lower the cover slip onto the slide so that it covers the object.

Step 3

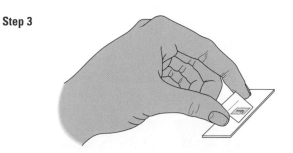

Preparing a Wet Mount

This method of preparing a microscope slide is called a wet mount, because water is used.

A wet mount is used for specimens that can dry out while you are examining them. For instance, when you use a specimen from a living thing, like an onion, the specimen must be very thin. This means that it can lose moisture rapidly: it needs to be kept moist or it will begin to shrivel and become more and more difficult to examine.

1. Find a small, thin, flat object.

2. Place the object in the centre of a microscope slide.

3. Place two drops of water on the object.

Step 3

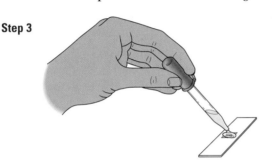

4. Holding the cover slip with your thumb and forefinger, touch the edge of the surface of the slide at a 45° angle. Gently lower the cover slip, allowing the air to escape.

Step 4

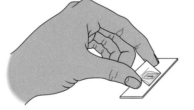

Positioning Objects Under the Microscope

1. Make sure the low-power objective lens is in place on your microscope. Then put either the dry or wet mount slide in the centre of the microscope stage. Use the stage clips to hold the slide in position. Turn on the light source.

Step 1

2. View the microscope stage from the side. Using the coarse-adjustment knob, bring the low-power objective lens and the object as close as possible to one another. Do not allow the lens to touch the cover slip.

Step 2

3. View the object through the eyepiece. Slowly move the coarse-adjustment knob so the objective lens moves away from the slide, to bring the image into focus. Note that the object is facing the "wrong" way and is upside down.

4. Using a compass or a petri dish, draw a circle in your notebook to represent the area you are looking at through the microscope. This area is called the field of view. Look through the microscope and draw what you see. Make the object fill the same amount of area in your diagram as it does in the microscope.

5. While you are looking through the microscope, slowly move the slide away from your body. Note that the object appears to move toward you. Now move the slide to the left. Note that the object appears to move to the right.

6. Rotate the nosepiece to the medium-power objective lens. Use the fine-adjustment knob to bring the object into focus. Note that the object becomes larger.

   🛑 Never use the coarse-adjustment knob with the medium or high-power objective lenses.

7. Adjust the object so that it is directly in the centre of the field of view. Rotate the nosepiece to the high-power objective lens. Use the fine-adjustment knob to focus the image. Note that you see less of the object than you did under medium-power magnification. Also note that the object seems closer to you.

Investigating Depth of Field

The depth of field is the amount of an image that is in sharp focus when it is viewed under a microscope.

1. Cut two pieces of thread of different colours.

2. Make a temporary dry mount by placing one thread over the other in the form of an X in the centre of a microscope slide. Cover the threads with a cover slip.

Step 2

3. Place the slide on the microscope stage and turn on the light.

4. Position the low-power objective lens close to, but not touching, the slide.

5. View the crossed threads through the ocular lens. Slowly rotate the coarse-adjustment knob until the threads come into focus.

6. Rotate the nosepiece to the medium-power objective lens. Focus on the upper thread by using the fine-adjustment knob. You will probably notice that you cannot focus on the lower thread at the same time. The depth of the object that is in focus at any one time represents the depth of field.

7. Repeat step 6 for the high-power objective lens. The stronger the magnification, the shallower the depth of field.

Determining the Field of View

The field of view is the circle of light seen through the microscope. It is the area of the slide that you can observe.

1. With the low-power objective lens in place, put a transparent ruler on the stage. Position the millimetre marks on the ruler immediately below the objective lens.

2. Using the coarse-adjustment knob, focus on the marks on the ruler.

3. Move the ruler so that one of the millimetre markings is just at the edge of

the field of view. Note the diameter of the field of view in millimetres, under the low-power objective lens.

Step 3

4. Using the same procedure, measure the field of view for the medium-power objective lens.

5. Most high-power lenses provide a field of view that is less than one millimetre in diameter, so it cannot be measured with a ruler. The following steps can be followed to calculate the field of view of the high-power lens.

    Calculate the ratio of the magnification of the high-power objective lens to that of the low-power objective lens.

$$\text{Ratio} = \frac{\text{magnification of high-power lens}}{\text{magnification of low-power lens}}$$

Use the ratio to determine the field of diameter (diameter of the field of view) under high-power magnification.

$$\text{Field diameter (high power)} = \frac{\text{field diameter (low power)}}{\text{ratio}}$$

Estimating Size

1. Measure the field of view, in millimetres, as shown above.

2. Remove the ruler and replace it with the object under investigation.

Step 2

3. Estimate the number of times the object could fit across the field of view.

4. Calculate the width of the object:

$$\text{width of object} = \frac{\text{width of field of view}}{\text{number of objects across field}}$$

Remember to include units.

Working with Scales and Balances

Mass is an important quantitative property that is frequently measured: it is the amount of matter a substance has. A balance will give you the same measurement of mass no matter where you are, because it compares the object to another object of fixed mass acting under the same gravitational force. The electronic balance, the platform balance, and the triple beam balance are commonly used in Science & Technology classrooms.

Weight is different from mass. Weight is the measure of the force of gravity working on an object. An object will weigh different amounts in a valley, on the top of Mount Everest, and on the Moon—but it will have the same mass. Spring scales are often used to weigh things in Science & Technology classrooms.

The Electronic Balance

Electronic balances are easy to use, but they are also usually expensive and sensitive pieces of equipment (**Figure 1**). To operate an electronic balance, you simply place the sample on the platform and read the measurement on the digital display. If you want to measure the mass of a substance without including the mass of the container it is in, you can place the container on the platform and "re-zero" or "TARE" the balance. This resets the scale to zero. You can then measure the mass of the substance that you add.

Figure 1

An electronic balance

The Platform Balance

A platform balance (or equal arm balance) operates on the same principles as old scales used in commerce and, figuratively, in justice. Look at **Figure 2**. Can you see why it is called a "balance"?

Figure 2

A platform or equal arm balance

To use a platform balance, you balance your sample with known masses. Be sure that your balance is "balanced" before you use it—you may have to adjust the adjustment weights. Add masses in small amounts to come as close as possible to a balanced state. Then adjust the rider to make the final balance.

The Triple Beam Balance

The triple beam balance uses the same principle as the platform balance, but it also uses the principle of leverage (**Figure 3**). You measure

Figure 3

A triple beam balance

the mass of a substance by systematically adjusting the three rider beams (starting with the largest scale and ending with the smallest scale) and combining the three readings (**Figure 4**). Again, you may have to initially "zero" the scale by adjusting the adjustment weights.

Measuring the mass of a beaker

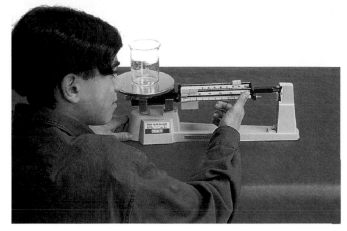

Try This — Measure Mass and Weight

Using one of the types of balances listed above, measure the following:
• the mass of a key
• the mass of the water in a glass (you may have to think about this if you are using either a platform balance or a triple beam balance)
• the mass of a spoon of sugar

How might you measure the weight of an object in water?

The Spring Scale

The spring scale is used to measure weight (**Figure 5**). In other words, a spring scale compares the force exerted by gravity (and any other forces that are acting—such as the buoyant force) to the counterforce applied by the spring and tells you where they balance, so the measurement varies with the force of gravity. It is particularly useful for items that do not fit on platforms or are different in shape. Spring scales come in various sizes. To use the scales, place the item to be measured on the hook of the spring scale and read the weight on the scale in the clear section of the tube.

Figure 5
Spring scales

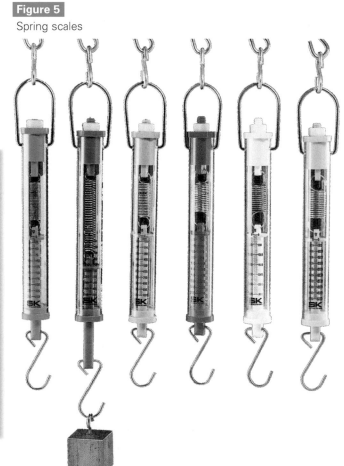

5C Using Other Scientific Equipment

You can do many investigations using everyday materials and equipment. In your Science & Technology classroom, there are other pieces of equipment. Some of these are illustrated below.

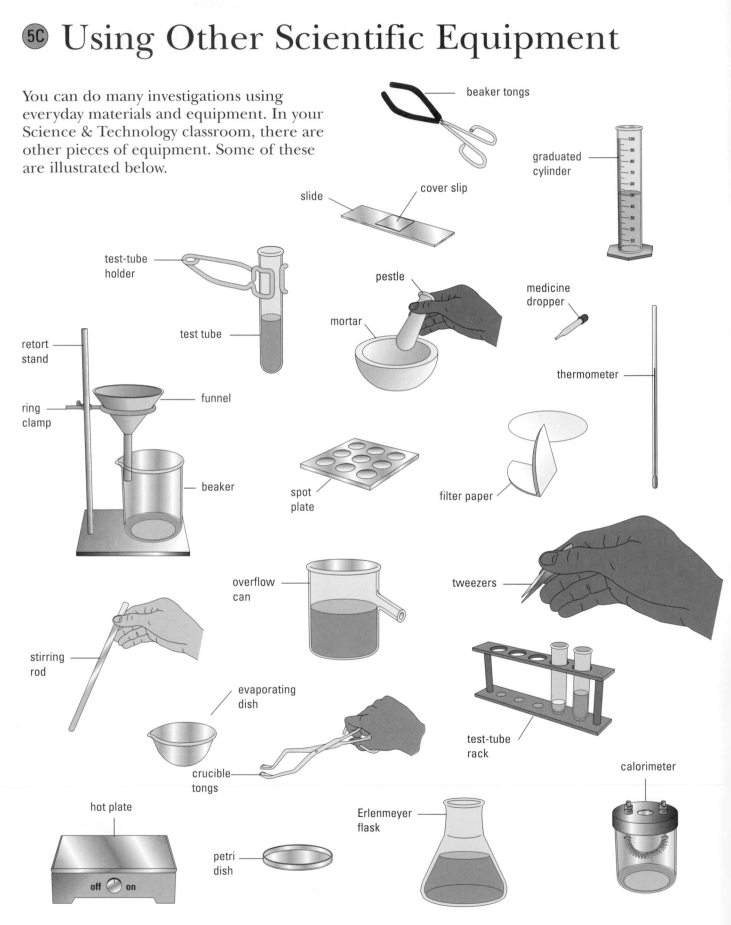

beaker tongs

graduated cylinder

slide

cover slip

test-tube holder

pestle

mortar

medicine dropper

test tube

thermometer

retort stand

ring clamp

funnel

beaker

spot plate

filter paper

overflow can

tweezers

stirring rod

evaporating dish

test-tube rack

crucible tongs

calorimeter

hot plate

off on

petri dish

Erlenmeyer flask

5D Using Technology Equipment

As you go through the design process, you will use various tools and materials to construct your prototypes. Some of these are illustrated below. (Refer to ① "Safety in Science & Technology," to review the safe use of saws, drills, paper drills, utility knives, snips, hammers, and screwdrivers.)

Tools

Sawing and Cutting

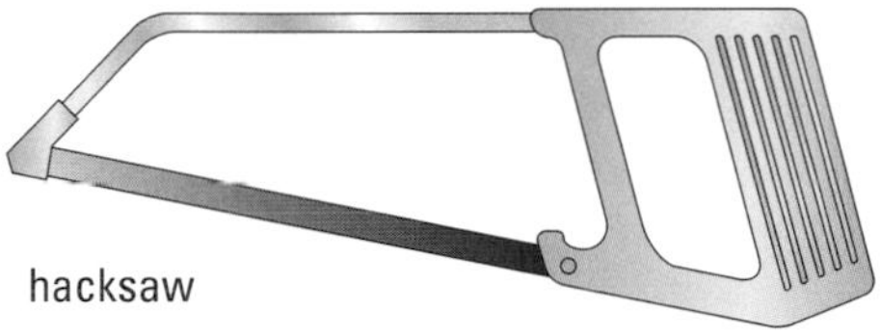

hacksaw

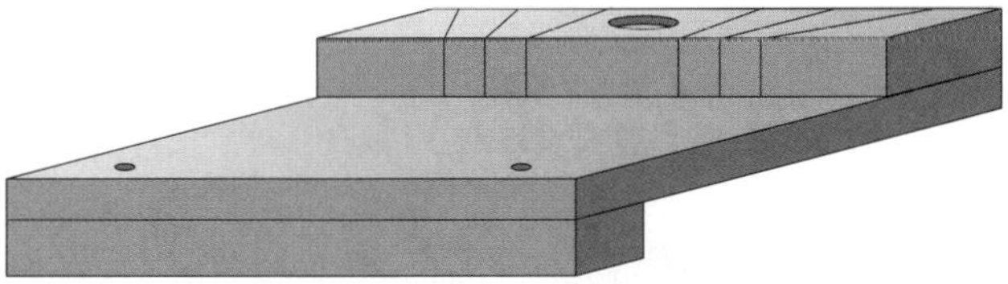

bench hook with mitre box

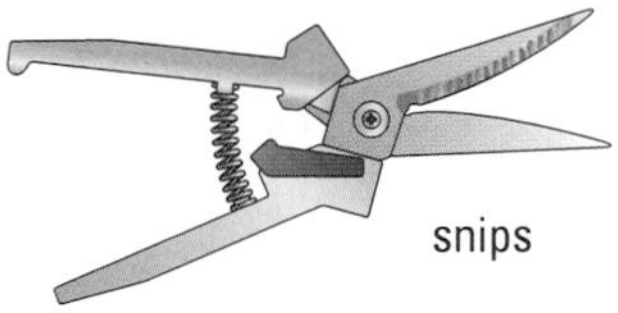

snips

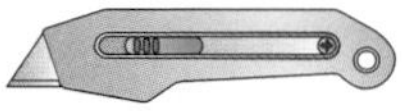

utility knife

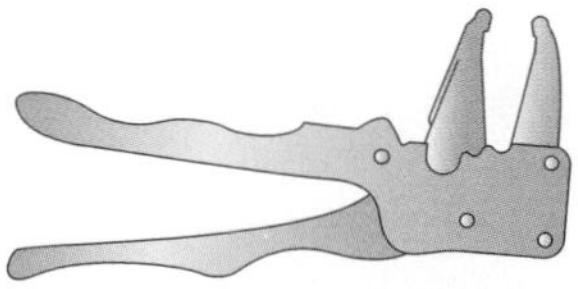

wire strippers

Joining

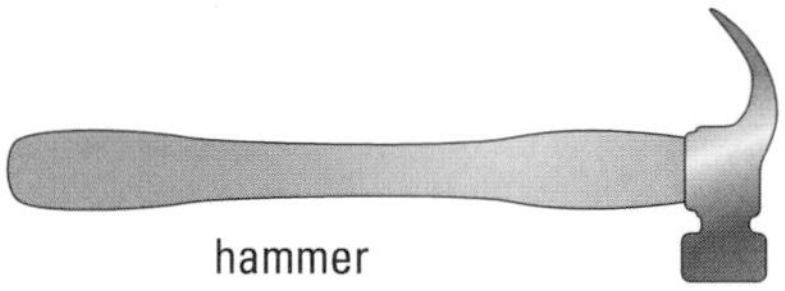

hammer

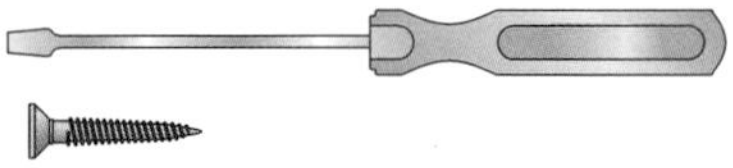

screwdriver and screw

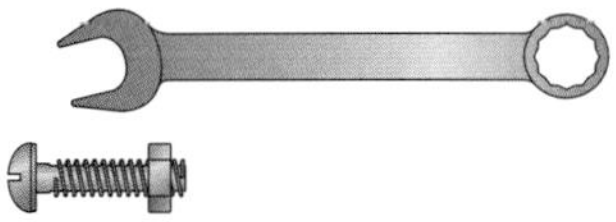

wrench, nut and bolt

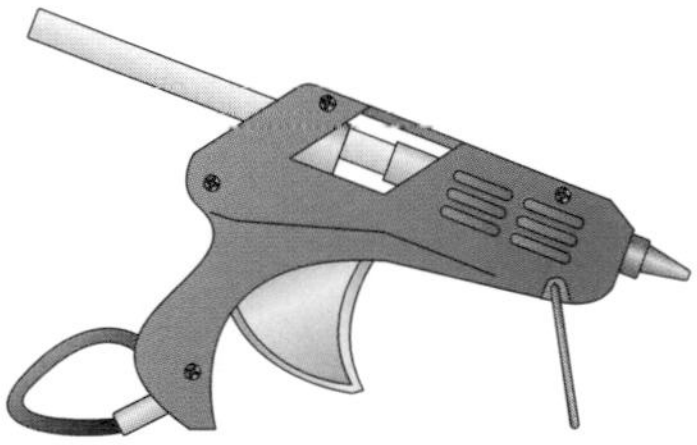

glue and glue gun

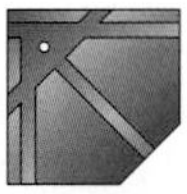

wood jointer

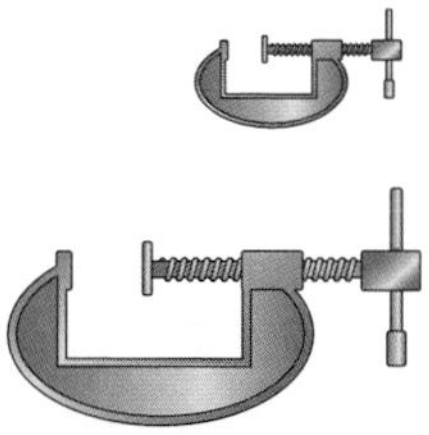

"C" clamps

Shaping

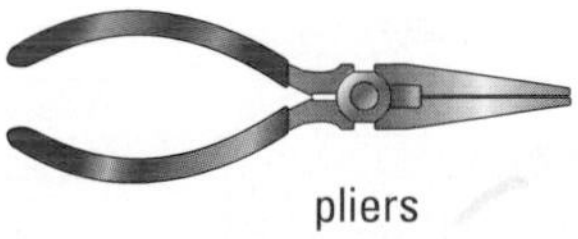

pliers

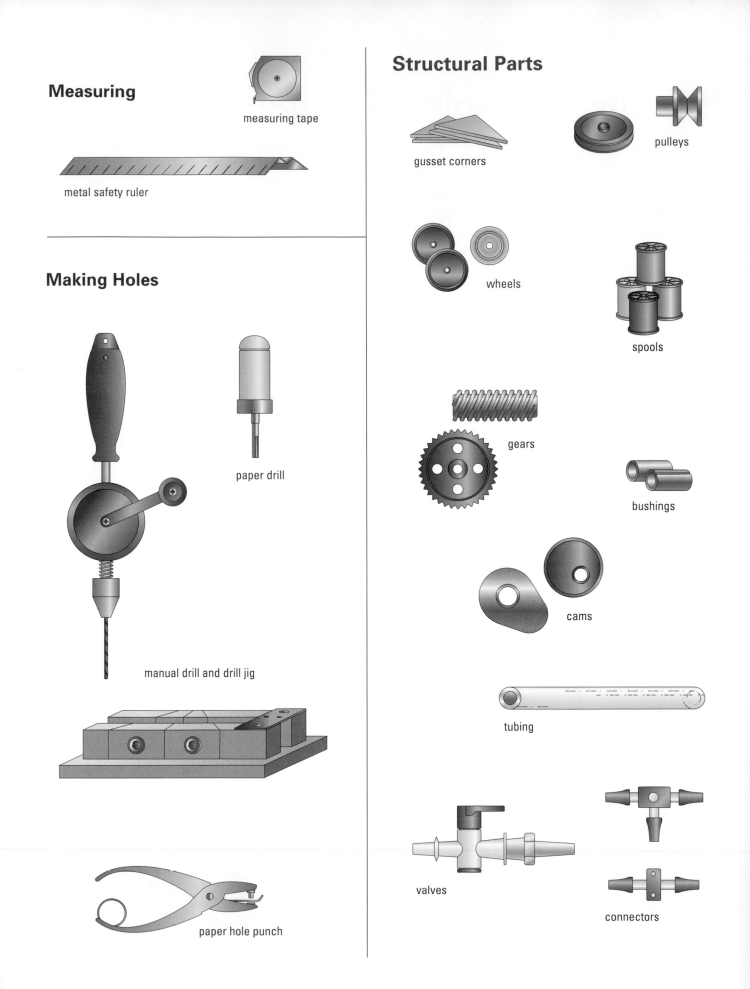

Measuring

measuring tape

metal safety ruler

Making Holes

paper drill

manual drill and drill jig

paper hole punch

Structural Parts

gusset corners

pulleys

wheels

spools

gears

bushings

cams

tubing

valves

connectors

motor

motor pulley

batteries

switches

bulb holder

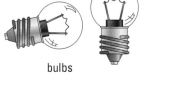
bulbs

Construction Materials

There are few limits to what materials you can use in construction. The more obvious materials include:

- wood (1 cm x 1 cm basswood)
- bristol board
- metal
- corrugated plastic
- fabric

You should also consider using materials that you encounter everyday, including:

- film containers
- bread tags
- polystyrene food trays
- aluminum pie plates
- fabric
- lids
- pizza "tables"

Try This Useful Materials

There is a wealth of construction materials available to you. Brainstorm a list of construction materials. Be as creative as possible. For each material, suggest a possible use.

 ⑤ᴇ Fabrication Techniques

There are many different fabrication techniques and skills that you can learn to help take your design from a plan to a prototype. The following section will help you learn some basic techniques. As you become more skilled, you will want to explore additional techniques. You can learn more by taking note of how things are built, by asking for expert help, and by using other information resources.

Structures

The following techniques will help you build a variety of different structures.

Joining with Adhesives

- Use the right adhesive for the materials you are using. Read labels carefully to get the best results and to work safely.
- If possible, it may be useful to roughen the surfaces being joined. A rough surface increases the gluing area and helps the glue hold.
- Make sure the surfaces being joined are in contact with each other. You may need to use a clamp or other device to apply the necessary pressure.

Figure 1 shows how to join two pieces of wood in a right angle. Spread glue on one side of a cardboard triangle, and place it on the wood so that a right angle is formed. When the glue has dried, do the same on the other side of the corner joint. This will prevent sideways twisting and keep the corner at a right angle.

Joining with Fasteners

Use the right fastener for the job. Nails, for instance, are used to join wood permanently whereas screws are better for joining things temporarily. **Figures 2–4** illustrate a few useful joining techniques.

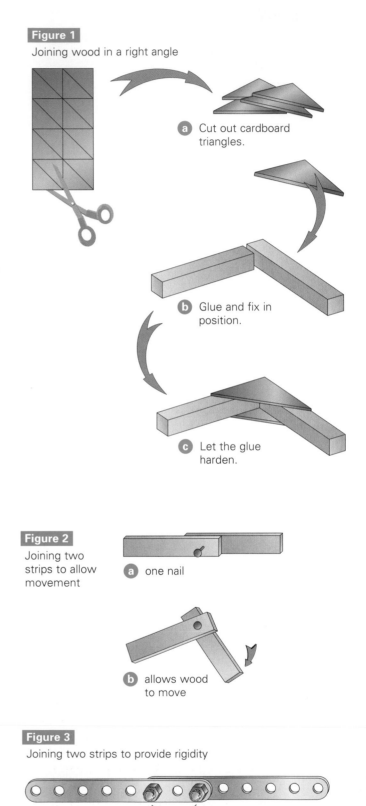

Figure 1
Joining wood in a right angle

a Cut out cardboard triangles.

b Glue and fix in position.

c Let the glue harden.

Figure 2
Joining two strips to allow movement

a one nail

b allows wood to move

Figure 3
Joining two strips to provide rigidity

nuts and bolts

Figure 4

Making holes in materials allows you to use many different fasteners that can help you control friction better. This is useful for constructing such things as levers.

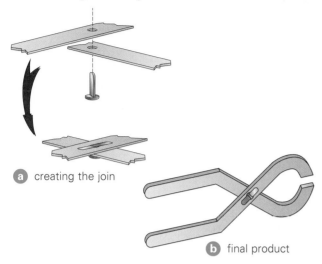

a creating the join

b final product

Wheels and Axles

There are two basic kinds of wheel systems: free wheels and fixed wheels. These can be understood by considering a bicycle (**Figure 5**). An axle runs through the centre of every wheel. On a bicycle, the back wheel is fixed to the axle. When the chain turns the axle, the axle turns the wheel. The front wheel is not fixed to the axle—the axle itself is fixed. When the bicycle moves forward, the front wheel turns.

Figure 5

A wheel depends upon friction to make it work. An axle runs through the centre of the wheel.

Free wheel: the bike moves forward, the tire cannot slip and so the wheel turns.

Fixed wheel: the axle turns the wheel, the tire cannot slip and so it pushes the bike forward.

- Wheels must be round. Ways of creating wheels include using ready-made wheels, using round objects as wheels, and cutting dowel into sections.

- Axles must be centred and straight. If not, the ride will be wobbly. Axles must also be loose enough or the wheels will stick.
- Wheels must have enough friction. This can be increased by roughening the surface of the wheel or covering it with a material like rubber.
- Wheels must be well attached to axles. Ways of keeping wheels on axles include plastic or rubber tubing, locking pins, and screws and washers.

Gears

A gear is a wheel with teeth. It can mesh with another gear to create different kinds of motion. Three useful types of gears are illustrated in **Figures 6–8**.

Figure 6

A worm gear drives a cog and turns the axis of rotation through 90°.

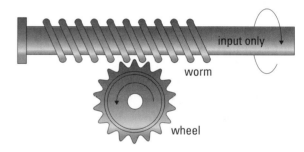

input only

worm

wheel

Figure 7

A rack and pinion gear converts circular movement to linear movement.

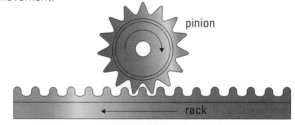

pinion

rack

Figure 8

A bevel gear has teeth cut at a 45° angle. It changes the direction of turning through 90°.

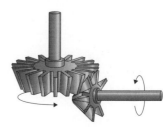

Gears are available ready-made. You can also make simple gears from corrugated cardboard and discs and dowel (**Figure 9**). For gears to work, their teeth must have a common factor. For example, a 12-tooth gear will mesh with a 4-tooth gear because they have a common factor of 3. A 12-tooth gear will not mesh with a 5-tooth gear, for example.

Figure 10
Different linkages

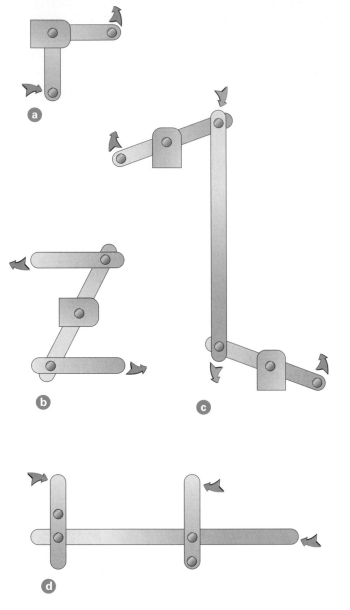

Figure 9
Gear construction

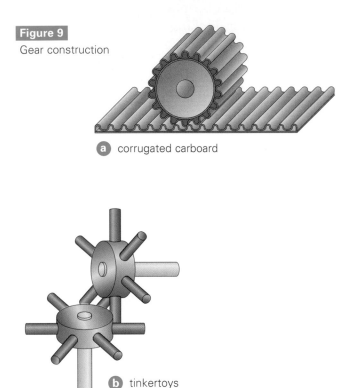

a corrugated carboard

b tinkertoys

Levers

Levers can be used to change the direction and size of a movement or force. A lever is a rigid rod with a turning point (pivot). There are standard ways of linking levers together that produce specific mechanisms. Some of these are illustrated in **Figure 10**. The best way to understand how levers work is to experiment with simple materials, like cardboard strips and paper fasteners.

If you are having trouble with your lever, check for the following problems:
- the pivots may be too tight or too loose
- the pivots may not be in the right place
- the linkages may be connected incorrectly
- the linkages may be the wrong length
- the linkages may be out of line.

Electricity

Many of the prototypes you build will use electricity. In these cases, you will need to draw and construct circuits to control electricity. The following section outlines the basic techniques for building circuits. When in doubt about any details, ask your teacher. Think safety first.

Safety Considerations

- Only operate a circuit after it has been approved by your teacher.
- Always ensure that your hands are dry, and that you are standing on a dry surface.
- Do not use faulty dry cells or batteries, do not connect different makes of dry cells in the same battery, and avoid connecting partially discharged dry cells to fully-charged cells.
- Take care not to short-circuit dry cells or batteries.
- Do not use frayed or damaged connectors.
- Handle breakable components with care.

The Parts of an Electric Circuit

Simple electric circuits have four basic parts, shown in **Figure 11**.

1. **A source of electrical energy:** You will typically use a combination of dry cells or a special device called a "power supply." These are direct current sources of electricity. They are much safer to use than wall outlets, which provide an alternating current source.

2. **An electrical load:** The load is the appliance that uses the electricity (e.g., lights, buzzers, motors).

3. **A circuit control device:** You will normally use one of a variety of switches (e.g., some switches turn things on and off, some switches reverse the direction of electric motors, etc.)

4. **Connectors:** These are often copper wires.

Drawing a Circuit Diagram

Before building a circuit, you should work it out on paper (**Figure 12**). There are some conventions to follow when drawing circuit diagrams: connecting wires are generally shown as straight linees or 90° angles, and

Figure 12

Schematic diagram of the closed circuit shown in Figure 11

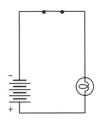

Figure 11

The parts of an electric circuit

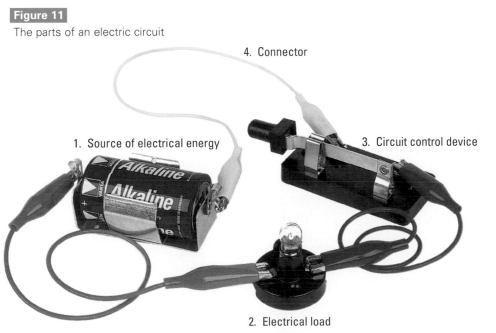

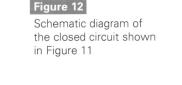

4. Connector

1. Source of electrical energy

3. Circuit control device

2. Electrical load

symbols (shown in **Table 1**) are used to represent all the components.

Table 1 **Symbols used in Circuit Diagrams**

	DC CIRCUITS	
Sources/Outlets	—+⊦−—	cell
	—+⊧⊧⊧−—	3-cell battery
Control Devices	—•⁄•—	switch
	—•∿•—	fuse
	—•⌢•—	circuit breaker
	—[ ]⁄—	switch and fuse
	▨	distribution panel
	S	switch
	S$_{WP}$	weatherproof switch
	▣	push button
Electrical Loads	—Ⓞ—	light bulb
	—Ⓒ—	clock
	—Ⓜ—	motor
	—Ⓣ—	thermostat
	—◇◇◇—	resistor
	—◇◇◇↗—	variable resistor (rheostat)
	[○]	fluorescent fixture
	◣	heating panel
Meters	—Ⓐ—	ammeter
	—Ⓥ—	voltmeter
Connectors	——	conducting wire
	—⊦—	wires joined
	⏚	ground connection

Constructing the Circuit

- Have your circuit diagram approved by your teacher.
- Check connections carefully when linking dry cells. Incorrect connections could cause shorted circuits or explosions. Ask your teacher for clarification if you are unsure.
- When attaching connecting wires to meters, connect a red wire to the positive terminal and a black wire to the negative terminal of the meter. This will remind you to consider the polarity of the meter when connecting it in the circuit.
- Sometimes the ends of connecting wires do not have the correct attachments to connect to the device or meter. Use extra approved attachment devices, such as alligator clips, but be careful to position the connectors so that they cannot touch one another.
- Open the switch before altering a meter connection or adding new wiring or components.
- If the circuit does not operate correctly, open the switch and check the circuit wiring and all connections to the terminals. If you still cannot find the problem, ask your teacher to inspect your circuit again.

Pneumatics and Hydraulics

Two additional systems can be used to create movement: pneumatic systems and hydraulic systems. Each of these systems is based on the fact that fluids (gas or liquid) can be "pushed" in order to make something else move. Hydraulic systems use a liquid. Water, for instance, works in low-pressure systems, whereas hydraulic oil is used in high-pressure systems. Pneumatic systems use a gas, such as air. The air must be compressed before it can be used.

These systems have three basic components:

1. Inputs: You need a reservoir of fluid and a way of moving the fluid into the system. For instance, gravity can be used to create water pressure.

2. Controls: You need a way of directing the flow of the fluid that is strong enough to withstand the pressure of the fluid. The parts of the control system include pipes to control the direction of the flow, connectors to extend the system, taps to control the amount of fluid in the system, and valves to control the direction of the flow.

3. Outputs: The moving fluid is used to activate a device.

A simple pneumatic system is illustrated in **Figure 13**. Air from the syringe is forced through the tubing and into the balloon. The balloon inflates and the hand is forced open.

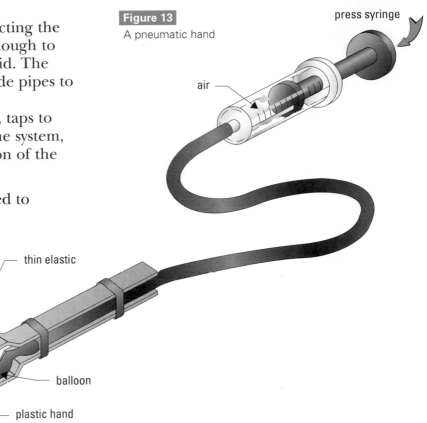

Figure 13
A pneumatic hand

press syringe

air

thin elastic

balloon

plastic hand

6A Obtaining Qualitative Data

Qualitative Observations

An observation is information that you get through your senses. Scientific questions and technological problems are usually based on observations. For instance, watching waves wash up onto a beach might make you wonder about the cause of tides or how to prevent soil erosion. When you describe the qualities of objects, events, or processes, the observations are qualitative (**Figure 1**).

Figure 1

The shape, the space available for sitting, and the colour of the chair are qualitative observations.

Making observations is a critical step in the process of scientific inquiry (see **2A** "Process of Scientific Inquiry," Step 6). Making observations is also critical to the process of design. Evaluating a prototype according to its design criteria requires careful observation (see **3A** "The Problem-Solving Cycle," Step 5). Both scientists and technologists have grouped qualitative observations into categories, based on the kind of qualities displayed and the purpose of the investigation.

Qualitative Observations in the Process of Scientific Inquiry

Common categories of qualitative observations used in the process of scientific inquiry appear below:

State of Matter: All substances can be classified as solid, liquid, or gas (**Figure 2**).

Figure 2

ⓐ Roller blades are solid.

ⓑ Water is a liquid.

ⓒ Air is a gas.

Colour: Objects can be described as being any colour or any shade of colour (**Figure 3**). Materials that have no colour should be described as colourless.

Figure 3

This leaf appears green because it reflects green light back to your eyes.

Smell: Also known as odour. There are many words to describe smells, including pungent, strong (**Figure 4**), spicy, sweet, and odourless.

Figure 4

Skunks can produce a very strong odour.

Texture: The surfaces of objects can have a variety of textures, including smooth, rough, prickly, fine, and coarse (**Figure 5**).

Figure 5

These cereal flakes have a coarse texture.

Taste: Objects can taste sweet, sour, bitter, or salty (**Figure 6**). Other tastes are combinations of these basic tastes. Objects that have no taste can be described as tasteless.

Figure 6

Black olives give this pizza a salty taste.

Shininess: Also known as lustre. Objects with very smooth surfaces that reflect light easily, like mirrors, are said to be shiny or lustrous

(**Figure 7**). Kitchen taps, mirrors, even well polished desktops can be described as lustrous. Objects with dull surfaces are said to be non-lustrous.

Figure 7

Most metals, such as copper and silver, appear shiny.

Clarity: Some substances let so much light through that letters can be read through them. These substances are said to be clear or transparent. Other substances that allow light through, but not in a way that allows you to see through them, are translucent. Objects that do not let light through are opaque (**Figure 8**).

Figure 8

Clarity ranges from transparent to opaque.

Other qualitative descriptions include form (the shape of a substance), hardness, brittleness (how easily the substance breaks), malleability (the ability of the object to be changed into another shape), and viscosity (a liquid's resistance to flow).

Another important characteristic that can be described qualitatively is the ability of substances to combine with each other.

Qualitative Observations in the Process of Design

The following list outlines design elements that often form the basis for qualitative observations in the process of design:

Shape: A shape is an area defined by a line. A shape can have two dimensions, like a square, or three dimensions, like a pyramid (**Figure 9**). The three dimensions are called: height, depth, and width.

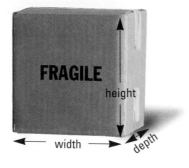

Space: Space is the area that surrounds an object or is contained within an object. All objects exist in space (**Figure 10**). We can only appreciate the form of an object by imagining or seeing the space around it.

Colour: Colour is important because it produces an instant response. Colour is used to enhance a design.

Texture: Texture has an effect on the appearance and function of a design.

Ergonomics: Ergonomics involves designing things so that they can be used easily and safely.

Try This Which Qualities?

Review the categories of qualities used in the processes of scientific inquiry and design. You will notice that some appear in both lists. Are there others that you think could be useful in both processes? Provide two or three examples.

⑥Ⓑ Obtaining Quantitative Data

Quantitative Observations

Observations that are based on measurements or counting are said to be quantitative, since they deal with quantities of things. The length of a rose's stem or a piece of wood, the number of petals on a flower, and the number of rotations of a gear are all quantitative observations.

Look at the two lines in **Figure 1**. Which looks longer? You will find that AB and CD are the same length. Our senses can be fooled. That is one of the reasons quantitative observations are important in science and technology and it is also the reason measurements must be made carefully.

Figure 1
Which line is longer? Use a ruler.

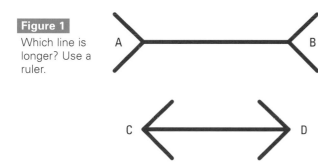

Standards of Measurement

Units of measurement used to be based on local standards that the community had agreed to. At one time, for example, there was a unit equal to the length of a line of 16 people standing close together. Horse heights are still measured in hands, based on the width of a human hand, and measured from the ground to the horse's shoulder.

These standards may sound strange, but the unit of length that replaced most local standards, the metre, was based on an arc on the Earth that ran from the equator, through Barcelona, Paris, and Dunkirk, to the North Pole (**Figure 2**). The length of this arc, divided by 10 000 000, equaled one metre. That also sounds strange, but it established the first standard unit of length that the whole world could use.

Figure 2
The early standard for the metre was 1/10 000 000 of the distance from the equator to the North Pole.

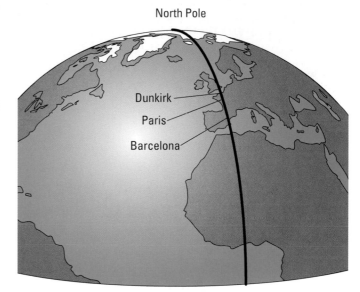

North Pole

Dunkirk
Paris
Barcelona

equator

The metric system, which includes units such as the metre and the kilogram, is the one adopted by Canada. You should be familiar with, and use, the units from this international system (also called the SI system, from the French name: Système International d'Unités).

Base Units and Prefixes

There are seven SI base units, shown in **Table 1**.

Table 1 **The Seven SI Base Units**

Quantity	Unit	Symbol
length	metre	m
mass	kilogram	kg*
time	second	s
electric current	ampere	A
temperature	kelvin	K
amount of substance	mole	mol
light intensity	candela	cd

*The kilogram is the only base unit that contains a prefix. The gram proved to be too small for practical purposes.

Larger and smaller units are created by multiplying or dividing the value of the base units by multiples of 10. For example, the prefix deca means multiplied by 10. Therefore, one decametre (1 dam) is equal to ten metres (10 m). The prefix kilo means multiplied by 1000, so one kilometre (1 km) is equal to one thousand metres (1000 m). Similarly, each unit can be divided into smaller units. The prefix milli, for example, means divided by 1000, so one millimetre (1 mm) is equal to 1/1000 of a metre.

To convert from one unit to another, you simply multiply by a conversion factor. For example, to convert 12.4 metres to centimetres, you use the relationship 1 m = 100 cm.

$$12.4 \text{ m} = ? \text{ cm}$$
$$12.4 \text{ m} \times \frac{100 \text{ cm}}{1 \text{ m}} = 1240 \text{ cm}$$

To convert 6.3 g to kilograms, you use the relationship 1000 g = 1 kg.

$$6.3 \text{ g} = ? \text{ kg}$$
$$6.3 \text{ g} \times \frac{1 \text{ kg}}{1000 \text{ g}} = 0.0063 \text{ kg}$$

Any conversion of the same physical quantities can be done in this way. The conversion factor is chosen so that, using cancellation, it yields the desired unit.

Once you understand this method of conversion, you will find that you can simply move the decimal point. Move it to the right when the new unit is smaller and to the left when the new unit is larger. As you can see from **Table 2**, not all the units and prefixes are commonly used.

Table 2 **Metric Prefixes**

Prefix	Symbol	Factor by which the base unit is multiplied	Example
giga	G	$10^9 = 1\ 000\ 000\ 000$	
mega	M	$10^6 = 1\ 000\ 000$	$10^6 \text{ m} = 1 \text{ Mm}$
kilo	k	$10^3 = 1\ 000$	$10^3 \text{ m} = 1 \text{ km}$
hecto	h	$10^2 = 100$	
deca	d	$10^1 = 10$	
		$10^0 = 1$	m
deci	da	$10^{-1} = 0.1$	
centi	c	$10^{-2} = 0.01$	$10^{-2} \text{ m} = 1 \text{ cm}$
milli	m	$10^{-3} = 0.001$	$10^{-3} \text{ m} = 1 \text{ mm}$
micro	μ	$10^{-6} = 0.000\ 001$	$10^{-6} \text{ m} = 1 \text{ μm}$

Table 3 shows quantities that you may need to be familiar with.

Table 3 **Common Quantities and Units**

Quantity	Unit	Symbol
length	kilometre	km
	metre	m
	centimetre	cm
	millimetre	mm
mass	tonne (1000 kg)	t
	kilogram	kg
	gram	g
area	hectare (10 000 m²)	ha
	square metre	m²
	square centimetre	cm²
volume	cubic metre	m³
	litre	L
	cubic centimetre	cm³
	millilitre	mL
time	minute	min
	second	s
temperature	degrees Celsius	°C
force	newton	N
energy	kilojoule	kJ
	joule	J
pressure	kilopascal	kPa
	pascal	Pa

Measuring Accurately

Many people believe that all measurements are accurate and dependable. But there are many things that can go wrong when measuring. The instrument may be faulty. Another similar instrument may give different readings. The person making the measurement may make a mistake.

Ask your teacher for two thermometers and check the room temperature. Are the readings identical? (You may want to check both thermometers over a range of temperatures—do the two thermometers always give the same readings?) Suppose you use only one thermometer, and it reads 21°C. Is the room temperature really 21°C? That depends on how reliable the thermometer is. If your thermometer is not accurate, the temperature of the room could be 19°C, 23°C, or some other value.

No matter what you are measuring, it is wise to repeat your measurement at least three times in order to be sure of an accurate result. If your measurements are close, calculate the average and use that number. To be more certain, repeat the measurements with a different instrument.

Measuring Tips

Measuring temperature: If you are measuring the temperature of a liquid, keep the bulb of the thermometer near the middle of the liquid (**Figure 3**). If the liquid is being heated and the thermometer is simply sitting in the container with its bulb at the bottom, you will be measuring the temperature of the bottom of the container, not the temperature of the liquid. (Do not use the thermometer as a stirring stick!) Similarly, if you are measuring the temperature of a solid, place the bulb of the thermometer as close to the centre of the solid as possible.

Figure 3
The thermometer is not resting on the bottom of the beaker.

Measuring length: Choose the right measuring instrument for the task at hand. If you are measuring something quite short, for instance, you need a tool that is quite precise (i.e., that indicates small increments.) Make sure you start measuring where "0" is indicated (**Figure 4**). Many rulers or metre sticks extend past this point.

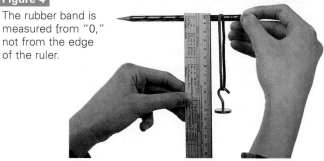

Figure 4
The rubber band is measured from "0," not from the edge of the ruler.

Measuring construction materials: Remember that when you cut some materials (e.g., wood) you will lose a bit of wood in cutting (**Figure 5**). This "bit" must remain the same to ensure square corners or exact angles. It will also affect how large the final pieces of your product are.

Figure 5
You will sometimes lose material when you cut it.

Measuring volume: As with length, it's important to choose the right measuring instrument. Make sure your measuring instrument is on a level surface. If you are measuring a solid, shake the container so that the surface is level. To measure the volume of a liquid using a graduated cylinder, measure from the bottom of the apparent curve (**Figure 6**).

Figure 6
The arrow indicates where the measurement should be taken.

Measuring time: Measuring short intervals of time introduces a strong possibility of human error (**Figure 7**). If you are using a stopwatch to time how many times a pendulum swings in 5 s, for instance, you have to start the stopwatch at precisely the same moment as the pendulum begins its first swing. Repeating the process and averaging the results is advisable.

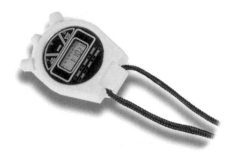

Figure 7
Accurate timing requires a lot of attention.

Measuring mass and weight: Refer to 5B "Working with Scales and Balances."

Try This — Measuring Quantities

Complete one of the following activities.

Activity A:
- You have been given a bag of balloons to provide motion for the balloon-powered car you have designed. Each balloon is advertised as being the same diameter. You want to verify this so that you can be certain all groups use the same volume of air to power their vehicles. Check to make sure that this is actually true.
- Decide how your group will prove or disprove this.
- Record all quantitative data in a table. What is the average balloon size?
- Compare your results with other groups.

Activity B:
- Find out what pH level means and the scale used to identify pH levels as acidic, neutral, and alkaline.
- With a partner, measure the pH levels of a variety of liquids.
- Compare your results with others in your class. Did everyone obtain the same results?

Scientific & Technical Drawing

Scientific drawings are done to record observations as accurately as possible. Technical drawings are used to visualize design ideas. Drawings are used to communicate, which means they must be clear, well-labelled, and easy to understand. Following are some tips that will help you produce useful scientific and technical drawings.

Before You Begin

- **Obtain some paper.** You will have to make a decision about which type of paper best meets your needs. Blank paper will be best when lines might obscure your drawing or make your labels confusing. Graph paper will be best when you are drawing something that requires exact measurements.
- **Find a sharp, hard pencil** (e.g., 2H or 4H). Avoid using pen, thick markers, or coloured pencils. Ink can't be erased—even the most accomplished artists change their drawings—and coloured pencils are soft, making lines too thick.
- **Plan your drawing.** Ensure that your drawing will be large enough that people can see details. For example, a third of a page might be appropriate for a diagram of a single cell or a gear train. If you are drawing the entire field of view of a microscope, draw a circle with a reasonable diameter (e.g., 10 cm) to represent the field of view. If you are drawing a three-dimensional object, plan for more than one view (e.g., top view, side view, etc.)
- **Leave space for labels.** In scientific drawings, the right side of the drawing is commonly used.

Scientific Drawing Tips

- **Make simple, two-dimensional drawings.**
- **Draw only what you see.** Your textbook may act as a guide, but it may show structures that you cannot see in your specimen.
- **Do not sketch.** Draw firm, clear lines, including only relevant details that you can see clearly.
- **Do not use shading or colouring.** A stipple (series of dots) shown in **Figure 1** may be used to indicate a darker area. Use double lines to indicate thick structures.

Figure 1
Using a stipple effect

Labelling

- **Label all drawings fully.** Avoid printing labels directly on the drawing.
- **Use a ruler.** Label lines must be horizontal and ruled firmly from the area being identified to the label (**Figure 2**).

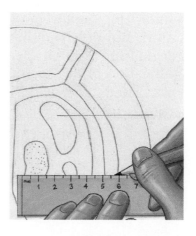

Figure 2
Neat labelling makes your drawing clear.

- **Label lines should never cross.**
- **Label drawings neatly.** In scientific drawings, it is preferable to list your labels in an even column down the right side.
- **Title the drawing.** Use the name of the specimen or prototype and any other specific information that will help identify the drawing. Underline the title.

Scale Ratio

To show the relation of the actual size to your drawing size, print the scale ratio of your drawing beside the title.

$$\text{scale ratio} = \frac{\text{size of drawing}}{\text{actual size of the specimen/prototype}}$$

For example, if you have drawn a nail that is 2 cm long (**Figure 3**) and the drawing is 8 cm long, then the scale ratio, which in this case is a magnification, is

$$\frac{8 \text{ cm}}{2 \text{ cm}} = 4\times$$

Figure 3
The nail as drawn is 4X larger than the actual nail.

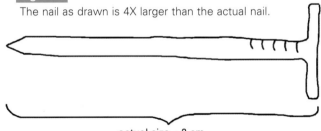

actual size = 2 cm

The magnification is always written with an "×" after it. In a fully labeled drawing, the total magnification of the drawing should be placed at the bottom right side of the diagram. If the ocular lens magnified a specimen 10×, the low-powered objective (4×) was used, and the diagram was drawn 3× larger that the original specimen, the total magnification of the diagram would be as follows:

Total Magnification = Ocular Lens × Low-Powered
 Objective Lens × Scale Ratio
 = 10 × 4 × 3
 = 120 ×

The total magnification should be written on the bottom right-hand side of the diagram, as shown in **Figure 4**.

Figure 4
The magnification is 120×.

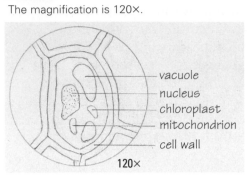

vacuole
nucleus
chloroplast
mitochondrion
cell wall
120×

Technical Drawing Techniques

The kind of drawing you produce during the process of technological design will depend on its purpose. Some drawings are little more than doodles—rough attempts to give shape to your ideas at the beginning of the process. Some drawings will help you explain your concept to others. Some drawings are used in the plan of a prototype, along with written instructions, to help in the construction.

Sketches

When you are first brainstorming ways of solving a problem, it is often useful to sketch your ideas. The sketches help you develop and record your concept. Often a sketch will include notes to help you keep track of an evolving idea (**Figure 5**). Sketches can also help you communicate your ideas to other members of your team.

Figure 5
A sketch for a game design

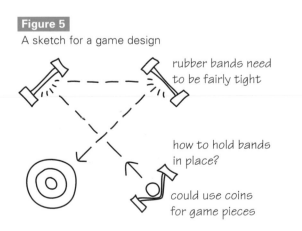

rubber bands need to be fairly tight

how to hold bands in place?

could use coins for game pieces

Isometric Drawings

As you refine your design, you will also refine your technical drawings. Drawings that are designed to help others understand or build your design need to be clear and accurate.

An isometric drawing represents an object in three dimensions with angles drawn at 30°. Often special isometric grid paper is used. It consists of three sets of parallel lines. Wherever the lines cross, there are three axes which represent depth, length, and height (**Figure 6**). This method of drawing allows you to use the actual measurements of the object you are drawing and provides others with a picture of the object that it easy to understand (**Figure 7**).

Figure 6

The parallel lines in an isometric grid run at 60° to one another.

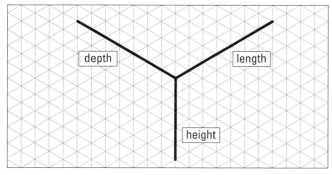

Figure 7

A model of a garage to be made from a shoebox

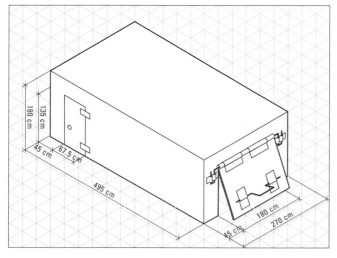

Orthographic Projection

It is often useful to create a working drawing that shows your prototype from three different views: the top, side, and front views. An orthographic projection is an accurate drawing that shows all the views and includes every detail and measurement (**Figure 8**). Each view is drawn square-on, in two dimensions. It is drawn so that the relation between the views is clear. Using graph paper makes this easier. One way of understanding the relation between each view is to imagine that the object is enclosed in a transparent box. If you drew what you saw from sides A, B and C on the box, then opened the box up, you could see how each view is related to the other two (**Figure 9**).

A complete working drawing often includes the orthographic projection, a list of parts, a list of materials used for each part, and detailed assembly instructions.

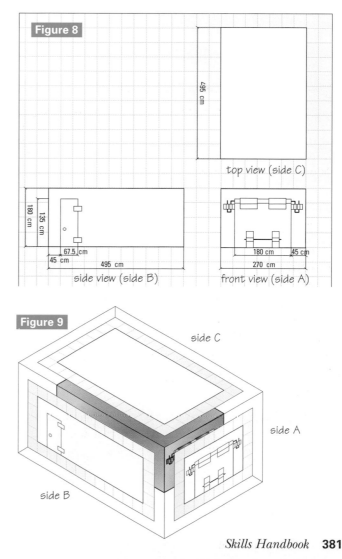

Other Views of an Object

In some cases, it may be useful to show the inside of an object. One way of doing this is to draw a cross-section (**Figure 10**).

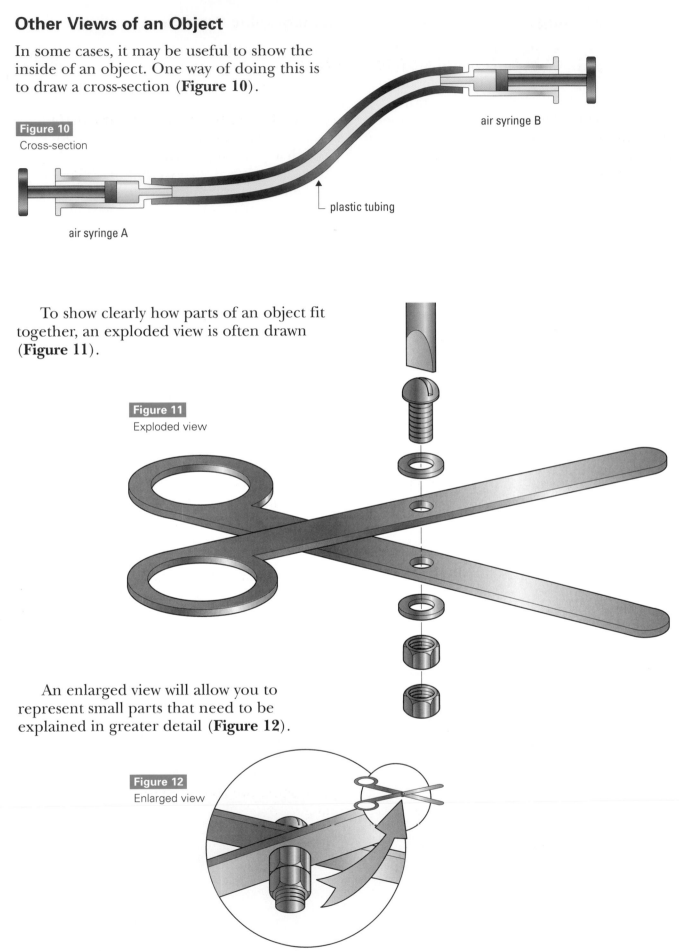

Figure 10
Cross-section

air syringe B

plastic tubing

air syringe A

To show clearly how parts of an object fit together, an exploded view is often drawn (**Figure 11**).

Figure 11
Exploded view

An enlarged view will allow you to represent small parts that need to be explained in greater detail (**Figure 12**).

Figure 12
Enlarged view

Creating Data Tables

Creating effective data tables in your investigations will help you record and analyze your data. Constructing a useful data table is one of the first steps in making sense of your experimental data. Take a look at **Tables 1, 2, and 3** which come directly from *Nelson Science & Technology 7/8*. What similarities exist? What strategies should you employ when constructing your data tables?

Table 1   Maturity Time and Yield of Tomato Varieties

Variety	Time to maturity (days)	Yield for determinate varieties (kg per plant)	Yield for indeterminate varieties (kg per plant every 10 d)
A	80	n/a	6.8
B	40	n/a	2.6
C	70	n/a	5.2
D	60	10	n/a
E	70	n/a	4.2
F	65	10	n/a
G	55	15	n/a
H	50	10	n/a
I	75	n/a	5.6

Table 2   Average Monthly Temperatures (°C) in Cities A and B

Month	Temperature (°C) in City A	Temperature (°C) City B
J	-7	-6
F	-6	-6
M	-1	-2
A	6	4
M	12	9
J	17	15
J	21	18
A	20	18
S	15	14
O	9	9
N	3	3
D	-3	-3

Table 3   Average Monthly Precipitation (cm) in Cities A and B

Month	Precipitation (cm) in City A	Precipitation (cm) in City B
J	4.6	14.7
F	4.6	11.9
M	5.7	12.3
A	6.4	12.4
M	6.6	11.1
J	6.9	9.8
J	7.7	9.7
A	8.4	11.0
S	7.4	9.5
O	6.3	12.9
N	7.0	15.4
D	6.6	16.7

The following checklist will help you construct effective data tables in your investigations:

- List the dependent variable(s) (the effect) along the top of the table.
- List the independent variable (the cause) along the side of the table.
- Be sure that each data table has a descriptive, yet concise, title.
- Be sure to include the units of measurement along with each variable when appropriate.
- If you include the results of your calculations in a table, be sure to show at least one sample calculation in your data analysis.

Refer to 9C "Using Your Computer Effectively" for information about using spreadsheet programs to create useful data tables.

7A The Need to Graph

Making Sense of Data

Scientists and technologists often create huge amounts of data while doing experiments and studies—maybe hundreds, even thousands, of numbers for every variable. How can this mass of data be arranged so that it is easy to read and understand? That's right—in a graph. The sample tables below don't have thousands of pieces of data, but there is enough to become confusing. Can you make sense of the data in **Table 1** by simple inspection?

A graph is an easy way to see where a relationship or pattern exists. As well, it allows you to see more precisely what the relationship is, so it can be accurately described in words and by mathematics. **Figure 1** is a point-and-line graph that shows the data from **Table 1**.

The graph in **Figure 1** shows the relationship between the two variables and highlights two temperature plateaus where a change of state is taking place. In more complex relationships such as this, the need for a graph is quite clear. Data trends are much easier to visualize and understand in the organized form of a graph than as numbers in a table.

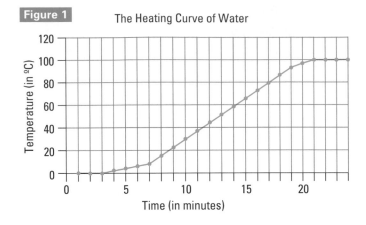

Figure 1 The Heating Curve of Water

Types of Graphs

There are many types of graphs that you can use when organizing your data. You must identify which type of graph is best for your data before you start drawing it. Three of the most useful kinds are point-and-line graphs, bar graphs, and circle graphs (also called pie graphs).

Point-and-Line Graphs

When both variables are quantitative, use a point-and-line graph. The graph in **Figure 2** was created after an experiment that measured the number of worms on the surface of soil (quantitative) and the volume of rain that fell on the soil (quantitative). It is based on the data in **Table 2**.

Table 1 The Heating Curve of Water

Time (minutes)	Temperature (°C)	Time (minutes)	Temperature (°C)
1	0	13	51
2	0	14	58
3	0	15	65
4	2	16	72
5	4	17	79
6	7	18	86
7	9	19	93
8	16	20	97
9	23	21	100
10	30	22	100
11	37	23	100
12	44	24	100

Table 2 Number of Worms Per Volume of Water

Volume of water (mL)	Number of Worms
0	3
10	4
20	5
30	9
40	22

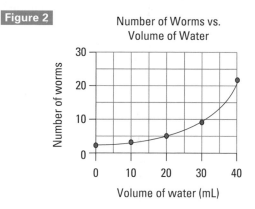

Figure 2

Number of Worms vs.
Volume of Water

make a circle graph like **Figure 4**. In a circle graph, each piece stands for a different category (in this case, the kind of music preferred), and the size of the piece tells the percentage of the total that belongs in the category (in this case, the percentage of students who prefer a particular kind of music).

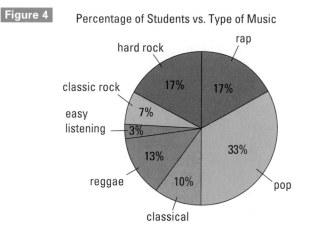

Figure 4 Percentage of Students vs. Type of Music

Bar Graphs

When at least one of the variables is qualitative, use a bar graph. For example, a study of the math marks of students (quantitative) who listened to different kinds of music (qualitative) while doing their math homework resulted in the graph in **Figure 3**. In this kind of graph, each bar stands for a different category, in this case a type of music. Notice also that the range on the vertical axis is chosen so that even the smallest bar is still visible.

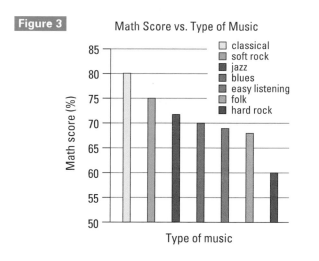

Figure 3 Math Score vs. Type of Music

Circle (or Pie) Graphs

Circle graphs and bar graphs are used for similar types of data. If your quantitative variable can be changed to a percentage of a total quantity, then a circle graph is useful. For example, if you surveyed a class to find the students' favourite type of music, you could

Try This Choose a Graph

Copy and complete **Table 3**. Determine the type of graph (point-and-line, bar, or circle) that is most suitable to illustrate the relationship between the variables in each pair.

Explain each of your choices.

Table 3

Pairs of variables	Most appropriate type of graph
1. Hardness of water Different cities/towns in Ontario	?
2. Amount of water used in a regular showerhead Amount of water used in a water-saver showerhead	?
3. List of five most abundant elements in the Earth's crust % abundance of elements	?
4. Surface area of an airplane wing Time the airplane stays aloft	?

7B Reading a Graph

When data from an investigation are plotted on an appropriate graph, patterns and relationships become much easier to see and interpret—it is easier to tell if the data supports your hypothesis or matches your design criteria. Looking at the data in a graph may lead you to a new hypothesis or to alter your design.

The graph in **Figure 1**, for example, clearly shows the relationship between the mass of an aircraft and the length of runway required for the aircraft to take off.

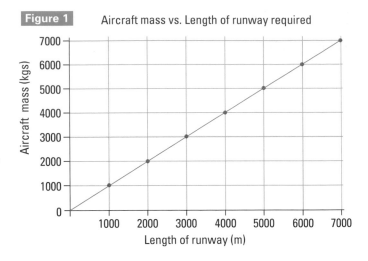

Figure 1   Aircraft mass vs. Length of runway required

What to Look for When Reading Graphs

Here are some guiding questions as you interpret the data on a graph:
- What variables are represented?
- Is there a dependent variable? Is there an independent variable? If so, identify each.
- Are the variables quantitative or qualitative?
- If the data are quantitative, what are the units of measurement?
- Are two or more sample groups needed? If so, are they included?
- What do the highest and lowest values represent on the graph?
- What is the range (the difference between the highest and lowest values) of values for each axis?
- What patterns, trends, functions, or relationships exist between the variables?
- If there is a linear (straight-line) relationship, what might the slope (steepness) of the line tell us and what is the impact?
- Is this the best graph for the data?

Try This   **Monitoring Water Quality**

What does the graph in **Figure 2** tell you?

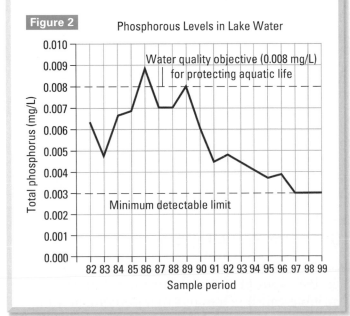

Figure 2   Phosphorous Levels in Lake Water

Constructing Graphs

Making Point-and-Line Graphs

Point-and-line graphs are common in mathematics, economics, geography, science, technology, and many other subjects. This section will help you become more skilled at drawing them, and at understanding point-and-line graphs produced by others.

As an example, the data in **Table 1** are used to produce a graph.

When making a point-and-line graph, follow these steps:

1. Construct your graph on a grid. The horizontal edge on the bottom of this grid is called the *x*-axis and the vertical edge on the left is called the *y*-axis (**Figure 1**). Don't be too thrifty with graph paper—if you draw your graphs large, they will be easier to interpret.

Table 1

Elevation (m)	Average height of tree (m)
1000	4
900	6
800	7
700	9
600	11
500	14
400	16
300	18
250	20
200	24
150	24
100	26
50	27
0	28

Figure 1

Step 1: Draw the axes.

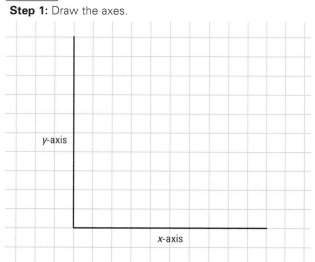

2. Decide which variable goes on which axis, and label each axis, including the units of measurement (**Figure 2**). It is common to plot the dependent variable (average height of tree in m) on the *y*-axis and the independent variable (elevation in m) on the *x*-axis.

Figure 2

Step 2: Label each axis.

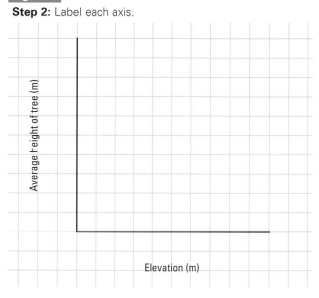

3. Determine the range of values for each variable. The range is the difference between the largest and smallest values. For the average height of tree, the maximum is 28 m, and the minimum is 4 m, so the range is: 28 m – 4 m = 24 m. For the elevation, the range is 1000 m – 0 m = 1000 m.

4. Choose a scale for each axis (**Figure 3**). This will depend on how much space you have and the range of values for each axis. Each line on the grid usually increases steadily in value by a convenient number, such as 1, 2, 5, 10, 20, 50, 100, etc. In the example, there are 10 lines for each axis. To calculate the increase in value for each line on the *x*-axis, divide the range by the number of lines:

$$\frac{28 \text{ m}}{10 \text{ lines}} = 2.8 \text{ m/line, which is rounded up to 3.}$$

Then, round up to the nearest convenient number, which in this case is 3. The scale on the "Average height of tree" axis should increase by 3 every space. Repeat the calculation for the *y*-axis:

$$\frac{1000 \text{ m}}{10 \text{ lines}} = 100 \text{ m/line}$$

Figure 3
Step 4: Choose a scale for each axis.

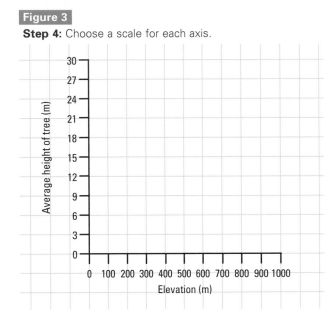

5. Plot the points (**Figure 4**). Start with the first pair of values from the data table, 1000 m elevation and 4 m trees. Place the point where an imaginary line starting at 1000 on the *x*-axis meets an imaginary line starting at 4 on the *y*-axis.

Figure 4
Step 5: Start plotting points.

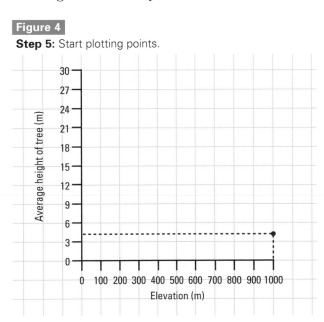

6. After all the points are plotted, and if it is possible, draw a line through the points to show the relationship between the variables (**Figure 5**). It is unusual for all the points to lie exactly on a line. Small errors in each measurement tend to move the points slightly away from the perfect line. You must draw a line that comes closest to most of the points. This is called the line of best fit—a smooth line that passes through or between the points so that there are about the same number of points on each side of the line. The line of best fit may be a straight line or a curved line.

Figure 5
Step 6: Draw a line of best fit.

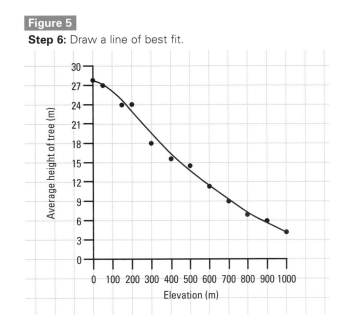

7. Title your graph.

Making Bar Graphs

Bar graphs are useful when working with qualitative data and when a variable is divided into categories. In the following example science students did a study of the kind of music students listen to while doing mathematics problems, and got the results listed in **Table 2**.

Table 2

Type of music	Math score (%)
easy listening	69
hard rock	60
jazz	72
blues	70
classical	80
folk	68
soft rock	75

Follow these steps to plot a bar graph of this data.

1. Draw and label the axes of your graph, including units (**Figure 6**). Some people prefer to have the bars based on the *x*-axis; others prefer to use the *y*-axis as the base. In the illustrations, the *x*-axis was chosen for the base.

Figure 6

Step 1: Draw the axes.

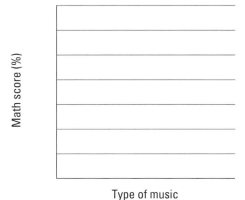

2. Develop a scale for the axis of the quantitative variable, just as you would for a point-and-line graph. In this example, the *y*-axis increases by fives, starting below the lowest value. In the illustration, 50 was chosen as the starting point, so all the bars would be visible.

3. Decide how wide the bars will be and how much space you will put between them. This decision is based on:
   - How much space you have. Measure the length of the axis on which the bars will be based, and divide that length by the number of bars. This will give you the maximum width of each bar.
   - How you want the graph to look. Decide how much less than the maximum width your bars will be, based on the visual appeal of thick and thin bars.

4. Draw in bars (**Figure 7**). Start by marking the width of each bar on the base axis. Then, draw in the top of each bar, according to your data table, and the sides. You can shade the bars equally or make each bar different from the others. It is important, however, to keep the graph simple and clear.

Figure 7

Step 4: Draw the bars.

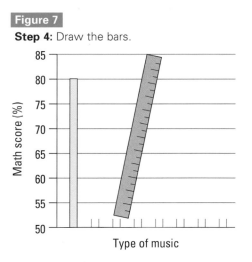

5. Identify each bar (**Figure 8**). There are several ways to do this. The best choice is the one that makes the graph easy to understand.

Figure 8

The completed bar graph

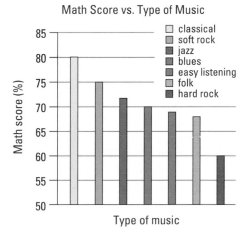

Math Score vs. Type of Music

- classical
- soft rock
- jazz
- blues
- easy listening
- folk
- hard rock

Making Circle (or Pie) Graphs

If your quantitative variable can be changed to a percentage of a total quantity, then a circle graph is useful. A sample circle graph is worked out below, using the data in **Table 3**.

Table 3

Type of music	Number of students who prefer that type	Percentage of total (% and decimal)	Angle of piece of pie (degrees)
rap	5	17% = 0.17	61.2
pop rock	10	33% = 0.33	118.8
classical	3	10% = 0.10	36.0
reggae	4	13% = 0.13	46.8
easy listening	1	3% = 0.03	10.8
classic rock	2	7% = 0.07	25.2
hard rock	5	17% = 0.17	61.2
TOTAL	30	100% = 1.00	360

Follow these steps to construct a circle graph.

1. Convert the values of your quantitative variable into percentages, and then into decimal form. In the sample, each number of students who prefer a type of music was turned into a percentage of the total number of students.

$$\text{Percentage} = \frac{\text{number}}{\text{total}} \times 100\%$$

$$\text{Percentage for rap} = \frac{5}{30} \times 100\% = 17\% \text{ (decimal version} = 0.17)$$

2. Multiply the decimal version of each percentage by 360 (there are 360° in a circle) to get the angle of each "piece of the pie" within the circle.

   Angle of piece of pie for rap = 0.17 x 360° = 61.2°

3. Draw a circle using a compass. To make the graph easy to read (and make), the circle should be big. The more pieces there are, the bigger the circle should be.

4. Draw in each piece of pie, using a protractor (**Figure 9**).

Figure 9
Step 4: Draw the pieces.

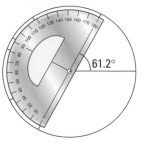

5. Shade each piece of pie using colours or patterns (**Figure 10**).

Figure 10
Step 5: Shade the pieces.

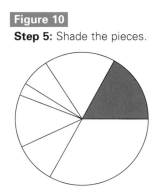

6. Label and title the graph (**Figure 11**). Put the percentage and the name of each category with its piece of pie (perhaps percentage inside and category outside the circle), or include them in a legend. Pick a title for your graph that describes the variables.

Figure 11
Step 6: The completed circle graph

Musical Preferences of Students

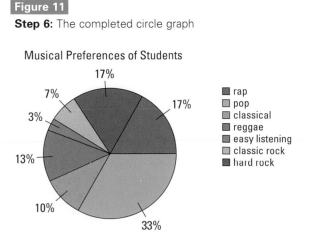

Using Computers for Graphing

You should be aware that there are many useful computer programs that can help with the graphing process. For example, Microsoft Excel is a very powerful spreadsheet/graphing program that allows for the construction of point-and-line, bar, and circle graphs as well as many other types of graphs (**Figure 12**). In addition, such programs can make use of statistical analysis to compute the best straight line or line of best fit.

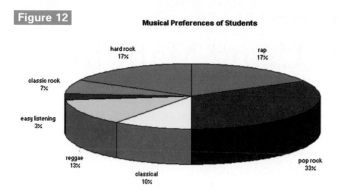

Figure 12

Musical Preferences of Students

hard rock 17%
rap 17%
classic rock 7%
easy listening 3%
reggae 13%
classical 10%
pop rock 33%

 **Graphing**

Perform the following tasks and graph the data that is given or that you collect.

1. Make labelled point-and-line graphs, with appropriate lines of best fit, for the data in **Table 4**.

2. Conduct a survey of your class or a larger group, and make bar and circle graphs from the data you collect. You could use one of the following variables or one of your own: most popular brand of sports shoe, favourite band, most interesting technological job, most well-known international structure or building.

Table 4 Amount of force needed to close a door vs. the position on the door where the force is applied

Distance from the fulcrum (hinges) in centimetres	Force applied in newtons
10 cm	80 N
15 cm	75 N
20 cm	70 N
25 cm	65 N
30 cm	60 N

7D Using Math in Science & Technology

Our world can often be analyzed, described, and predicted mathematically. For example, the mass and volume of a pure substance, when viewed in a point-and-line graph, prove to be directly proportional to one another. That is to say, as the volume of the object increases the mass of the object increases as well. If we set up a ratio of

$$\frac{\text{the mass of an object (m)}}{\text{the volume of an object (V)}} = \text{density of an object (D)}$$

we can define a new property—density—for a substance. This is just one example of how a mathematical relationship allows for the extension of our understanding.

While mathematics can sometimes appear abstract and daunting, as a scientist or technologist your ability to understand some fundamental mathematical concepts will improve your analytical ability.

Scientific Notation

In your studies, you use some very large and some very small numbers. For example, the average distance from the centre of the Earth to its crust is 6 400 000 m (**Figure 1**) and the average radius of a hydrogen atom is 0.000 000 000 05 m (**Figure 2**).

Because we don't want to spend the better part of our day writing out zeros, it is convenient to use a mathematical abbreviation known as scientific notation. The scientific notations for these two values are 6.40×10^6 m and 5.0×10^{-11} m, respectively. Can you see how this works? Essentially,

multiply by the number 10 a total of 6 times

$$6.4 \times 10^6 = 6.4 \times 10 \times 10 \times 10 \times 10 \times 10 \times 10$$

$$5.0 \times 10^{-11} = \frac{5.0}{(10 \times 10 \times 10 \times 10 \times 10 \times 10 \times 10 \times 10 \times 10 \times 10 \times 10)}$$

divide by the number 10 a total of 11 times

Figure 1

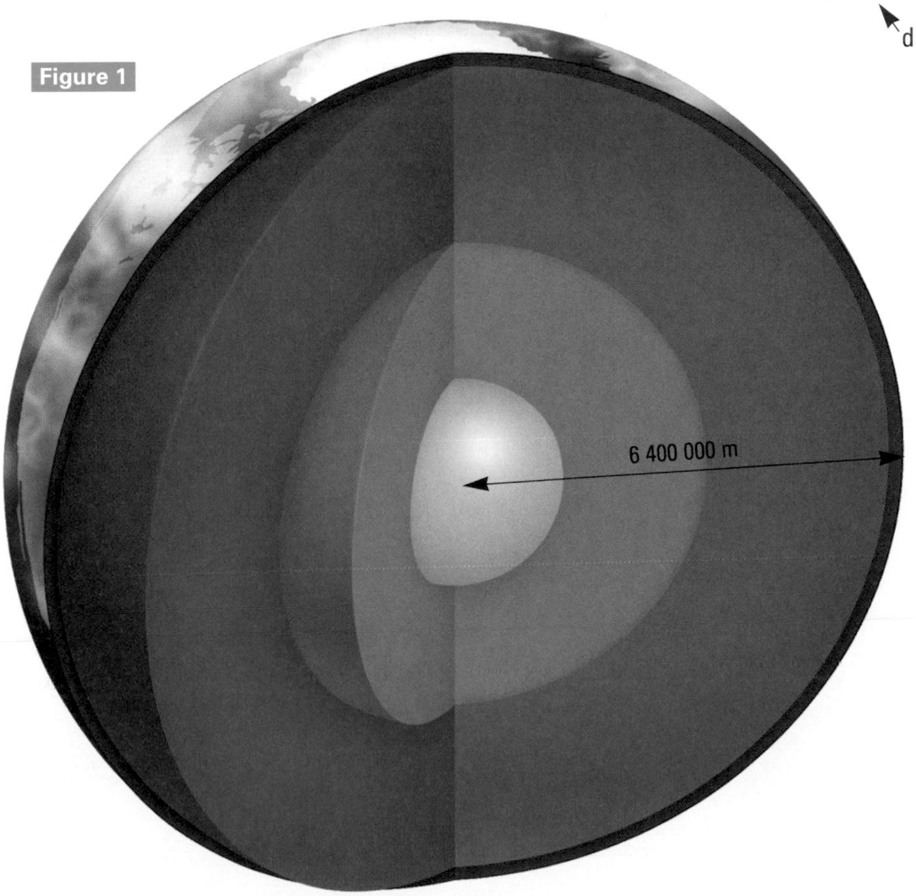

6 400 000 m

Figure 2

0.00000000005 m

hydrogen atom

Significant Figures

Imagine you are given two pieces of string and you wish to find the total length of string that you have (**Figure 3**). You measure the length of one piece of string with an accurate scale ruler and find that it is 12.72 cm long. You measure the length of the other piece of string with an old metre stick and find that piece of string to be 14 cm long. What is the total length of string that you have? If you claim the total length to be 26.72 cm, you have assumed that the second piece of string is 14 cm—was your old metre stick able to give you this level of precision? No. You can only come to the conclusion that you have a total length of 27 cm.

Figure 3

When we take measurements and manipulate numbers in science and technology, we must look at the number of significant digits (or figures) in a number. The number of significant digits represents how carefully, and with what level of accuracy or precision, the measurement was taken.

Calculating Averages

There are many statistical methods that help us analyze the quantitative data that we collect. One of the most important of these is finding the average of a set of numbers. Calculating the average of a set of numbers allows you to reduce your findings to one representative value. For example, if we measure the heights of four students,

Suzanne = 175 cm   Jan = 185 cm
Omar = 145 cm   Molly = 180 cm

we could calculate that the average height of the group is

$$\text{average height} = \frac{175 + 185 + 145 + 180}{4} = 171 \text{ cm}$$

Predicting Using Formulas

Using various mathematical or experimental techniques, we can connect and explain phenomena by a mathematical formula. For example, you will study the following relationship:

$$\text{pressure} = \frac{\text{force}}{\text{area}}$$

If you know this formula, and you know any two of the quantities, you can predict the third. For instance, consider two people on a toboggan. If you know the area of a toboggan (1 m^2) and the force exerted on it by the two people sitting on it (1000 N), you can predict the pressure:

$$\frac{1000 \text{ N}}{1 \text{ m}^2} = 1000 \text{ N/m}^2 \quad \text{also known as 1 kilopascal (kPa)}$$

Try This **What Pressure?**

A pile of scrap metal with a force of 20 000 N is dumped on a platform with an area of 25 m². What is the pressure on the platform?

7E Reaching a Conclusion

Scientific investigations mean very little, if anything, unless the scientist states a conclusion about the results. A conclusion is a statement that explains the results of an investigation. This statement should refer back to your original hypothesis. It should reveal whether the results support, partially support, or reject your hypothesis. Don't worry if your hypothesis is incorrect—scientists usually need to revise and repeat experiments many times in order to obtain the solutions they are seeking. Remember, science is a repetitive process. How many experiments do you think have been repeated in order to learn what we now know about cancer treatments?

In the process of design, the evaluation of the prototype is the stage at which conclusions are reached (see 3F "Testing and Evaluating a Prototype"). Your evaluation will take into consideration how effectively you solved the initial design problem. The design process is also a repetitive process: products and processes are tested and modified and, ultimately, improved.

Checking Your Hypothesis

Suppose you wanted to find out about the relationship between the amount of time spent doing homework per week and the mark you receive on your tests. Your hypothesis may be "As I increase the amount of time I spend on Science & Technology homework, my level of success on tests increases." Over a period of 10 weeks, you increase the number of hours you study by 2.5 h per week.

At the end of each week, you are given a test and record your results. At the end of 10 weeks your results have improved.

One conclusion that could be made from these results might read, "My hypothesis was correct. The results show that when I spend more time on Science & Technology homework, there is an increase in my test

Figure 1
Consider all the variables when you reach your conclusion.

scores because I understand the material better." There may be other possible hypotheses and conclusions that would explain these results. When reaching a conclusion, it is important to consider all the variables, e.g., your study methods, the environment in which you studied, and the time of day (**Figure 1**).

Reaching conclusions in Science & Technology investigations allows you to critically analyze results using a mix of logic, common sense, understanding, and patience.

 **Think Again**

Consider the variables that you would have had to control in order to conduct a sound investigation to test the effect of hours of study on test results. What possible hypotheses might you want to consider before settling on your final conclusion?

⑦F Reflecting on Your Work

It is always important to reflect on events in order to learn from them. This is one aspect of inquiry in science and technology that is sometimes neglected, especially with beginners. Once you have been through either the process of inquiry or design, it is always advantageous to step back and think about what you did. What went well? What were the challenges? What could be improved? What would you do differently if you were to go through the process again? It is through reflection that you will improve your work and increase your learning.

When reflecting back on the process of inquiry or design, be sure to identify the types of error that may have emerged. These sources of error should be identified in the conclusion or discussion of your results and be used as the basis for improving the process the next time. For example, let's say you completed an experiment and were able to conclude that plants did grow toward sunlight. What sources of experimental error could have occurred while performing this experiment? These could include such things as variations in air temperature, inconsistent exposure to light, or differences in soil composition. Be as specific as possible when stating experimental errors. It is not good enough to simply state: "It was due to human error." Reflection is equally important when evaluating the design process. For example, once you've developed the prototype for a new type of school chair, you need to think about what modifications or improvements you should make.

In the process of scientific inquiry, experimental errors decrease the validity of an experiment. But, more importantly, they allow you to revise your procedure. That revision will increase the reliability of the results the next time you perform the same investigation. Remember, experiments are a repeating process. By repeating the process, you are improving your ideas and investigative skills.

In any investigation, it is important to recognize that what may appear to be an error in one phase may ultimately turn out to be the means to improvement or innovation.

 If You Did It All Over…

Complete one of the tasks below:
- Think back to an argument you had with your parents or a friend. Now, reflect on the conflict from beginning to end. List all the things that you would do differently if you were ever in that situation again.
- Think back to a scientific experiment or technology project you have done in the past. Now, reflect on the work you did from beginning to end. List all the things that you would do differently to make it more reliable.
- Think back to a prototype you have built in the past and identify the modifications you would make in order to improve it.

8A Writing a Report

All investigators use a similar format to write reports, although the headings and order may vary slightly. Indeed, your report should reflect the process of scientific inquiry that you used in the investigation.

The Features of a Report

Cover Page: Make a cover page (**Figure 1**) that includes the following:
• the title of your investigation
• your name
• name of your partner(s) (if applicable)
• your instructor's name
• the due date

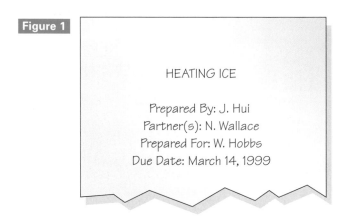

Figure 1

HEATING ICE

Prepared By: J. Hui
Partner(s): N. Wallace
Prepared For: W. Hobbs
Due Date: March 14, 1999

Title: At the beginning of your written report, write the title of your experiment.

Introduction: Always begin with a brief explanation of pertinent theory underlying the experiment. This includes the information you discovered by researching your topic. This section is also referred to as your "review of literature."

Purpose, Question, or Problem: Make a brief statement about your investigation. This can be written as a question.

Hypothesis: Write the hypothesis. Remember this is your "educated guess," based on your previous knowledge and the research you completed.

Materials: These include consumables (e.g., water, paper towels). Be specific about sizes and quantities. These also include non-consumables (e.g., test tube, beaker). Make a detailed list of the materials you used.

Diagram: Make a full-page diagram of the materials and equipment you used in the experiment (**Figure 2**). Remember to label and title the diagram. Your diagram can be placed at the end of your report, following the applications.

Figure 2

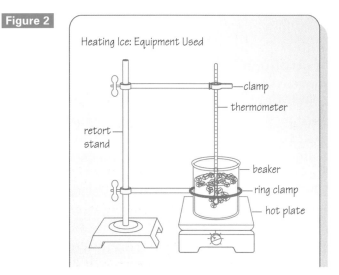

Heating Ice: Equipment Used

clamp
thermometer
retort stand
beaker
ring clamp
hot plate

Experimental Design: List the independent, dependent and controlled variables in your experiment and summarize the procedure.

Procedure: The most important part of an investigation, when others are trying to determine if it is "good" or "bad" science, is the procedure. To be sure that your work is judged fairly, make sure you leave nothing out! Remember to write this in numbered steps, past tense, and passive voice.

Observations/Results: Present your observations and results in a form that is easily understood. The data should be in tables, graphs, or illustrations, each with a title. Include any calculations that are used. The results of the calculations can be shown in a table.

Analysis/Conclusion: Summarize the investigation as you would if you were writing a book report. Refer back to your hypothesis. Was it correct, partially correct, or incorrect? Explain how you arrived at your conclusion(s). Justify your method and describe your results. Suggest a theory to support or interpret your results. If you were assigned questions with an investigation, you would answer them here. Discuss any sources of experimental error that may have affected your findings.

Applications: Describe how the new knowledge you gained from doing the investigation relates to your life and our society. It should answer the question, "Who cares?"

References/Bibliography: Give credit for the resources you used in your research. Always cite your source(s). Failing to do so is considered plagiarism (unacknowledged copying). It is unethical and illegal.

Citing Your Information Sources

Giving Credit for Material Used Within the Report

Whenever you give credit to an author (including yourself from previous reports!) for the use of graphs, tables, diagrams, or ideas, use the following technique:

Immediately after the information is used, give the last name of the source, the date of the publication, and the page reference. For example:

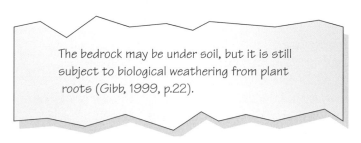

The bedrock may be under soil, but it is still subject to biological weathering from plant roots (Gibb, 1999, p.22).

Writing a Bibliography

The bibliography appears at the end of your report and includes the full reference for every source you cited within your report as well as any sources you used for general

reference, fact-checking, etc. It should be in alphabetical order of authors' last names. Be sure to use hanging paragraphs. The format for books, journals, web sites, newspapers, and CD-ROMs differ. To make sure you cite your sources correctly, refer to the following examples:

- **Information from a book:**

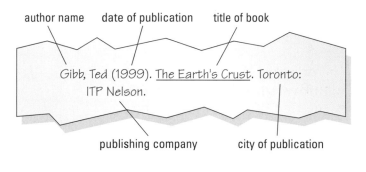

author name   date of publication   title of book

Gibb, Ted (1999). <u>The Earth's Crust</u>. Toronto: ITP Nelson.

publishing company   city of publication

- **Information from a journal or a magazine:**

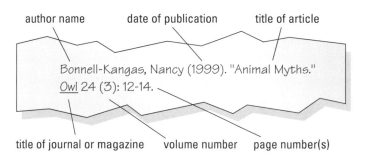

author name   date of publication   title of article

Bonnell-Kangas, Nancy (1999). "Animal Myths." <u>Owl</u> 24 (3): 12-14.

title of journal or magazine   volume number   page number(s)

- **Information from a newspaper:**

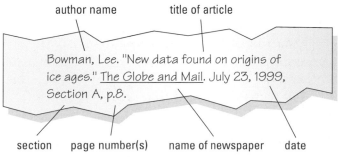

author name   title of article

Bowman, Lee. "New data found on origins of ice ages." <u>The Globe and Mail</u>. July 23, 1999, Section A, p.8.

section   page number(s)   name of newspaper   date

- **Information from a web site:**

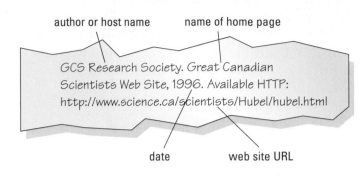

author or host name

name of home page

GCS Research Society. Great Canadian
Scientists Web Site, 1996. Available HTTP:
http://www.science.ca/scientists/Hubel/hubel.html

date

web site URL

- **Information from a CD-ROM:**

title of CD-ROM

Oxford English Dictionary Computer File: On
Compact Disc. 2nd ed. CD-ROM. Oxofrd. Oxford
UP, 1992.

year of publication

city of publication

Checklist for Writing a Report

Refer to this checklist whenever you are
required to write a scientific report.
✓ Cover page
✓ Title of the investigation
✓ Introduction
✓ Purpose/Question
✓ Hypothesis
✓ Materials
✓ Diagram
✓ Experimental Design
✓ Procedure
✓ Observations/Results
✓ Analysis /Conclusion
✓ Application
✓ References/Bibliography

Creating a Design Folder

It is a good idea to create a folder that communicates important information about your design. The end product (or process) will rarely speak for itself. You should be able to explain why your design is useful, what steps you took in the design process, and how well the prototype meets the needs for which it is designed. In fact, you should summarize all the steps you took in the process of design as outlined in ③Ⓐ "The Problem-Solving Cycle."

Features of a Design Folder

Cover Page: Create a cover page (**Figure 1**) that includes:
- name of the product or process you designed
- your name
- your partner(s) name (if applicable)
- the date the folder was completed

Figure 1

Wind Generating Systems

Prepared By: D. Fisher
Partner(s): M. Fong, B. Hedney, S. Taylor

May 28, 1999

Title: At the beginning of your folder, write the name of your product or process.

Problem: State your problem briefly and clearly and define any key terms.

Introduction: Provide background information on your problem. What was the context for your design? How did you assess the need that your design is intended to satisfy? If you conducted any interviews or surveys, summarize the results here. (Details can be placed in an appendix.) Summarize any research you did on existing products or processes that might meet your need, and explain if and how these were adapted to solve the problem you identified.

The Best Alternative: Explain how you chose the solution you did. List all the constraints, and explain and rate the design criteria. Itemize all the alternatives that you considered as possible solutions to the problem, and explain how you rated them. Include any useful charts or graphs. For instance, if you used the problem-solving matrix to choose the best alternative, include the results in this section (**Figure 2**).

Figure 2

Rating Scale: 0=Bad

Alternatives	Safety	Cost	Durability		Total
	0-10	0-9	0-8		
Solar Paneled Ceilings	6	2	3		11
Water Wheel	4	0	2		6
Windmills	8	6	6		20

Specifications spans the Safety / Cost / Durability columns.

Design Plan: Explain how your prototype was put together and how it is supposed to function. Include well-labelled sketches and drawings to support your explanation (see ⑥Ⓒ "Science & Technical Drawing" for samples.) Include a list of necessary materials and tools. If appropriate, include operating instructions.

Tests and Evaluation: Present the results of your prototype tests. Be sure that your tests measured the prototype against the specific design criteria you used. Use tables and graphs, and/or qualitative observations to illustrate your results. Write a brief paragraph evaluating how well the prototype met your design criteria—how well did it solve your problem?

Summary: From all of your experience and data, draw conclusions as appropriate. Be certain the conclusions are based on the data obtained from the construction of your prototype, the test results, and from a thorough literature survey. Describe what worked and what didn't. Indicate what could be improved if the prototype were rebuilt. Present evidence to support your conclusions.

References/Bibliography: In addition to citing various sources (see 8A "Writing a Report" for the correct format for citing sources of information), include a list of all the people who have made substantive contributions to your project.

Checklist for Creating a Design Folder

Refer to this checklist whenever you are required to create a design folder.
✓ Cover page
✓ Name of the product or process
✓ Introduction
✓ Problem
✓ The Best Alternative
✓ Design Plan
✓ Tests and Evaluation
✓ Summary
✓ References/Bibliography

8C Multimedia Presentations

Multimedia presentations provide a lot of scope for creativity. They allow you to use a combination of colour, computer graphics (even animation), sound and video clips to communicate information in an interesting, interactive way. When you read a book, for example, you tend to get information in a linear fashion, one page after another. When you interact with a multimedia presentation (e.g., web sites, computer games, CD-ROMs, kiosks) you have much more control over what information you see and when you see it.

There are a number of different software programs that can help you create effective multimedia presentations. There are specific skills you need to use specific programs. What you can create will depend on what hardware and software you have available to you, and how well you know how to use them (or how much time you have to learn!). There are some general tips you should bear in mind, no matter what kind of multimedia presentation you are creating.

General Tips

- Be sure to have a definite and well-articulated purpose. Be sure that you know who your audience will be.
- Start by considering your introduction (where you state your main goals) and your conclusion (where you restate your main goals).
- Create a flowchart for your presentation (**Figure 1**). Consider how your audience might want to make use of the information you are presenting, and provide logical links from one place to another.
- Consider the length of your presentation. Be clear and concise!

Figure 1

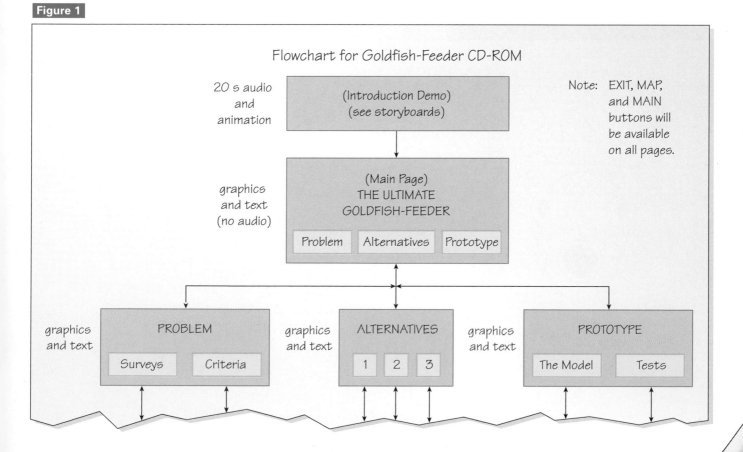

Flowchart for Goldfish-Feeder CD-ROM

20 s audio and animation — (Introduction Demo) (see storyboards)

Note: EXIT, MAP, and MAIN buttons will be available on all pages.

graphics and text (no audio) — (Main Page) THE ULTIMATE GOLDFISH-FEEDER — Problem | Alternatives | Prototype

graphics and text — PROBLEM — Surveys | Criteria

graphics and text — ALTERNATIVES — 1 | 2 | 3

graphics and text — PROTOTYPE — The Model | Tests

- Draw storyboards for your presentation (**Figure 2**). Be sure to consider all media: what are people going to see and hear at any given moment?
- Choose your audio-visual material carefully. Remember that the special effects you use should have a purpose. They should make your presentation more memorable and clarify any information you are presenting.

 **What Makes a Good Site?**

Search the Internet for three good web sites. Choose one and analyze the way the information is presented. What are the strengths? List three ways you would improve the site. Write an e-mail to the webmaster stating what you like about the site and how it could be improved. The next time you access the site, some of your suggestions may have been implemented!

Figure 2

Frame #: 1	Length of shot: 2 s
	Visual: Black
	Audio: no sound

Frame #: 2	Length of shot: 3 s
	Visual: Fade-in on front-view of goldfish. Bubbles coming from mouth. Mouth opening and closing. Background becoming lighter—turning a clear blue.
	Audio: Bubbling sound of fish tank.

8D Exploring an Issue

In *Nelson Science & Technology 7/8*, you will have opportunities to explore many issues. Advances in technology and science need to be evaluated from many different perspectives—particularly since these advances are being made at an ever-increasing rate.

Figure 1 shows a helpful way of organizing the advantages and disadvantages of a given issue related to technology or science.

Figure 1
Should you use an electric toothbrush?

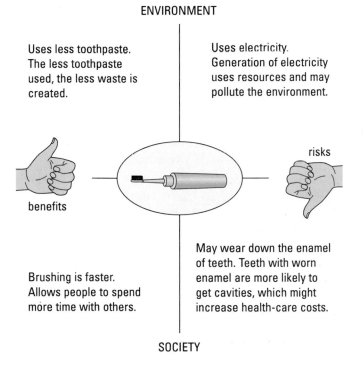

ENVIRONMENT

Uses less toothpaste. The less toothpaste used, the less waste is created.

Uses electricity. Generation of electricity uses resources and may pollute the environment.

benefits

risks

Brushing is faster. Allows people to spend more time with others.

May wear down the enamel of teeth. Teeth with worn enamel are more likely to get cavities, which might increase health-care costs.

SOCIETY

Toward an Educated Opinion

The following process will help you evaluate the advantages and disadvantages of an issue, and provide supporting evidence and arguments to the position you ultimately take on that issue.

1. Initial Research

Choose an issue that really interests you. Gather sources of information about it.

Consider all the sources of information available to you (see 4A "Research Skills").

2. Formulation of a Question

Put together a question around the issue. The question should be answerable, important to our society, and debatable. You are encouraged to try this question out on your classmates, teacher, and others.

3. Further Research

Continue your research on this topic. Find at least two additional sources of information on the issue. Be sure to scrutinize the credibility of your information. Remember PERCS (see 4A "Critical Thinking")!

4. Reaching Your Position

Answer your question. Explain your position thoroughly. Be sure to consider the following:
- Have you included information from at least three articles?
- Have you stated your position clearly?
- Have you shown why this issue is relevant and important to our society?
- Have you included at least two solid arguments (with solid evidence) backing up your position?
- Have you included at least two arguments against your position and shown their respective faults?
- Have you analyzed the strong points and weak points of each perspective?

5. Communicating Your Position

There are several ways of communicating your position, each with its own format:
- Write a brief essay.
- Participate in a formal debate.
- Participate in a role-play activity, taking on the role of a specific, affected party.
- Write a letter to the editor of a newspaper.

9A Setting Goals and Monitoring Progress

Think back to the time you spent in school last year. What classes did you do really well in? Why do you think you were successful? What classes did you have some difficulty with? Why do you think you had those troubles? What could you do differently this year that would help you do better than you did last year?

What you have just done is reflect on your past behaviour in an attempt to make positive change. The things that you want to accomplish today, this week, this year—throughout your life, for that matter—are called goals. Learning to set goals and planning toward their achievement takes skill and practice.

Setting Goals

- **Honestly assess your strengths and weaknesses.** Setting goals starts with reflection. Maybe you've noticed that you do better on projects and reports than you do on tests. Your strengths may include teamwork, independent research, and analysis. Your weaknesses may include inattention in class, anxiety or stress during tests, and poor note-taking skills.
- **Brainstorm a list of realistic goals that are important to you.** Don't set yourself up to fail by setting goals that you can't achieve, or that you don't care about. State your goals in relation to your expectations of yourself—not in comparison with the performance of others. For instance, "I will increase my test results by 10% by the end of the semester" is a better goal than "I'll have the highest test results in the class by the end of the semester."
- **Make sure your goals are measurable.** You will find it easier to keep trying to reach your goals if you can tell whether or not you are getting any closer to them. Again, "I will increase my test results by 10% by the end of the semester" is a better goal than "I'm going to do a lot better on my tests."

- **Discuss your goals with someone you trust.** Other people can often help you clarify your goals. People who know your strengths and weaknesses may think of possibilities you haven't considered. Sharing your goals with someone else is also a good way of enlisting outside support.

Planning Toward Your Goals

Once you have a list of realistic goals, you need to create a plan to achieve them. There are two essential components to your plan: actions and target dates.

Taking Action

The first thing to do is to make a list of actions that might help you reach your goals (**Figure 1**). If you've made an honest assessment of your strengths and weaknesses, you know what you have to work on to achieve your goals. If note-taking is one of your weaknesses, you could strengthen that skill by arranging to meet regularly with someone who could help you develop it. If

Figure 1

Goal: To increase my test results by 10% by the end of the semester

Possible actions:
- call Mark and Akim. Ask them if they want to start a study group for tests
- meet with Mrs. Rankin to ask how I could learn to take better notes
- increase the amount of time I study each evening by 30 minutes (NOTE: this will mean giving up something else! Must decide what!)
- reorganize my desk and bookshelf
- buy a day-timer
- schedule my homework time each day
- take Fridays off if I keep my schedule from Monday to Thursday

working in groups is one of your strengths, you could build on it by starting a study group to help you prepare for tests. The key is to identify what is preventing you from achieving your goal and to plan ways of overcoming those obstacles.

When you are making your list, include incentives and rewards. If overcoming obstacles starts feeling like a punishment, you won't work at it as long or as hard.

Making a Schedule

Your goal is a target. You need to know what you want to achieve, and you need to know how long it should take to achieve it. Once you've made a list of actions, you can assign dates to them. These dates provide short term targets that, if you hit them, will make it easier to hit your overall target.

Work backwards from your ultimate target date. For instance, if you hope to achieve a 10% increase in test results by the end of the semester, how much time have you got? How many tests are scheduled between now and then? What can you achieve before the first test? What more can you achieve before the second test?

Go back to your list of actions and write in a date beside each one. Stay flexible. Your plan will evolve as you put it into action. Often, your plan relies on other people and will change depending on their schedule. A working schedule is represented in **Figure 2**.

Once you've roughed out a schedule that looks manageable, transfer the actions from your list onto a calendar. Keep your calendar in a prominent place in your study area, and make it a habit to refer to it on a daily basis.

Monitoring Progress

When you reach your ultimate target date, you have to be able to assess whether or not you've achieved your goal. It is also important to measure your progress along the way. The more detailed and specific your plan is, the easier this will be. In fact, your plan should include regular monitoring. You might decide to review your progress at the end of every week, for instance. How many of the things that you scheduled did you actually do? For example, did you have any tests that week? If so, did your results show an increase?

The results of this monitoring may be a change in plan. For example, maybe the study group idea isn't working very well, and you're spending more time talking than studying. It's always possible to change your plan.

Don't be too hard on yourself when you review your progress. If you missed some small targets, put it behind you and keep moving forward. Adjust your goal if you have to, but don't give up.

Figure 2

Sept. 19:	Organize study space
Sept. 20:	Meet with Mrs. Rankin: 3:55 p.m.
	Buy day-timer
Sept. 22:	First study group (plan to meet every Wednesday)
Sept. 23:	Science & Technology Study: 4:15-5:15 (same time every Mon., Tues., Thurs.)
Sept. 24:	TEST: 11:00 a.m.
	Meet Sara at Mike's: 4:10 p.m. (if goals met during the week)

 Your Goals

On a piece of paper, write three personal goals that you would like to accomplish by the end of the term or semester. Identify ways in which you will try to reach each of these goals. State how you will celebrate when you reach your goals.

9B Good Study Habits

Understanding anything—whether it is a life-saving technique in the swimming pool, a trumpet solo, or a Science & Technology lesson—is an active process. Studying takes on many forms. It involves learning and understanding material. Developing the following study skills can help you in your learning. You can modify these tips to help you in other school courses and in recreational activities.

Your Study Space

- **Organize your working area.** The place where you study at home and at school should be tidy and organized. Papers, books, magazines, or pictures that are strewn all over your working area will distract you from focusing on the work at hand.
- **Maintain a quiet study space.** Make sure that the place where you study is removed from distractions such as the phone, stereo system, TV, friends, and brothers and sisters. Popular study spaces include the school library, the public library, and your bedroom at home (if it has a working area). Any quiet place where you can be productive will work.
- **Make sure you feel comfortable in your study space.** You will be the most productive and study effectively if you are working in an area where you feel at ease—personalize your space.
- **Be prepared with all the materials you will need.** It is important that you have all your notebooks, textbooks, computer equipment, paper, pencil, pen, ruler, dictionary, thesaurus, and anything else you use for your work in your study space. If you have to continually get up to find a book or eraser, you won't be able to accomplish as much as you had hoped.

Study Habits

- **Prepare for class by reading material ahead of time.** It is also helpful to read or view materials from other sources, such as science magazines, newspapers, the Internet, and television programs.
- **Take notes.** To make note-taking easier, you may want to make up a shorthand method of recording ideas.
- **Review any notes you made in class the same day and add comments.** Then have a friend or relative quiz you on the material in the notes. Reinforce your understanding by answering the questions in the textbook—even if they are not assigned.
- **Use your notes and the textbook to prepare summaries.** Studying is most effective with a pen or pencil or your word processor, so you can write down the important ideas (**Figure 1**). You may want to write or type study cards to assist in making effective, point-form summaries of your notes. Look at the example in **Figure 2**. Notice there is a title at the top and all the information has been condensed into a point-form, easy-to-learn format. It's much more effective than learning material that is in paragraph form. Condense, condense, and condense!

Figure 1

- **Use graphic organizers to help you summarize a unit, or lesson.** (see **9E** "Graphic Organizers"). You may want to use unit summaries in the student resources.
- **"Practice makes perfect."** This is as true for Science & Technology as it is for playing piano and shooting baskets. If you practise your study skills until they become almost automatic, you will have more time to think about how you will use them.
- **Schedule your study time.** This will help you avoid that most ineffective of all study methods, "cramming" before assignments and tests. Use a daily planner and take it with you to every class. Write all homework assignments, tests, projects, and extra-curricular commitments in it. This will assist you in organizing a daily "To Do" list that will ensure maximum use of your time.
- **Know your strengths and your weaknesses.** Take advantage of all opportunities to get help with areas in which you may have trouble. Use your strengths to help yourself and others. Form a study group and have regular meetings. You may be able to help others in some parts of the course. In turn, you may receive help from them.
- **Teach the material you have learned to someone who has not yet learned it.** Their questions will help you see what areas of the subject you need to learn more about and what areas you don't completely understand (**Figure 3**).

- **Take study breaks.** It is important that you set study goals and take a short study break after meeting each of the goals you set. For example, you could decide that you will take a study break after crossing two items off your "To Do" list. Taking study breaks will help you rejuvenate for the next tasks on your list and will assist you in completing all your work effectively and accurately.

Study Checklist

✓ Organize your study environment. (Is it quiet? Comfortable? Organized?)
✓ Read material ahead of time.
✓ Take notes.
✓ Review.
✓ Summarize. (Make study cards, if that technique works for you.)
✓ Use graphic organizers.
✓ Practise.
✓ Schedule study time. (Use your daily planner and make a "To Do" list.)
✓ Know your strengths and weaknesses.
✓ Teach what you have learned.

Try This Making Study Cards

Condense the information in this section of the *Skills Handbook* (**9B**) onto study cards. Remember to put a title at the top of each study card and make point form notes.

Figure 2
A study card

The Visible Spectrum

White Light = Roy G. Biv
- red
- orange
- yellow
- green
- blue
- indigo
- violet

Figure 3

9C Using Your Computer Effectively

Computers are becoming more and more common in your learning. Most students have access to this technology at some point every week. Like your notebook, it is important to keep your computer files organized. It is also necessary to use your computer effectively—there is a time for computer work and a time for computer games and recreational surfing of the Internet. The following hints can assist you in using your computer effectively in your learning. Remember these hints can be modified to suit your needs.

General Computer Hints

- **Create a folder for all your science and technology work.** It is important that any computer work you do is kept in one folder. Otherwise, your work could be saved in lots of different locations on your computer and this means that it could become easily misplaced or even lost.
- **Organize your science and technology units in your folder.** Now that you have created a science and technology folder, organize this folder into the various units that you will

study this year. Refer to **Figure 1** for a detailed glimpse of what your folders might look like.

- **Think carefully about what to name each of your documents.** Make sure that the names you give will allow you to easily identify what a particular document contains. Work that is called *Science & Technology 1*, for instance, provides no indication of what the work actually is. Be as specific as possible.
- **Back up your work.** Always make an extra copy of any work you do on the computer. Copy your work onto a disk or onto your school network. Too often students lose their work because they do not take the time to do this. It's much easier than having to complete a report or assignment all over again.
- **Maintain correct posture and form.** It is important that you don't sit too close to the screen and that you sit in an upright position with your hands formed correctly while typing. Incorrect hand positioning can eventually cause carpal tunnel syndrome. The study of how people interact effectively and safely with computers is a part of what is termed "ergonomics."

Figure 1

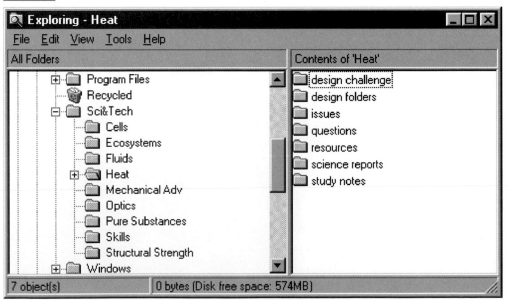

Using Spreadsheets and Databases

The computer is a powerful tool for storing, organizing, and analyzing data. Using databases and spreadsheets, you can record observations from science experiments or information acquired during the design process. You can use these software programs to sort information in different ways and to discover important relationships among variables. You can also use this software to create graphs and charts. The best way to get an overview of how spreadsheets and databases work is to explore different programs by using their built-in tutorials.

Spreadsheets

You can think of a spreadsheet as an electronic data table. To be as useful as possible, it has to be well designed. When you create any kind of data table, you should start by thinking carefully about what information you need to record, and how you will ultimately use that information.

In scientific inquiry, your spreadsheet will often be built on the variables you are using. If you are observing the viscosity of different fluids, your variables are the kind of fluid and the amount of time it takes for an object (e.g., a marble) to fall to the bottom of the receptacle containing that fluid (see **Figure 2**).

Your spreadsheet, like any data table, should have a title. The rows and columns of your spreadsheet should be well-labelled. Specific data is entered where a given row and column intersect. This space, which you can identify by referencing the number of the row and the letter of the column, is known as a cell. Some information you will enter yourself as numbers or text. In other cells, however, you will enter a formula that tells the program to perform a mathematical function using data in other cells. For instance, in **Figure 2**, you do not type in the numerical averages—the program does this for you based on the formula you have entered. To find out what formula is required, simply use the help function of the program you are using.

As you change or add data, the results of the calculations will change. The information in your spreadsheet will also be available as graphs—and these are also automatically updated as data is changed (**Figure 3**.)

Figure 3

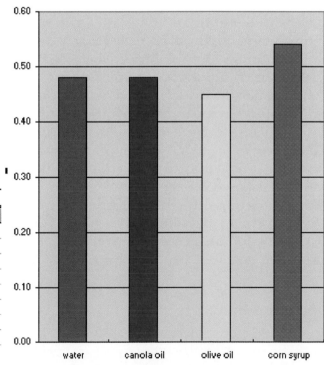

Time taken for marble to fall through the liquid (s)

Figure 2

E7	▼	=SUM(B7:D7)/3		
	A	**B**	**C**	**D**	**E**
1	Viscosity of Various Liquids				
2		Time taken for marble to fall through the liquid			
3	Liquid	Trial #1	Trail #2	Trial #3	Average
4	water	0.48	0.48	0.47	0.48
5	canola oil	0.57	0.56	0.54	0.56
6	olive oil	0.45	0.42	0.47	0.45
7	corn syrup	0.52	0.54	0.55	0.54
8					

Databases

A database is another powerful tool for managing data. A good database will help you find specific information with ease, see relationships between different pieces of information, chart trends, create graphs, charts and reports, etc. Again, however, you have to spend some time designing this tool for your specific needs. A database can only give you what you need if you have designed it well.

First, you will need to become familiar with the power and uses of a database. The tutorials that are packaged with database software are good places to start. In general, a database is organized into records and fields. You can think of a record as an index card that lists all the information you need about a specific thing, person, or process. For instance, if you have conducted a survey about public reaction to the use of CFCs, each record would contain the information provided by one respondent.

Each record in a database is set up in the same way. The structure of each record is a "form" (**Figure 4**). You fill in the form with information you have gathered. Each piece of information is entered into a "field." Like spreadsheets, these fields have specific "electronic addresses." In fact, you can view information in a database as a list (**Figure 5**).

You can use the database for sophisticated analysis of your results. For instance, you can look for trends in responses to certain survey questions based on age, region, gender, etc. You can also use the data for other purposes (e.g., to create a mailing list). And, of course, you can generate accurate graphs and charts from the data.

Try This Use a Database

Complete the tutorial for a popular database program. Now think of one project that you are working on now, or have recently completed, that would be enhanced by using a database. Design a form for that project.

Figure 4

A form designed for aircraft parts inventory

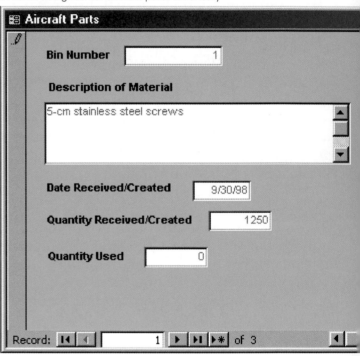

Figure 5

Inventory database in list view, showing 3 records

	Bin Number	Description of Material	Date Received	Quantity Received	Quantity Used
	1	5-cm stainless steel screws	9/30/98	1250	0
	2	5-cm stainless steel nuts	9/30/98	1250	0
	3	wheels	11/15/98	12	0

9D Working Together

Technological and scientific progress is almost always made by teams of people working together. Scientists share ideas, help each other design experiments and studies, and sharpen each other's conclusions. Technologists most frequently work in interdisciplinary teams, in which each person brings different expertise to the problem-solving process. We have all worked in a group at one time or another. In the "real world," group work is necessary and usually more productive than working alone. It is therefore important for us to be able to work in teams.

 **The Barge Contest**

Your group will compete against other design groups to create the barge capable of carrying the greatest number of marbles.

To solve this problem, you will build a model. Models are used as small-scale tests for larger, more expensive future experiments. Cheap models also allow a trial-and-error approach that would be far too expensive for full-scale tests.

Figure 1

Materials
- water
- large bucket
- marbles
- 250 g of modelling clay

Procedure

1. Working with all the members of your group, create a diagram for the barge's design. Everyone in the group must agree on this design (**Figure 1**).

2. Build your barge using only the modelling clay you have been given.

3. Fill the bucket with water and place your barge on the surface of the water.

4. Add marbles to your barge, until it begins to sink (**Figure 2**).

5. Record the maximum number of marbles that could be added.

6. Evaluate your teamwork.

Figure 2

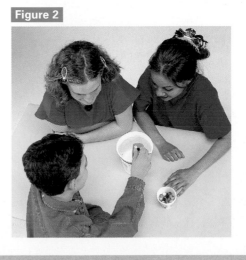

Teamwork Tips

While working with *Nelson Science & Technology 7/8*, you will spend much of your time working in teams. Whenever you do, it is useful to take the following tips into account:

- Encourage all members to contribute to the work of the group.
- Respect everyone's contributions. There are many points of view and all perspectives should be considered. Keep an open mind.
- Be prepared to compromise.
- Share the work fairly.
- Keep focused on the task at hand. Divide the various tasks between all group members.
- Support the team's final decision.
- When you are given the opportunity of picking your own team, be sure that the students you decide to work with complement your strengths and weaknesses.

Can you think of any more tips that should be considered during group work?

Evaluating Teamwork

After you've completed a task with your team, evaluate the team's effectiveness—the strengths, weaknesses, opportunities, and challenges. Answer the following questions:

1. What were the strengths of your teamwork?

2. What were the weaknesses of your teamwork?

3. What opportunities were provided by working with your team?

4. What possible challenges did you see with respect to your teamwork?

⑨ᴱ Graphic Organizers

When you are trying to describe objects and events, it is sometimes helpful to write your ideas down so that you can see them and compare them with those of other people. Instead of writing these ideas down in sentences, they can often be represented visually. There are a number of ways of organizing information graphically that may help you express concepts and relationships.

Concept Maps

A concept map is a collection of words (representing concepts) or pictures that you connect to each other with arrows and short descriptions. The map is a drawing of what is happening in your brain.

You may have seen concept maps similar to the one in **Figure 1**. This concept map, called a food web, shows one way of thinking about animals and what they eat. The arrowhead points to the animal that eats the animal or plant at the other end of the arrow. The

arrows describe the relationship between the organisms.

Concept maps can also be drawn of other topics and in other ways. For instance, the relationships between family members can be drawn using a concept map like the one in **Figure 2**.

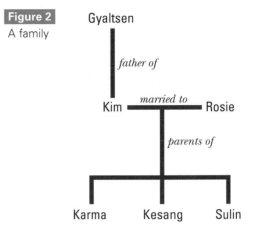

Figure 2
A family

Gyaltsen
father of
Kim — *married to* — Rosie
parents of
Karma   Kesang   Sulin

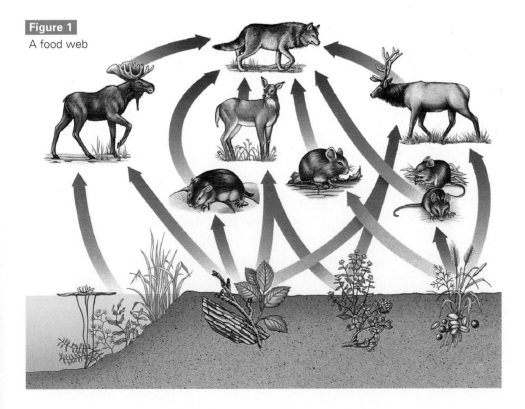

Figure 1
A food web

Concept maps can also be drawn to show a series of cause-and-effect relationships (**Figure 3**). You may find making this kind of map useful during the processes of scientific inquiry and design.

Sometimes concept maps can be used to show how your ideas change and become more complex as you work on a topic. You can see an example of this type of concept map in **Figure 4**.

Figure 3
Causes and effects related to plant growth

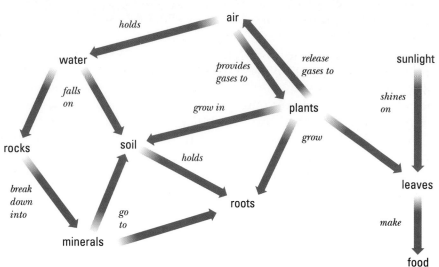

Figure 4
Concept maps evolve as your ideas evolve

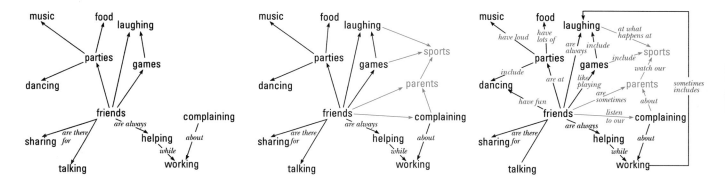

Making a Concept Map

Here are some steps you can take to help you make a concept map.

1. Choose the central idea of your concept map.

2. Write the central idea and all related ideas on small scraps of paper.

3. Move the scraps of paper around the central idea so that the ones most related to each other are close to each other. Ask yourself how they are related, and then use that information in the next steps.

4. On a big sheet of paper, write down all of your ideas in the same pattern that you have arranged the scraps. Draw arrows between the ideas that are related.

5. On each arrow, write a short description of how the terms are related to each other.

As you go, you may find other ideas or relationships. Add them to the map. When you gain new ideas—whether from research, from your investigations, or from other people—go ahead and change your concept map. You may want to add new ideas in a different colour of ink, to indicate your new ways of thinking about the ideas.

Comparison Matrix

It is often useful to use a comparison matrix to compare things according to a variety of criteria (**Table 1**). For instance, you might want to compare the properties of different materials in order to choose the best one for a particular design.

Venn Diagram

Another simple diagram used for comparing and contrasting things is the Venn diagram (**Figure 5**). Similarities between two items are written in the area of overlap; differences are written in the separate circles.

Hierarchical (Branching) Diagram

Some concepts can be broken down into subcategories. A hierarchical diagram is a useful way of representing these relationships (**Figure 6**).

Table 1	The Heating Curve of Water			
	Properties			
	Malleable	**Lustrous**	**Strong**	**Affordable**
Gold	X	X		
Silver	X	X	X	
Copper	X	X	X	X

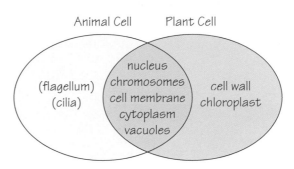

Figure 5

Comparing Plant and Animal Cells

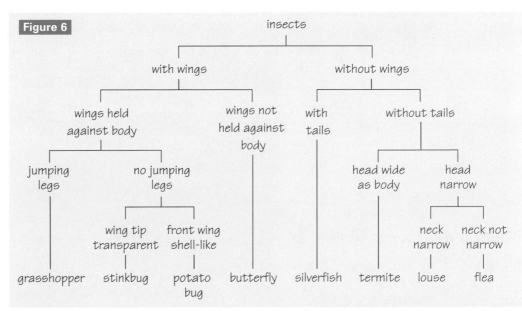

Figure 6

Target Diagram

A target diagram is often used to illustrate which item best applies to a given criterion. (**Figure 7**).

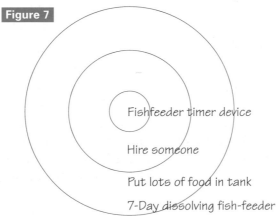

Figure 7

Fishfeeder timer device

Hire someone

Put lots of food in tank

7-Day dissolving fish-feeder

Photo Credits

Cover: J. McGrail/First Light.

Table of Contents: p. 5 Images B.C./T. W. Image Network; p. 6 CORBIS/Jeffrey L. Rotman; p. 7 Visuals Unlimited/Glenn M. Oliver.

Unit 1: Cells

Unit Opener (pp. 10–11): Prof. P. Motta/Dept. of Anatomy/University *La Sapienza*, Rome/Science Photo Library; p. 12 Corel, inset Thomas Kitchin/First Light; p. 14 top Professor P. Motta/Science Photo Library, bottom Professor P. Motta and S. Correr/Science Photo Library; p. 15 CORBIS/David Muench; p. 16 clockwise from top right Visuals Unlimited/Science VU, Visuals Unlimited/Glenn M. Oliver, Visuals Unlimited/R. Lindholm, Visuals Unlimited/G. Murti, Visuals Unlimited/M. F. Brown; p. 17 top Visuals Unlimited/Tim Hauf, middle Visuals Unlimited/Bruce Berg, bottom Visuals Unlimited/L. Bassett; pp. 18–19 Dave Starrett; p. 22 left and centre Dave Starrett, right Visuals Unlimited/John D. Cunningham; p. 23 top Dave Starrett, top inset Visuals Unlimited/Martha Powell, bottom inset Visuals Unlimited/D. M. Phillips, middle Dave Starrett; p. 24 top Utrechts Universiteits Museum, top inset Harold V. Green/VALAN PHOTOS, bottom CORBIS/Dave Reid, bottom inset D. P. Wilson/Photo Researchers; p. 25 top Visuals Unlimited/Stanley Flegler, top inset Dr. Ann Smith/Science Photo Library, bottom Visuals Unlimited/SIU, bottom inset Visuals Unlimited/R. Kessel, C. Y. Shih; p. 26 top Visuals Unlimited/D. W. Fawcett, bottom Visuals Unlimited/R. Bolender, D. Fawcett; p. 27 top Visuals Unlimited/Don W. Fawcett, bottom Visuals Unlimited/K. G. Murti; p. 28 Jeremy Jones; p. 30 Jeremy Jones; p. 31 Chuck Savage/First Light; p. 32 Leonard Lessin; p. 34 Dave Starrett; p. 35 top Visuals Unlimited/Jeff Greenberg, middle pair Dave Starrett; p. 37 Visuals Unlimited/Doug Sobell; p. 38 top courtesy of Dr. Thomas Chang, middle pair Corel, bottom PhotoDisc; p. 39 Corel; p. 42 top Visuals Unlimited/SIU, middle Visuals Unlimited/Gary Carter; p. 43 Jan Hinsch/Science Photo Library; p. 45 Visuals Unlimited/John D. Cunningham; pp. 52–53 Dave Starrett; p. 55 Ken Edward/Science Source/Photo Researchers; p. 56 Visuals Unlimited/John Gerlach; p. 57 CORBIS/Lester V. Bergman; p. 64 CORBIS/Stuart Westmorland; p. 66 Dave Starrett; pp. 70–71 Dave Starrett; p. 73 Visuals Unlimited/Jackson Lab; p. 74 top Alex Bartel/Science Photo Library, bottom PhotoDisc; p. 75 (both) Dr. P. Marazzi/Science Photo Library; p. 76 Visuals Unlimited/Bruce Berg; p. 79 clockwise from top left Carolina Biological Supply Co., CORBIS/Science Pictures Limited, CORBIS/Lester V. Bergman, (next two) CORBIS/Science Pictures Limited, CORBIS/Lester V. Bergman.

Unit 2: Fluids

Unit Opener (pp. 82–83): B. Fraunfelter/First Light; p. 84 left V. Wilkinson/VALAN PHOTOS, right Images B.C./T. W. Image Network; p. 85 top CORBIS/Christine Osborne; p. 86 top William H. Mullins/Photo Researchers, top inset Dan Guravich/Photo Researchers, bottom CORBIS/Jennie Woodcock/Reflections Photolibrary, bottom inset courtesy Dutchmaster Nurseries (www.dutchmasternurseries.com); p. 87 Images B.C./T. W. Image Network; p. 88 CORBIS/Henry Diltz; p. 89 CORBIS/Joel W. Rogers; p. 90 Tim Davis/Photo Researchers; p. 91 CORBIS, inset CORBIS/Roger Ressmeyer; pp. 92–94 Dave Starrett; p. 95 top Mark Williams/Tony Stone Images, bottom Dave Starrett; p. 96 top courtesy of Randy Droniuk, bottom CORBIS/Richard T. Nowitz; p. 97 courtesy Randy Droniuk; pp. 100–101 Dave Starrett; p. 102 F. Frances/Photo Researchers; p. 103 Visuals Unlimited/Mark. E. Gibson; p. 104 Dave Starrett; p. 105 PhotoDisc; p. 107 top CORBIS/Ralph A. Clevinger, bottom CORBIS/The Mariners' Museum, box Jeremy Jones; p. 108 top Larry Wells/T. W. Image Network, bottom Dave Starrett; p. 109 CORBIS; p. 110 top PhotoDisc, top inset courtesy Seaco Marine Dock Systems, bottom courtesy Nora Alexander; p. 111 Y. R. Tymstra/VALAN PHOTOS; p. 112 Dave Starrett; p. 113 top CORBIS/Richard Hamilton Smith, bottom Dave Starrett; p. 116 Michigan Deptartment of the Environment; p. 117 Peter Yates/Science Photo Library; p. 119 Peter Skinner/Photo Researchers; p. 120 top Cornelius Van Ewyk, bottom Boily; p. 121 left Canadian Press CP/Andrew Vaughan, right Cornelius Van Ewyk; pp. 122–123 Dave Starrett; p. 124 PhotoDisc; p. 125 CORBIS/Catherine Karnow; p. 128 CORBIS/Jonathan Blair; pp. 129–130 Dave Starrett; p. 131 top left PhotoDisc, bottom left COMSTOCK, top right CORBIS/Christian Sarramon; p. 132 left K. Cooke/VALAN PHOTOS, top right Bill Aaron/Photo Researchers, bottom right CORBIS/Bob Krist; p. 133 top James King-Holmes/SPL/Photo Researchers, Inc., bottom (illustration) courtesy of the Toronto Transit Commission; p. 134 top CORBIS/Amos Nachoum, bottom (stamp) courtesy Canada Post; p. 135 top Canadian Press SSM/Keith Stephen, bottom CORBIS/Robert Pickett; p. 136 left Larry Wells/T. W. Image Network, top right CORBIS/Roger Ressmeyer, bottom right CORBIS/Christian Sarramon; p. 137 top and bottom left Dave Starrett, bottom right K. Cooke/VALAN PHOTOS; p. 140 Visuals Unlimited/Michael Gabridge; p. 141 top left

PhotoDisc, top right V. Wilkinson/VALAN PHOTOS, bottom right V. Wilkinson/VALAN PHOTOS.

Unit 3: Mechanical Advantage and Efficiency
Unit Opener (pp. 142–143): Alan Marsh/First Light; p. 144 left (main and inset) CORBIS/Sandy Felsenthal, right CORBIS/Kevin R. Morris; p. 145 CORBIS/BB Pictures/Eye Ubiquitous; p. 146 left CORBIS/Roger Ressmeyer, top right CORBIS/Neil Rabinowitz, bottom right Joyce Photographics/VALAN PHOTOS; p. 147 CORBIS/Michael S. Yamashita, inset CORBIS/Kevin Fleming; p. 148 Dave Starrett; p. 149 Archive Photos; p. 152 CORBIS/Franck Seguin/TempSport; p. 154 Dave Starrett; p. 155 top PhotoDisc, bottom Visuals Unlimited/Robert Clay; p. 156 top CORBIS/Jeffrey L. Rotman, bottom CORBIS/Roger Ressmeyer; p. 157 CORBIS/Ed Eckstein; p. 162 CORBIS/Charles O'Rear; p. 163 CORBIS/Charles E. Rotkin; p. 164 top Andrew Syred/Science Photo Library, bottom CORBIS/Geoffrey Taunton/Cordaiy Photo Library; p. 168 Dave Starrett; pp. 170–171 courtesy Kim Parker and Maureen de Sousa; p. 172 Dave Starrett; p. 173 (main and inset) CORBIS/Kevin R. Morris; p. 174 Dave Starrett; p. 175 CORBIS/Mark Gibson; pp. 176–177 Kennon Cooke/VALAN PHOTOS; p. 178 Dave Starrett; p. 179 top PhotoDisc, bottom pair Dave Starrett; p. 181 CORBIS/George Hall; p. 182 Dave Starrett; p. 183 CORBIS/Owen Franken; p. 184 D. Young Wolff/Photo Edit; p. 186 top Dave Starrett, bottom PhotoDisc; p. 187 top Carol Glegg, bottom John Fowler/VALAN PHOTOS; pp. 188–189 top CORBIS/Karl Weatherly, bottom Corel; p. 190 top Visuals Unlimited/Bernd Wittich, bottom CORBIS/James L. Amos; p. 191 top John Fowler/VALAN PHOTOS, bottom CORBIS/Tony Arruza; p. 192 Richard Laird/FPG; p. 194 left CORBIS/Jim Winkley, Ecoscene, right Harold V. Green/VALAN PHOTOS; p. 195 John Fowler/VALAN PHOTOS; p. 196 CORBIS/Charles O'Rear; p. 197 top left PhotoDisc, bottom left CORBIS/Tony Arruza, top right Dave Starrett, bottom right CORBIS/Roger Ressmeyer; p. 198 Jeremy Jones; p. 200 top and middle Corel, bottom CORBIS/Kevin Fleming; p. 201 Corel.

Unit 4: Water Systems
Unti Opener: (pp. 202–203): Joseph Van Os/The Image Bank; p. 204 left Visuals Unlimited/Edward Hodgson, right Visuals Unlimited/C. McCutcheon; p. 205 CORBIS/Jay & Becky Dickman; p. 206 left NASA/Oxford Scientific Films, top right PhotoDisc, bottom right CORBIS/Charles E. Rotkin; p. 207 Johnny Johnson/VALAN PHOTOS; p. 208 NASA; p. 209 left Francis Lepine/VALAN PHOTOS, right CORBIS/Yann Arthur-Bertrand; pp. 210–211 Dave Starrett; p. 214 CORBIS/Natalie Fobes; p. 215 Harold V. Green/VALAN PHOTOS; p. 217 Dave Starrett; p. 218 top Visuals Unlimited/Marty Snyderman, bottom CORBIS/Sergio Dorantes; p. 219 Pam E. Hickman/VALAN PHOTOS; p. 222 courtesy of Hazel

Breton; p. 223 © Doug Dealey; p. 225 left Michel Julien/VALAN PHOTOS, right Ian Davis Young/VALAN PHOTOS; p. 226 top Visuals Unlimited/Roy David Farris, bottom Visuals Unlimited/Glenn M. Oliver; p. 228 Deborah Vanslet/VALAN PHOTOS; p. 229 top Stephan J. Kraseman/VALAN PHOTOS, right inset CORBIS/Jonathan Blair; p. 230 Dave Starrett; p. 231 top Visuals Unlimited/Charles Preitner, middle Visuals Unlimited/Mark E. Gibson, bottom Dave Starrett; p. 232 Dave Starrett; p. 237 CORBIS/Robert Holmes; p. 238 Dave Starrett; p. 239 V. Wilkinson/VALAN PHOTOS; p. 240 top Visuals Unlimited/Neville Coleman, middle & bottom CORBIS/Ralph White; p. 241 top courtesy of Graham Standen, Geoforce Consultants Ltd., Dartmouth, Nova Scotia, bottom NASA/Oxford Scientific Films; p. 242 top right National Archives of Canada/C-12101, bottom right Greg Locke/Stray Light Pictures, St. John's, NFLD; p. 243 left Visuals Unlimited/John Lough, right Visuals Unlimited/API; p. 244 Visuals Unlimited/Science VU; p. 248 Dave Starrett; p. 249 top Francis Lepine/VALAN PHOTOS, bottom Harold V. Green/VALAN PHOTOS; p. 250 top CORBIS/Lester V. Bergman, bottom CORBIS/Douglas P. Wilson, Frank Lane Picture Agency; p. 251 top Visuals Unlimited/Martin G. Miller, bottom pair Dave Starrett; p. 252 middle Visuals Unlimited/Inga Spence, bottom CORBIS/Gunter Marx; p. 254 left Wayne Shiels/VALAN PHOTOS, right Visuals Unlimited/Joel Arrington; p. 255 CORBIS/Natalie Fobes; p. 256 left Visuals Unlimited/Roy David Farris, top right Visuals Unlimited/Edward Hodgson, bottom right V. Wilkinson/VALAN PHOTOS; p. 257 left CORBIS/Lester V. Bergman, top right CORBIS/Ralph White, middle right Greg Locke/Stray Light Pictures, St. John's, NFLD., bottom right CORBIS/Sergio Dorantes; p. 258 Corel.

Unit 5: Optics
Unit Opener (pp. 262–263): Telegraph Colour Library/FPG International; p. 264 top Pekka Parviainen/Science Photo Library, bottom CORBIS/W. Cody; p. 265 courtesy Alan J. Hirsch; p. 266 top CORBIS/Layne Kennedy, bottom CORBIS/Gunter Marx; p. 267 Dave Starrett; p. 269 top centre Gerald Brimacombe/The Image Bank, top right CORBIS/Philip Gould, bottom Kalus Guldbrandsen/Science Photo Library; p. 270 Joe Azzara/The Image Bank; p. 271 Visuals Unlimited/Ken Lucas; pp. 272–274 Dave Starrett; p. 275 left Val Whelan/VALAN PHOTOS, right Joyce Photographics; pp. 278–279 Dave Starrett; p. 280 CORBIS/John McAnulty; p. 281 J. L. Peleaz/First Light; pp. 282–284 Dave Starrett; p. 285 top CORBIS/Michael S. Yamashita, middle courtesy Belmont Equipment Corp., bottom Dave Starrett; p. 287 T. W. Image Network/Omni Photo Communications Inc.; pp. 289–290 Dave Starrett; p. 293 CORBIS/Larry Lee;

pp.296–297 Visuals Unlimited/Steve McCutcheon; p. 300 Visuals Unlimited/Jay Pasachoff; p. 301 top CORBIS/AFP, middle (both) courtesy of Gemini North, bottom CORBIS/NASA/Roger Ressmeyer; p. 302 Dave Starrett; p. 303 T. Svensson/First Light; p. 306 Courtesy of Brad Dickson; p. 309 Kharen Hill/T. W. Image Network; p. 312 left John Cancalosi/VALAN PHOTOS, right CORBIS/Chinch Gryniewicz, Ecoscene; p. 314 left Francois Morneau/VALAN PHOTOS; right Photo Edit/Myrleen Ferguson; p. 315 PhotoDisc; p. 316 top Kalus Guldbarndsen/Science Photo Library, bottom left CORBIS/Larry Lee, bottom right Dave Starrett; p. 317 top left Dave Starrett, top right CORBIS/Philip Gould, middle courtesy of Gemini North; bottom CORBIS/Chinch Gryniewicz; p. 320 Andrew Farquhar/VALAN PHOTOS; p. 321 CORBIS/Adam Woolfitt.

Skills Handbook
Unit Opener (pp. 322–323): collage of (clockwise from top left) Corel, Alan Marsh/First Light, Visuals Unlimited/Derrick Ditchburn, B. Fraunfelter/First Light; p. 325 top Ian Crysler, bottom Dave Starrett; pp. 326–328 Dave Starrett; p. 329 Paul Till; p. 332 Dave Starrett; pp. 333–336 Ian Crysler; pp. 337–339 Dave Starrett; p. 340 PhotoDisc; p. 342 Visuals Unlimited/Jeff Greenberg; p. 343 CORBIS/Richard T. Nowitz; p. 344 Dave Starrett; p. 346 Dave Starrett; p. 350 top to bottom PhotoDisc, Todd Ryoji, Dick Hemingway, Omni Photo Communications Inc./T. W. Image Network; p. 352 Dave Starrett; pp. 354–355 Dave Starrett; p. 357 Dave Starrett; p. 360 top Visuals Unlimited/Richard L. Carlton, rest Boréal; p. 361 top left Ian Crysler, bottom right Boréal; p. 369 Dave Starrett; p. 372 top left CORBIS/Rodney Hyett/Elizabeth Whiting & Associates, top right R. W. Jones/First Light, middle right (b) Bob Semple, (c) First Light, bottom right Rom Watts/First Light; p. 373 top left Visuals Unlimited/R. Lindholm, middle left Joe Lepiano/Artbase, bottom left Dave Starrett, top right Dave Starrett, bottom right Andrea Pistolesi/The Image Bank; p. 374 top left Dave Starrett, bottom left Gary Russ/The Image Bank; p. 377 left Dave Starrett, top right Joe Lepiano/Artbase, middle right Dave Starrett, bottom right Chuck Savage/First Light; p. 378 Paul Till; pp. 393–395 Dave Starrett; pp. 406–407 Dave Starrett; p. 411 Ian Crysler.

Glossary

A

acid precipitation: precipitation, usually snow or rain, that contains small amounts of sulfuric or nitric acid

additive colour mixing: the process of adding colours of light together to produce other colours

aerodynamics: concerns the flow of air around solid objects or the effect of air on objects moving through it

angle of incidence: the angle between the incident ray and the normal

angle of reflection: the angle between the reflected ray and the normal

angle of refraction: the angle between the refracted ray and the normal

aquifer: an underground zone of rock or soil that contains and yields water

aquitard: an impervious layer of clay, silt, or rock through which water cannot move quickly

Archimedes' principle: the buoyant force on an object is equal to the weight of the fluid that the object displaces

artery: a blood vessel that carries blood away from the heart

B

bacteria: the most common form of microorganism; unicellular organisms that have no nucleus, no mitochondria, and no ribosomes

ballast: any substance that acts as a weight and alters buoyancy of a vehicle, such as a ship, submarine, hot-air balloon, or dirigible

basin: a natural depression in the ground where water can gather

bioluminescence: any process used by living things to transform chemical energy into light energy

block and tackle: a rope and pulley system used to move objects

buoyancy: the upward force that a fluid exerts on an object less dense than itself

C

capillary action: the upward movement of water through soil due to the attraction of water molecules to soil particles

cell membrane: the cell structure in plant and animal cells that covers the entire cell and acts as a gatekeeper, controlling the movement of materials into and out of the cell

cell specialization: every cell of a multicellular organism has a function that it is designed to perform; as a result, cells in the same organism come in a variety of sizes and shapes

cell wall: the plant-cell structure that protects and supports the plant cell

chemiluminescence: the process of transforming chemical energy into light energy with little or no change in temperature

chlorination: the addition of chlorine to water to kill microorganisms

chloroplast: the plant-cell structure containing many molecules of a green pigment called chlorophyll that helps plants to make their own food

chromosomes: the parts of the cell that contain hereditary or genetic information

circulatory system: an organ system that includes the heart, arteries, and veins; carries nutrients to all the cells of the body and carries away wastes

complementary light colours: any two colours of light that produce white light when added together

compressed: pressed into less volume or smaller space

compressible: the ease with which a substance reduces its volume under external force

concave lens: a lens that is thinner in the middle than at its outside edge

concave mirror: a curved mirror that has its reflecting surface on the inside of the curve

condensation: a change in state from a gas to a liquid (e.g., water vapour changing into liquid water)

Continental Divide: the ridge of land that separates waters flowing into the Pacific Ocean from those flowing north and east

continental shelf: the area offshore from a continent that slopes gently before the steep drop to the deep ocean floor

convection current: the movement of a fluid, often in a circular pattern, caused by differences in temperature and density

convex lens: a lens that is thicker in the middle than at its outside edge

convex mirror: a curved mirror that has its reflecting surface on the outside curve

current: water or another fluid moving in a specific direction

cylinder: a cylindrical chamber in a hydraulic system; it houses a piston that moves under fluid pressure

cytoplasm: the fluid area of the cell in which nutrients are absorbed, transported, and processed, and wastes are stored until proper disposal can be carried out

D

density: the mass of a substance per unit volume of that substance; calculated by dividing the mass of a substance by its volume

diaphragm: a device that controls how much light enters the camera

diffuse reflection: the reflection of light off an irregular surface; reflection that produces no image

diffusion: the movement of molecules from an area of high concentration to an area of lower concentration

digestion: the process multicellular animals use to break large food molecules into smaller molecules for fuel, growth, and repair

digestive system: an organ system that includes the esophagus, stomach, intestines, and liver; breaks down food molecules into smaller molecules that can be used by cells for energy, to build new cells, and to repair damage

disease: a condition that interferes with the well-being of an organism

displacement: a technique used to measure the volume of small irregular solids, using the formula: volume of object = (volume of water + object) − (volume of water)

diversity: a measure of the number of different types of organisms in an area

drag: a force that acts to slow a body moving through a liquid

dynamic: relating to systems involving moving fluids

E

effort force: the push or pull (force) required to move an object

electric discharge: the process by which a gas emits light because of electricity passing through it

electromagnetic spectrum: the entire range of radiant energies, from radio waves through visible light to gamma rays

endocrine system: an organ system that includes the pancreas, adrenal glands, and pituitary glands; creates chemical messengers that travel to the cells of the body; helps to coordinate the body's response to external and internal events

endoplasmic reticulum: a series of canals that carry materials throughout the cytoplasm of the cell

ergonomics: the study of designing products intended to maximize safety, efficiency, and ease

erosion: the carrying away of soil particles by wind, water, or glacial ice

esthetics: the qualities, such as texture, colour, and pattern, that make a product attractive

estuary: an area where fresh water from rivers and salt water from the oceans mix to form moderately salty (brackish) water

evaporation: a change in state from a liquid to a gas (e.g., liquid water changing to water vapour)

excretory system: an organ system that includes the kidneys, bladder, liver, ureters, and urethra; eliminates waste from the body

F

field of view: the area visible through a microscope

flocculation: the formation of clumps from particles suspended in a fluid

flood plain: a relatively flat area next to a river's banks that experiences periodic flooding

flow rate: the speed that a fluid moves in a given amount of time

fluorescence: the process of emitting light while receiving energy from another source

focal length: the distance from the principal focus to the middle of the mirror or lens

fresh water: water that contains a low concentration of dissolved salts

friction: the force that resists the movement of one object or surface moving across another

G

gear ratio: the relationship between the circumferences of the gears; determined by counting the number of teeth on each gear

gear train: two or more wheels with meshed teeth used to speed up or slow down motion

glacier: a large mass of ice and snow that slowly flows over land

Golgi apparatus: an organelle in which protein molecules are stored

ground water: water that has soaked into the earth, often between saturated soil and rock

guyot: a volcanic island with an eroded top that lies below the surface of the ocean

gyre: the circular flow of ocean waters composed of several major currents

H

hormone: a chemical messenger from the organs of the endocrine system that tells cells in other organs how to adjust to what's going on inside and outside the body

hydraulic fluid: a liquid under pressure in a hydraulic system that enables the system to work

hydraulic system: a confined system that uses a liquid under pressure to operate

hydraulics: confined, pressurized systems that use moving liquids to operate

hydrodynamics: the motion of liquids, usually water, around solid objects

hydrometer: an instrument used to measure the density of liquids

I

incandescence: the process of emitting light because of a high temperature

incident ray: a ray of light that travels toward a reflecting surface

irrigation: the watering of crops by diverting water from a river, lake, or underground water source

L

laminar flow: the movement of water in straight or almost straight lines

laws of reflection: a summary of what is known about regular reflection: the angle of incidence equals the angle of reflection; the incident ray, normal, and reflected ray all lie in the same plane

lens: a curved, transparent device designed to cause light to refract in a particular way as it passes through

light: a form of radiant energy that travels in electromagnetic waves and can be detected by the human eye; higher in energy than infrared radiation but lower than ultraviolet radiation

linkage: a connection of two or more levers used to transmit force and motion

load force: the force exerted by the load

luminous: describes an object that emits its own light

lysosome: organelle that breaks down large molecules within the cytoplasm and destroys damaged or worn-out cells

M

machine: a device that makes work easier to do; a machine can transform energy, change the direction of a force, transfer a force from one location to another, change the magnitude of a force, and/or increase or decrease speed

mass: the amount of matter in an object, measured in milligrams (mg), grams (g), or kilograms (kg)

mechanical advantage: the amount that a machine multiplies a force, measured by dividing the load force by the effort force

mechanism: a system of moving parts that changes an input motion and force into a desired output motion and force

microorganism: a living thing that can be seen only with the aid of a microscope

mitochondria: (singular is mitochondrion) cell organelles that provide the cells with energy through a process called respiration

multicellular organism: an organism composed of many cells

N

negative buoyancy: the tendency of an object to sink in a fluid because the object weighs more than the fluid it displaces

nervous system: an organ system that includes the brain, spinal cord, nerves, and sensory organs such as the eyes; carries electrical signals throughout the body

neutral buoyancy: the tendency of an object to remain level in a fluid because the object weighs the same as the fluid it displaces

nonluminous: describes an object that does not emit light but only reflects light from other sources

normal: the line drawn from the point of incidence at 90° to the optical device

nucleus: the cell structure in plant and animal cells that acts as the control centre and directs all of the cell's activities

O

opaque: describes a material that does not transmit any light; all of the light hitting an opaque material is absorbed or reflected

optical device: any device that produces an image of an object

organ systems: groups of organs that have related functions

organ: large structure composed of several different types of tissues that are specialized to carry out a specific function

organelles: tiny cell structures within the cytoplasm that are specialized to carry out a function

organism: an individual living thing

osmosis: the diffusion of water through a selectively permeable membrane

overturn: mixing of the upper and lower levels of a body of water, usually caused by convection currents

P

particle theory: a theory used to explain matter and heat transfer, which suggests that all matter is made up of tiny particles too small to be seen. These particles are constantly in motion because they have energy. The more energy they have the faster they move.

Pascal's law: the principle that an external force exerted on a confined fluid is distributed evenly in all directions inside the surface area of the container

penumbra: the part of a shadow where some light from the source reaches

percolation: the process of seeping through a porous material

phloem vessel: a tube in a plant that moves sugars from the leaves to the stems and roots for storage

phosphorescence: the process of emitting light for some time after receiving energy from another source

piston: a cylinder or disk inside a larger cylinder that moves under fluid pressure

plane mirror: a flat surface that produces an image by regular reflection

pneumatic system: a confined, pressurized system that uses moving air or other gases

pneumatics: confined, pressurized systems that use moving air or other gases

positive buoyancy: the tendency of an object to rise in a fluid because the object weighs less than the fluid it displaces

precipitation: water that has gathered in the clouds and falls to Earth as rain, hail, sleet, or snow

pressure: a measure of the distribution of force over a given area; written as

$$\text{Pressure} = \frac{\text{Force}}{\text{Area}}$$

primary light colours: red, green, and blue, the three colours of light that the cones in human eyes detect

primary pigment colours: yellow, cyan, and magenta; each of these pigments absorbs one primary colour from white light and reflects the other two

principal axis: a line through the centre of a mirror or lens that includes the principal focus

principal focus: for a lens or mirror, the position where parallel light rays come together

productivity: a measure of how well organisms reproduce

protists: microorganisms that live in moist areas; protists have a nucleus and contain mitochondria, ribosomes, and lysosomes

R

real image: an image that can be placed on a screen

reflected ray: a ray of light that bounces off a reflecting surface

refraction: the bending of light as it travels from one material into another

regular reflection: the reflection of light off a smooth, shiny surface

respiratory system: an organ system that includes the lungs, windpipe and blood vessels; delivers oxygen to the blood for distribution to all the cells of the body and eliminates waste carbon dioxide

runoff: water flowing along the surface of the ground

S

salinity: the concentration, or amount, of dissolved salts in water

saturated zone: the area beneath the water table where water fills the spaces in the gravel, sand, silt, or rock

seamount: an underwater mountain

secondary light colours: cyan, yellow, and magenta; each is produced by combining two of the primary light colours

secondary pigment colours: red, green, and blue; each of these pigment colours absorbs two primary light colours from white light and reflects the third

sediment: material such as sand, silt, and mud that is carried and deposited by wind, water, or ice

seiche: a back-and-forth movement of water in a lake that results in the rising and falling of the surface

selectively permeable: allowing certain substances to enter or leave but not others

self-correcting: able to adjust to a situation automatically

shadow: an area where light has been blocked by a solid object

solar cell: a device that converts light energy into electrical energy

solar panels: a collection of solar cells, designed to increase the output of electricity

streamlined: a smoothly curved, narrow shape that allows an object to move easily through a fluid, disturbing the fluid as little as possible

subtractive colour theory: the explanation of how pigments mix to produce other colours; called subtractive because each pigment absorbs (subtracts) different colours from white light

system: a combination of interacting or interdependent parts that form a unified whole

T

tidal range: the difference between water levels at high tide and low tide

tide: the rising and falling of the ocean surface due to the different gravitational pulls of the sun and the moon

tissue: a group of cells similar in shape and function

translucent: describes a material that transmits light, but also reflects and absorbs light; a clear image cannot be seen through a translucent material

transparency: a measure of how much light can pass through a material; materials are classified as transparent, translucent, or opaque

transparent: describes a material that transmits light; a clear image can be seen through the material

trench: a steep-sided depression in the ocean floor that forms when one of Earth's plates slides under another

tributaries: small rivers and streams that join a larger river

tsunami: a large ocean wave caused by earth movement or a volcanic eruption on the ocean floor

turbulent flow: a broken or choppy movement of water usually caused by rapids, eddies, or whirlpools

turgor pressure: water pressure in a plant cell that pushes the cytoplasm against the nonliving cell wall, causing the plant cell to stay rigid

U

umbra: the part of a shadow where no light from the source reaches

unicellular organism: an organism that has only one cell

V

vacuole: a fluid-filled space in plants and animal cells that can store food and water

vein: a blood vessel that carries blood toward the heart

velocity ratio: the relationship between the distance that an effort force moves and the distance that a load force moves; written as

$$\text{Velocity Ratio} = \frac{\text{distance effort force moves}}{\text{distance load force moves}}$$

virtual image: an image that cannot be placed on a screen; a virtual image can be seen only by looking at or through an optical device

viscometer: an instrument that measures the resistance of a fluid to flow and movement

viscosity: the physical property of a liquid that limits its ability to flow

viscous: having relatively high resistance to flow

visible spectrum: the band of colours visible to the eye; the spectral colours are red, orange, yellow, green, blue, and violet

volume: a measure of the amount of space occupied by matter; measured in cubic meters (m^3), litres (L), cubic centimeters (cm^3), or millilitres (mL)

W

water cycle: the movement of water as it changes state around Earth

water table: the upper boundary of the saturated zone

watershed: an area surrounded by high land in which all water runs to a common destination (such as a river)

wavelength: the distance between the crest of one wave and the crest of the next (can also be measured from trough to trough)

weight: a measure of the force of gravity pulling on an object; measured in newtons (N)

X

xylem vessel: a tube in a plant that carries water and minerals to the leaves

Ind

A

Acid lakes, 219
Acid precipitat...
Acid rain, 219
Additive colou...
Adrenaline, 63
Aerodynamics,
Aerodynamic sh...
Air compressor,
Airplanes
  and fluid syst...
  and hydrauli...
  and wind tun...
Algae, 248–249
Algae blooms, 2...
Alpine glaciers,
Amoeba, 44–45
Anaerobic bacteria, 221
Anal pore, in paramecium, 44
Angle of incidence, 279
Angle of reflection, 279
Angle of refraction, 288
Animal cells, 20
  compared with plant cells, 22–23
  specialized, 49
Animals
  digestive systems in, 68–69
  fluid movement in, 64–67
  organ systems in, 62–63
Antarctica, 228
Antibodies, 48, 51
Apple juice test, 15
Aquatic plants, and buoyancy, 114
Aquifers, 216
Aquitard, 216
Aral Sea, 252
Archimedes' principle, 109–110
Arteries, 64–65
Artificial arms, 157
Atrium, 65
Avalanches, 215
Axle, and wheel, 158

B

Bacteria, 42, 51
Ballast, 115
Ballast water, contaminated, 116–117
Ball bearings, 165
Basins, 213, 225
Bay of Fundy, 239
Bicycles
  designs for, 188–189
  gears on, 160
  wheel and axle on, 158
Big Chute Marine Railway lock, 131
Binoculars, magnification of, 277
Bioluminescence, 271
Birds, digestive system in, 68–69
Black light, 299
Block and tackle, 166
Blood, 14
Blood pressure, 127
Blood tissue, 48

neutral, 110
positive, 110
and temperature, 119
Buoyancy compensator vest, 114

C

Calypso, 240
Camera, and human eye, 294–295
Canadarm, 148, 157
Can openers, 147, 148–149
Canyons, 225
Capacity, 98
Capillarity, 56
Capillary action/force, 56, 217
Capsule, 42
Carbon dioxide, 106
Cars
  advantages/disadvantages of, 190
  and brakes, 124, 165, 179, 181
  in cities, 191
  designed for older people, 186
  gears on, 161
  and hydraulics, 181
  lubricants in engines of, 165
  modified controls for, 186
  wheel and axle on, 158
Cell division, need for, 46–47
Cell membrane, 20, 28
  in bacteria, 42
Cells
  animal, 20, 22–23, 49
  artificial, 39
  designing/building model or
    simulation of, 74–75
  models of, 39
  organization of, 40–41
  parts of, 26–27
  plant, 16, 21–23, 48
  reproduction, 16
  size of, 47
Cell specialization, 48–49
Cell systems, 40–41
Cell theory, 17
Cell wall, 21
  in bacteria, 42
Cell wars, 50–51
Chairs, design of, 184
Challenger Deep, 225

...nas, 39
...268
...nce, 271
...58
..., 96–97
...44
Ciliary muscles, 294
Circulatory system, 40–41, 62, 64–65
Classrooms, student-friendly, 184–185
Clear-cut logging, 214
Climate, 234–235
Cohen, Stanley, 72
Coliform bacteria, 218
Colour blindness, 305
Colour mixing, 302–303
  additive, 304
  subtractive, 310–311
Colour printing, 311
Colours, 266
  complementary light, 304
  primary light, 304
  secondary light, 304
  spectral, 296–297
Colour vision, 304
Columbia Icefield, 227
Complementary light colours, 304
Compound light microscope, 18–19, 24
Compressed, 176
Compressible, 125
Computer monitors, hydraulic system
  for, 182–183
Concave lenses, 291
Concave mirrors, 284–285
  in telescopes, 300
  using, 286–287
Concentration, 30–31
  and osmosis, 36–37
Condensation, 212
Cone cells, 304
Cones, 295
Confederation Bridge, 120–121
Confined fluids, under pressure,
  124–125
Conservation Authorities, 222
Continental Divide, 227
Continental glaciers, 228
Continental shelves, 224
Contour ploughing, 214
Contractile vacuole
  in euglena, 43
  in paramecium, 45
Controls, machines and, 149
Convection currents, 232
Convex lenses, 291, 300
Convex mirrors, 284–285

Handwritten note (overlay):

Definitions

cylinder = a cylindrical chamber in a hydraulic system; it house a piston that move under fluid pressure

Pressure = a measure of the distribution of force over a given area

$$pressure = \frac{force}{Area}$$

Viscometer = an instrument that measures the resistence of a fluid to flow and movement.

using, 286–287
Cool light, 271
Copper, 106
Coral reef, 246
Cornea, 294
Cousteau, Jacques, 240
Credit Valley Conservation Authority, 222
Crest, of a wave, 236
Currents, 232–233
Curved mirrors, 284–285
    using, 286–287
Cuticle, 58, 61
Cylinder, in hydraulic system, 126
Cytoplasm, 20, 26

D

Dams, 225
Dead Sea, 208
Decomposers, 246
Deep Tow Seismic System, 241
Density, 102–103, 210
    calculating, 102
    of common substances, 102
    comparing, 106–107
    and temperature, 118–119
Deposition, 214
Deserts, 213
Desks, design of, 185
Diabetes, 29
Dialysis machine, 38
Dialysis tubing, 34
Diamonds, 291
Diapers, 193
Diaphragm, 129, 295
Diatoms, 43
Dickson, Brad, 306–307
Diffuse reflection, 281
Diffusion, 28–29
    observing osmosis and, 34–35
Digestion, 68
Digestive enzymes, 27
Digestive system, 41, 62, 68–69
Dikes, 215
Dirigibles, 107, 115
Disease, 50
Displacement, 99
Divers, and buoyancy, 114
Diversity
    in fresh water, 244–245
    in salt water, 246–247
Drag, 90
Dragline excavators, 162
Dredging, 214
Droniuk, Randy, 96–97
Dynamic systems, 88

E

Earthworms, 64, 66
    digestive system in, 68–69
Echo sounding, 241
Ecosystems, 244–247
Efficiency of a mechanism, 153
Effluent, 221
Effort force, 150
Egg osmosis meter, 33
Electrical energy, 268, 269
Electric discharge, 270

Electromagnetic spectrum, 298–299
Electrons, 25
El Niño, 235
Endocrine system, 41, 63
Endoplasmic reticulum, 26
Energy, 16
Enzymes, 68
Epidermis, 58
Epithelial tissue, 40
Ergonomics, and bike design, 188–189
Erosion, 214
Esthetics, 184
Estuaries, 208, 213
Euglena, 43
Evaporation, 212
Excretory system, 41, 62, 66–67
Exotic species, 116
Exxon Valdez, 255
Eye, human, 294–295
Eyespot, in euglena, 43

F

Fats, 28
Fat tissue, 48
Fertilizers, 248–249
Field of view, 18
Filters, and subtractive theory, 311
Fir, 61
Fish, and buoyancy, 114
Fisheye lens, 293
Fishing rod, 151
Flagellum, 21
    in bacteria, 42
    in euglena, 43
Floating, 110–111
Flocculation, 220
Flood plains, 222, 226
Floods, 215, 222–223
Flow rate, defined, 88
Fluid flow around objects, 90–91
Fluid movement in animals, 64–67
Fluid power systems
    designing, 130–131
    and hydraulics, 126–127
    and pneumatics, 128–129
    uses of, 132–133
Fluids
    confined, 124–125
    defined, 88
    and forces, 176
    under pressure, 122–125
    vs. solids, 89
Fluid systems
    human impact on, 116–117
    and hydraulics, 126–127
    and pneumatics, 128–129
    pressure in, 180–181
Fluorescence, 270
Focal length, 286, 291
Food chains, 245, 246
Food vacuole
    in amoeba, 44
    in paramecium, 45
Food webs, 245, 246
Force
    and confined fluids, 124
    effort force, 150
    load force, 150

and Jaws of Life, 132
    of gravity, 98, 108–109
    and pressure, 174
Fossil fuels, 242
Fraser River, 227
Fresh water, 208, 209
    compared with salt water, 210–211
    diversity in, 244–245
Freshwater marshes, 209, 213, 244–245
Freshwater swamps, 209, 244
Friction
    defined, 164
    and levers, 166
    and mechanical advantage, 166–167
    positive effects of, 165
    and pulleys, 166
    reducing, 165
    testing for, 167
Frog-bacteria cross, 72
Fuel pump, 127
Fulcrum, 150
Fungus, 45
Fun house, designing, 314

G

Galileo, 300
Gamma rays, 299
Gamma ray telescopes, 301
Gas, and electric discharge, 270
Gases, 16
    and compression, 125
    and pneumatics, 128–129
    pressure on, 176–177, 178–179
Gas exchange, in leaves, 58–59
Gas flow, and wind tunnels, 91
Gear ratio, 160, 189
Gears, 160–161
Gear train, 160
Gemini North, 301
Genetic engineering, 72–73
Glaciers, 209, 213, 225, 228–229
Glass, 274
    low-emissivity, 275
Global warming, 61, 229
Golgi apparatus, 27
    in euglena, 43
Grand Banks, 224
GRAND project, 252
Gravity, 216
    force of, 98, 108
Great Barrier Reef, 246
Great Lakes, ballast water in, 116
Greenland, 228
Gregory, James, 300
Ground water, 213
Guard cells, 59
Gullet, in paramecium, 45
Guyots, 224
Gyres, 233

H

Heart, 14, 40–41, 65
    as pressurized fluid system, 127
Helium, 103, 106, 108, 111
Helium-neon laser, 287
Hemoglobin, 48
Hibernia oil project, 242
Hindenburg, 107

Hormones, 63
Hot air balloons, 115, 118
Hovercraft, 164
Hubble Space Telescope, 301
Human growth hormone, 73
Human Movement laboratory, 170–171
Hydra, 68
Hydraulic fluid, 126
Hydraulic press, 180
Hydraulics, 126
Hydraulic system, 124, 180
   and cars, 181
   composition of, 126
   for computer monitors, 182–183
   designing, 130–131
   uses of, 132–133
Hydrodynamics, defined, 88
Hydrogen, 106, 216
Hydrometer, 112

I

Ice, 118
Icebergs, 107, 229
Images
   characteristics of, 277
   describing, 276–277
   in eye and camera, 295
Immune system, 51
Impermeable, 28
Impervious layer, 216
Incandescence, 269
Incidence, point of, 279
Incident ray, 279
Indirect lighting, 281
Infection, 50
Infrared radiation, 298
Insects, excretory system in, 67
Insulin, 29
Intestine, small, 49
Iodine, 22
Iris, 294
Irrigation, 36–37, 252

J

Jackhammers, 128
Jaws of Life, 132

K

Kepler, Johannes, 300
Kerosene lamp, 269
Kidney, 35, 38, 67
Kilopascals, 175

L

Lakes, 225, 244
   acid, 219
   freezing of, 118
Laminar flow, 90
Lava, 119
Laws of reflection, 279, 280
Leaves, 58–59, 61
Leeuwenhoek, Anton van, 24
Lenses, 267
   in camera, 294–295
   combining, 291
   concave/convex, 291
   in human eye, 294
   investigating, 292–293

   refracting light in, 290–291
Levees, 215
Levers, 148
   classes of, 150
   efficient, 153
   and ergonomics, 187
   friction and, 166
   linked, 153
   and mechanical advantage, 152
   in pianos, 155
Light
   absorbing and reflecting, 275
   defined, 268
   designing device/system to control,
      314–315
   reflected off plane mirror, 278–279
   speed of, 298
   white, 297
Light bulb, 269
Light energy
   sources of, 268–271
   viewing, 266–267
Lighting
   stage, 308–309, 315
   television, 306–307
Lightning, 270
Linkage, 153
Linkage system, designing, 154–155
Lipids, 28
Liquids
   measuring density of, 112–113
   measuring volume of, 98–99
   mixing, 104–105
   pressure on, 176–177, 178–179
Living things
   building blocks of, 14–15
   characteristics of, 16–17
Load force, 150
Logging, 214
Lubricants, 165
Luminous, 268
Lungs, 74
Lungs, as pneumatic system, 129
Lysosomes, 27, 51

M

Machines
   and controls, 149
   designing, 148–149
   giant, 162–163
   as systems, 148
Macronucleus, in paramecium, 45
Magnification, 277
Maple, 61
Maple syrup, 112–113
Mariana Trench, 225
Markers, 51
Marshes
   freshwater, 209, 213, 244–245
   saltwater, 208, 213, 246
Mass
   defined, 98
   related to volume, 100–101
Materials, and light energy, 275
Matter, measuring, 98–99
Mechanical advantage
   defined, 151
   and friction, 166–167

   of hydraulic system, 180
   and levers, 152
   of pulley systems, 159
Mechanical engineer, 170–171
Mechanisms
   defined, 148
   efficiency of, 153
Melanin, 46
Meltwater, 209
Meniscus, 99
Mercury, 106
Mercury vapour, 270
Metals, recycling, 192
Meteorologists, 241
Meteors, and friction, 164
Microbes, 42–45
Micronucleus, in paramecium, 45
Microorganisms, 42–45
Microscopes
   compound light, 18–19, 24
   lenses in, 291
   magnification of, 277
   scanning electron, 25
   single-lens, 24
   technological advances of, 24–25
   transmission electron, 25
   using, 18–19
Microspheres, 39
Microwaves, 298
Mid-Atlantic Ridge, 224
Middle lamellae, 48
Mid-Ocean Ridge, 224
Mirrors, 267
   curved, 284–285, 286–287
   and laws of reflection, 280
   plane, 278–279, 282–283
Mitochondria, 26
   in euglena, 43
Modelling, 38–39
Moon, 268
   force of gravity on, 98
Moss, 61
Motor neurons, 70
Mountain bikes, vs. road bikes, 188–189
Mountains, 213
   plants on, 61
   underwater, 224
Multicellular organisms, 40, 42, 48

N

Nautile, 240
Negative buoyancy, 110
Neon, 270
Nerve tissue, 48
Nervous system, 40, 63
   and reaction time, 70–71
Neutral buoyancy, 110
Newton, Isaac, 98, 297, 300, 302
Newtons, 98, 175
Niagara Falls, 206
Nonluminous, 268
Normal, 279
North Atlantic Gyre, 233
Nuclear energy, 268
Nucleus, 20
   in euglena, 43

O

Observatories, 301
Ocean currents, 232–233
   and climate, 235
Oceans, 208
   exploration of, 240–241
   oil underneath, 242–243
Oil
   flow rate of, 94–95
   underneath ocean floor, 242–243
Oil spills, 103, 243, 255
Oil Springs, Ontario, 242, 243
Opaque, 274
Optical device, 276
Optic nerve, 294
Oral groove, in paramecium, 44–45
Organelles, 26
Organisms, 16
   multicellular, 40, 42, 48
   productivity of, 248–249
   unicellular, 42–45
Organochlorines, 193
Organs, 40
Organ systems, 41, 62–63
Osmosis, 30–33
   concentration of solution affecting,
      36–37
   observing diffusion and, 34–35
Overturns, 232
Oxygen, 106, 119, 216

P

Palisade, 58
Pantograph, 153
Paper, recycling, 193
Papua New Guinea, 236
Paramecium, 44–45
Parasites, 42, 218
Parker, Kim, 170–171
Particle theory
   and confined fluids under pressure,
      125
   and density, 106
   explaining flow using, 89
   and temperature change, 119
   and viscosity, 92
Pascal, Blaise, 176
Pascal's Law, 176, 180
Pectin, 48
Pellicle, 43
Penicillin, 45
Penumbra, 272
Percolation, 216
Permafrost layer, 60
Permeable, 28
Perspiration, 33
Phloem vessels, 57–58
Phosphates, 248–249
Phosphorescence, 269
Photography, 277
Photosynthesis, 53, 55, 58–59, 247
Phytoplankton, 219
Pianos, levers in, 155
Pigments, 310–311
Pili, 42
Pine, 61
Pinhole camera, 276
Pistons, 180

in hydraulic system, 126
Plane mirror
   reflecting light off, 278–279
   viewing images in, 282–283
Plant cells, 16, 21
   compared with animal cells, 22–23
   specialized, 48
Plants, 15
   environments of, 60–61
   leaves of, 58–59
   transpiration in, 209
   water movement in, 52–53, 54–57
Plastic bottles, 110
Plastics, recycling, 193
Plate tectonics, 224
Plimsoll lines, 111
Plimsoll, Samuel, 111
Pneumatics, 128–129
Pneumatic systems, 128–129, 180–181
   designing, 130–131
   uses of, 132–133
Point of incidence, 279
Polar icecap, 228
Pollution, 213, 218–219, 248–249. *See
   also* Oil spills
   from cars, 190–191
   and products, 192–193
Pollution, and ballast water, 116–117
Positive buoyancy, 110
Potatoes, 36–37
Power shovels, 163
Precipitation, 212–213
Pressure
   calculating, 175
   confined fluids under, 124–125
   and fluids, 122–123
   in fluid systems, 180–181
   force and, 174
   on liquids and gases, 176–177,
      178–179
   reducing, 175
   and temperature, 177
Pressurized fluid systems
   and hydraulics, 126–127
   and pneumatics, 128–129
Primary light colours, 304
Primary pigment colours, 310–311
Principal axis, 286, 291
Principal focus, 286, 291
Prism, 297
Producers, 246
Productivity of organisms, 248–249
Products
   designed for people with special
      needs, 186–187
   recycling, 192–193
Propane, 103, 125
Proteins, 26
Protists
   animal-like, 44
   plantlike, 43
Pseudopod, 44
Pulleys, 158–159
   friction and, 166
   large weights raised with, 168–169
Pumps, 127
Pupil, 294
Pus, 51

R

Radiant energy, 298
Radiation in space, 298
Radio telescopes, 300
Radio waves, 298
Rainbows, 296
Rainforest, in British Columbia, 214
Reaction time, 70–71
Real image, 276
Recycling products, 192–193
Red blood cells, 48, 74
Red River Valley flood, 215, 222–223
Reflected ray, 279
Reflecting telescope, 286, 300
Reflection
   diffuse, 281
   laws of, 279, 280
   regular, 280
   terms related to, 279
Refraction, 288–289
   in lenses, 290–291
Regular reflection, 280
Remote video, and underwater
   exploration, 240
Respiration, 26
Respiratory system, 41, 49, 62
Retina, 294, 295, 304
Ribosomes, 26
Rivers, 226
Road bikes, vs. mountain bikes,
   188–189
Robots, 156–157
Rocky Mountain Trench, 252
Rods, 295
Root hairs, 54
Root pressure, 56
Root systems, 61
Rotary motion, 158
Runoff, 213, 214

S

Sailboats, modified, 187
Salinity, 208, 250–251
Salt, 32, 36–37
Salt water, 208
   compared with fresh water, 210–211
   diversity in, 246–247
Saltwater marshes, 208, 246
Saltwater swamps, 208, 246
Satellite dishes, 285
Satellite imaging, 241
Saturated zone, 216
Sault Ste. Marie boat lock, 134
Scanning electron microscope, 25
Scavengers, 246
Screwdriver, 150, 158
Scuba divers, 240
Seamounts, 224
Secondary light colours, 304
Secondary pigment colours, 311
Sediment, 214
Seesaw, 166
Seiches, 239
Selectively permeable, 28
Self-correcting controls, 149
Sensory neurons, 70
Septic bed, 221
Septic tanks, 221

Sewage treatment, 221
Shadows, 272–273
Ships
    and ballast, 115–117
    and buoyancy, 110
Shoes, testing, 172–173
Shovels, power, 163
Shutter, 295
Single fixed pulley, 159
Single-lens microscope, 24
Single moveable pulley, 159
Skin, artificial, 75
Slide projector, 276
Sludge, 221
Snails, 64
Snowshoes, 175
Sodium vapour, 270
Solar cells, 312
Solar panels, 312–313
Solids
    measuring volume of, 99
    vs. fluids, 89
Solid water, 209
Solute, 31
Solvent, 31
Sonar, 240–241
Special needs, designing products for
    people with, 186–187
Spectral colours, 296–297
Spectrum, visible, 296–297
Spiny water flea, 116
Sponges, 64
Sports balls, 91
Springs, 226
Spruce, 61
Stage lighting, 308–309, 315
Stars, twinkling, 301
Steam, 119
Steering wheel, 158
Stoma, 59
Stomach, 49
Streamlined shape, 90
Strip logging, 214
Strollers, 153
Sublimation, 213
Submarines, 115, 240
Subsystems, 148–149
Subtractive colour mixing, 310–311
Subtractive colour theory, 311
Sun, 16, 266
    and solar panels, 312–313
    as source of light, 268
Swamps, 213
    freshwater, 209, 244
    saltwater, 208, 246
Swimmer's itch, 218
System, defined, 206
Systems, machines as, 148

T
Telescopes
    early, 300
    radio, 300
    reflecting, 286, 300
Television lighting director, 306–307
Temperature

and density, 106, 118–119
and pressure, 177
and viscosity, 94–95, 118–119
Tennis racket, 150, 152
Thermal energy, 268, 269
Thumbtacks, 174
Tidal range, 238
Tidal waves, 236
Tides, 238–239
Tile bed, 221
Tissue, 40
Titanic, 229, 240
Translucent, 274
Transmission electron microscope, 25
Transparency, 274–275
Transpiration, 56, 209, 212
Transpiration pull, 56
Trenches, 225
Tributaries, 226
Trough, of a wave, 236
Tsunamis, 236
Tunnel Boring Machine, 133
Turbulent flow, 90
Turgor pressure, 32
Turnbull, Wallace Rupert, 91

U
Ultraviolet (UV) radiation, 270, 299,
    305
Umbra, 272
Umbrellas, 153
Underwater exploration, 240–241
Underwater mountains, 224
Unicellular organisms, 42–45

V
Vaccines, 51
Vacuole, 20–21
Vacuum, 298–299
Valves, 127
Veins
    in animals, 64–65
    in plants, 58
Velcro, 186
Velocity ratio, 152
    and friction, 166
    in pulley systems, 159
Ventricle, 65
Vents, 246
Vesicle, 27
Video cameras, and underwater
    exploration, 240
Virtual image, 276
Virtual reality, 277
Viruses, 50
Viscometer, 93, 97
Viscosity
    and chocolate making, 96–97
    defined, 92
    measuring, 93
    and temperature, 94–95, 118–119
Viscous, 92
Visible light, 298
Visible spectrum, 296–297
Volcanoes, 16, 224–225
Volume

defined, 98
measuring, 99
related to mass, 100–101
Von Braunhut, Harold, 250

W
Waste disposal, 221
Wastes, 17
Water
    absorption/transport in plants,
        52–57
    brackish, 208
    chemical formula for, 216
    damage from, 254
    density of, 106
    fresh, 208, 209
    making safe for drinking, 254
    obtaining samples of, 207
    and osmosis, 30–31
    power of, 214–215
    salt, 208
    solid, 209
    and temperature change, 118
    three states of, 209
    transparency of, 275
    and turgor pressure, 32
Waterbeds, 176
Water cycle, 212–213
Water distribution, 208
Water features, 224–227
Watersheds, 227
Water table, 216–217
Water treatment, 220–221
Water vapour, 209
Wavelength, 236, 298–299
Waves, 236–237
    and energy and light, 299
    radio, 300
Weather, 234–235
    and climate, 234–235
Wedge, 148
Wegener, Alfred, 224
Weight, 98
Wells, 216, 217, 221
Wetlands, 209
Wet mount, 22
Whales, 125
Wheel and axle, 158
Wheelbarrow, 150
White blood cells, 48, 51
White light, 297, 304
Winds, 235
    and waves, 236
Wind tunnels, and gas flow, 91

X
X rays, 299
X-ray telescopes, 301
Xylem vessels, 55, 58

Y
Yeast, 45

Z
Zebra mussels, 117–118